B

Maths Links

112

Dave Capewell

Mike Heylings

Pete Mullarkey

Nina Patel

8

OXFORD

OXFORD
UNIVERSITY PRESS

Great Clarendon Street, Oxford OX2 6DP

Oxford University Press is a department of the University of Oxford.
It furthers the University's objective of excellence in research,
scholarship, and education by publishing worldwide in

Oxford   New York

Auckland   Cape Town   Dar es Salaam   Hong Kong   Karachi
Kuala Lumpur   Madrid   Melbourne   Mexico City   Nairobi
New Delhi   Shanghai   Taipei   Toronto

With offices in

Argentina   Austria   Brazil   Chile   Czech Republic   France   Greece
Guatemala   Hungary   Italy   Japan   Poland   Portugal   Singapore
South Korea   Switzerland   Thailand   Turkey   Ukraine   Vietnam

Oxford is a registered trade mark of Oxford University Press
in the UK and in certain other countries

British Library Cataloguing in Publication Data

Data available

ISBN: 978-0-19-915292-6

10 9 8 7 6 5 4 3 2

Printed in Singapore by KHL Printing Co. Pte Ltd

Paper used in the production of this book is a natural, recyclable product made from wood
grown in sustainable forests. The manufacturing process conforms to the environmental
regulations of the country of origin.

Acknowledgements

The editors would like to thank Pete Crawford for his work in creating the case studies;
Stefanie Sullivan, Nottingham Shell Centre, for her advice with the Case Studies.

p9 Donna Beeler/Photographers Direct; **p17** Dave Capewell; **p42** Awilli/zefa/Corbis;
Fertnig/iStockphoto; Zoom Studio/iStockphoto; Feng Yu/Dreamstime; Ann Murie/Dreamstime;
Yahoo/Dreamstime; Stocksnapper/Dreamstime; William Mahar/iStockphoto; Marc
Brown/iStockphoto; Dmitry Rukhlenko/Dreamstime; **p42/3** Maksym Bondarchuk/Dreamstime;
Unopix/Dreamstime; **p43** Martin Trebbin/Dreamstime; www.mastergames.com **p45** Luke
MacGregor / Reuters; **p61** Bibliothèque de Genève; **p95** Dr Gary Settles/Photolibrary;
p111 Photographers Direct/ Ottmar Bierwagen; **p125** Photographers Direct/ Ottmar
Bierwagen; **p133** Dave Capewell/Ann Cresswell; **p135** Dennis Hallinan / Alamy; **p136** Dave
Capewell/Ann Cresswell; **p148** Durham Cathedral Library; Wolfgang Amri/Dreamstime;
Thomas Dobner/Dreamstime; lishenjun/iStockphoto; imacon/iStockphoto;
samoyloff/iStockphoto; samoyloff/iStockphoto; kcastagnola/iStockphoto; Bram
Janssens/Dreamstime; Seagrave/Dreamstime; illuminated-design.co.uk; **p149** Bora
Ucak/Dreamstime; **p155** Stefano Bianchetti/Corbis; **p151** Jupiterimages/ Gerhard Joren;
p194 timsa/iStockphoto; Zoom Studio/iStockphoto; wdstock/iStockphoto;
IvanPhoto/Dreamstime; Stockbyte/OUP PictureBank; **p195** Viktor Kitaykin/iStockphoto;
RonPeigl/iStockphoto; Rcmathiraj/Dreamstime; Feng Yu/Dreamstime; Joas/iStockphoto
p197 Victor Yee /Photographers Direct; **p224** Ken Freeman/ Shutterstock; **p250** Thomson;
chert61/iStockphoto; **p251** Felix Moeckel/iStockphoto; Kroeger/Gross/Getty Images; Kirsty
Pargeter/iStockphoto; Mark Mason/OUP PictureBank; Tomasz Trojanowski/Dreamstime;
Egidijus Skiparis/Shutterstock **p261** Amy Clarke

Figurative artworks are by

p149 Jane Starr Weils;

All other figurative artworks are by Matt Latchford.

Contents

First page of a chapter
The first page of each chapter shows you real-life maths in context and also includes levelled Check in questions.

Consolidation
The Consolidation pages offer additional practice for each lesson in the chapter.

Summary
The Summary page for each chapter contains Assessment criteria, a levelled worked exam-style question and levelled past KS3 exam questions.

Case Study
The Case Studies bring maths alive through engaging real-life situations and innovative design.

> **Lesson^2**
> A 'squared' lesson exists outside of the running page order and either consolidates or extends a topic.

1 Number

Integers and decimals

Factors and multiples show you how numbers and quantities relate to each other. In particular, they let you work out how many of one quantity fit inside another one exactly.

What's the point? Knowing about factors and multiples helps when you're tiling a floor or patio – so you don't have lots of awkward gaps to fill!

✔ Check in

1 Put these numbers in order from smallest to largest.
   a 0.5, 0.512, 0.55, 0.47, 0.52
   b 3, -4, 5, -6, 9, -10

2 Calculate
   a $4 - 9$ **b** $-8 + 5$ **c** $-6 - 3$

3 Calculate
   a 7×5 **b** $12 \div 4$ **c** 9×6 **d** $72 \div 8$

4 **a** Write down the first three **multiples** of 7.
   b List all the **factors** of 12.

5 Write down the first five **prime** numbers.

- Compare the size of negative decimals
- Order positive and negative decimals
- Add and subtract integers

Keywords

Decimal   Order
Integer   Positive
Negative   Place value

- To compare the size of **negative decimals**, check the **place value** of the digits, beginning with the first non-zero digit.

Remember:
< means less than and
> means greater than.

example

Which is smaller, -1.3 m or -1.29 m?

. . . .

Compare the tenths digit.
    -1.3 has a tenths digit of 3
    -1.29 has a tenths digit of 2
so -1.3 < -1.29
because -1.3 is further below zero than -1.29.

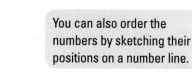

-1.29 m   -1.3 m

To put decimals in **order**, for example 0.3   -0.1   -0.15   -0.2, check the sign and then the place value:
0.3 is the only **positive** number
    -0.1   -0.15   -0.2   0.3

-0.2 is smaller than -0.1 and -0.15 as it has tenths digit of 2
    -0.2   -0.1   -0.15   0.3

-0.15 < -0.1 as it has a hundredths digit of 5
    -0.2   -0.15   -0.1   0.3

You can also order the numbers by sketching their positions on a number line.

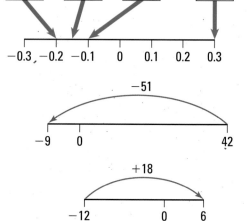

- Adding a negative integer is the same as subtracting a positive integer.
  42 + -51 = 42 − 51   (Adding -51 is the same as
       = -9   Subtracting 51)

- Subtracting a negative integer is the same as adding a positive integer.
  -12 − -18 = -12 + 18   (Subtracting -18 is the
       = 6   same as Adding 18)

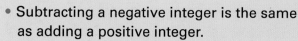

Exercise 1a

1 Place < or > between these pairs of numbers to show which number is the larger.

   a -8 and 6   **b** -7 and -5   **c** -5 and -4.5
   d -3.2 and -3   **e** -1.5 and -1.49   **f** -2.7 and -2.8
   g -0.37 and -0.39   **h** -0.0235 and -0.024

2 Put these numbers in order from smallest to largest.

a -8	-6	3	5	-12
b 0.5	1.4	-3.5	-1.5	-8
c 3.2	-1.4	-2.9	4.7	-1.6
d -2.5	1.35	-2.9	-2.3	-3

The lowest temperature possible is -273 °C, or **absolute zero**. No known substances exist at this temperature.

3 Calculate

   a $3 + 12$ **b** $15 - 7$ **c** $14 - 18$
   d $12 - 21$ **e** $6 - 26$ **f** $-4 + 3$
   g $-5 + 9$ **h** $-12 + 8$ **i** $-14 + 20$

4 Calculate

   a $7 + -7$ **b** $4 + -4$ **c** $8 + -5$
   d $-6 + -5$ **e** $-9 + -5$ **f** $7 - -4$
   g $6 - -8$ **h** $3 + -3$ **i** $-7 - -10$
   j $-11 - -15$ **k** $-13 - -8$ **l** $-16 + -9$

5 Solve each of these problems.

   a Aftab owes £13 to his dad and £8.50 to his mum. How much money does he owe altogether?

   b Bella and Carson are on holiday. Bella is swimming 3.5 m under water. Carson is standing on the diving board directly above Bella. He is 2.5 m above the water. How far below Carson is Bella?

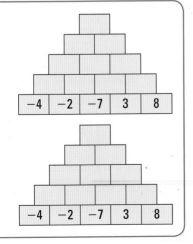

puzzle

In these pyramids the brick which sits directly above two bricks is the sum of these two bricks.

   a In this pyramid, add the right-hand number and the left-hand number to find the number directly above it.

   b In this pyramid, subtract the right-hand number from the left-hand number to find the number directly above it.

-4	-2	-7	3	8

-4	-2	-7	3	8

- Multiply and divide integers

Keywords
Integer   Negative
Inverse   Positive

A good rule to remember when multiplying or dividing a pair of **integers** is:
- if the signs are different the answer will be **negative**
- if the signs are the same the answer will be **positive**.

Multiply or divide	Positive Integer	Negative Integer
Positive Integer	+ Answer	– Answer
Negative Integer	– Answer	+ Answer

example

Calculate

a -2 × 3   **b** -2 × -3

- -

a -2 × 3

Multiply the numbers	2 × 3 = 6
Check the sign	Negative × positive = negative
Write the answer	-2 × 3 = -6

b -2 × -3

Multiply the numbers	2 × 3 = 6
Check the sign	Negative × negative = positive
Write the answer	-2 × -3 = 6

A number line shows this is correct:

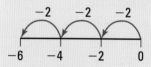

You can think of -2 × 3 as three lots of -2.

example

Calculate

a -6 ÷ -2   **b** -6 ÷ 3   **c** 6 ÷ -2

- -

a -6 ÷ -2

Divide the numbers	6 ÷ 2 = 3
Check the sign	Negative ÷ negative = positive
Write the answer	-6 ÷ -2 = 3

b -6 ÷ 3

Divide the numbers	6 ÷ 3 = 2
Check the sign	Negative ÷ positive = negative
Write the answer	-6 ÷ 3 = -2

c 6 ÷ -2

Divide the numbers	6 ÷ 2 = 3
Check the sign	Positive ÷ negative = negative
Write the answer	6 ÷ -2 = -3

From the first example, you know that -2 × 3 = -6 so it follows that -6 ÷ -2 = 3 This is the **inverse** relationship.

Exercise 1b

1 Ffion is trying to write out the negative times tables.
Copy and complete these.

a $7 \times 3 = 21$	**b** $-5 \times 3 = -15$	**c** $-9 \times 3 = \square$
$7 \times 2 = 14$	$-5 \times 2 = \square$	$-9 \times 2 = \square$
$7 \times 1 = \square$	$-5 \times 1 = \square$	$-9 \times 1 = \square$
$7 \times 0 = \square$	$-5 \times 0 = \square$	$-9 \times 0 = \square$
$7 \times -1 = \square$	$-5 \times -1 = \square$	$-9 \times -1 = \square$
$7 \times -2 = \square$	$-5 \times -2 = \square$	$-9 \times -2 = \square$
$7 \times -3 = \square$	$-5 \times -3 = \square$	$-9 \times -3 = \square$
$7 \times -4 = \square$	$-5 \times -4 = \square$	$-9 \times -4 = \square$

2 Copy and complete the multiplication grid on the right.

3 Use the multiplication grid from question **2** to answer
these questions.
   a What is two lots of -3?   **b** What is -3×-2?
   c How many -4s are there in -12?
   d What number do you multiply by -4 to make 12?
   e The answer is -12. What is the question?

×	-4	-3	-2	-1	0	1	2	3	4
4					0				
3					0				
2					0				
1					0				
0	0	0	0	0	0	0	0	0	0
-1					0				
-2					0				
-3					0				
-4					0				

4 Calculate
   a 3×-4 **b** -2×5 **c** -4×-3 **d** -5×-7 **e** -10×4
   f -3×-8 **g** 5×-5 **h** -9×-9 **i** -11×11 **j** -15×-10
   k $-20 \div -5$ **l** $-30 \div 10$ **m** $-26 \div -2$ **n** $-33 \div -3$ **o** $60 \div -20$
   p -11×4 **q** -5×12 **r** -15×-6 **s** $-42 \div -7$ **t** $-80 \div 5$

5 Eric's classwork has been marked by his teacher.
Explain why each of the questions that have been marked
with a cross is wrong, and write the correct answer.
   a $2 \times -3 = 6$ ✗   **b** $10 \div -2 = 8$ ✗   **c** $-40 \div -8 = -5$ ✗
   d $-4 \times 2 = -8$ ✓   **e** $7 \times -4 = -3$ ✗   **f** $-12 \div 3 = 4$ ✗

6 Copy and complete these calculations.
   a $5 \times \square = -20$ **b** $-30 \div \square = -6$ **c** $-4 \times \square = 28$
   d $-40 \div \square = 8$ **e** $\square \times -7 = -49$ **f** $-6 \times \square = -54$
   g $\square \div -4 = 9$ **h** $\square \div -9 = -4$

puzzle

Copy and complete this multiplication grid.

×	4		-6	
		-10	12	
3		15		
	-28		-56	
			-72	

- Recognise and use multiples and factors
- Use divisibility tests

Keywords
Divisibility   Multiple
Factor   Product

- The **multiples** of a number are those numbers that divide by it exactly, leaving no remainder.

You can find the first three multiples of 25 by writing out the 25 times table:

$$1 \times 25 = 25 \qquad 2 \times 25 = 50 \qquad 3 \times 25 = 75$$

The first three multiples of 25 are 25, 50 and 75.

> All these numbers will divide by 25 and leave no remainder.

- Any whole number can be written as the **product** of two **factors**. Most numbers have more than two factors.

You can find the factors of 36 by listing the factor pairs:

$$1 \times 36 = 36 \qquad 2 \times 18 = 36 \qquad 3 \times 12 = 36$$
$$4 \times 9 = 36 \qquad 6 \times 6 = 36$$

The factors of 36 are {1, 2, 3, 4, 6, 9, 12, 18 and 36}

> The factors of a number are numbers that divide into it exactly.

- You can use simple **divisibility** tests to help you find all the factors of a number.

Divisibility tests	
÷2	the number ends in a 0, 2, 4, 6 or 8
÷3	the sum of the digits is divisible by 3
÷4	half the number is divisible by 2
÷5	the number ends in a 0 or a 5
÷6	the number is divisible by both 2 and 3

÷7	there is no check for divisibility by 7
÷8	half the number is divisible by 4
÷9	the sum of the digits is divisible by 9
÷10	the number ends in a 0
÷11	the alternate digits add up to the same sum
÷12	the number is divisible by both 3 and 4

example

Is 9 a factor of 189?

Yes, because $1 + 8 + 9 = 18$, and 18 is a multiple of 9.

Check $189 \div 9 = 21$

$$
\begin{array}{r}
21 \\
9\overline{)189} \\
-180 \\
\hline
9 \\
-9 \\
\hline
0
\end{array}
$$

$9 \times 20 = 180$

$9 \times 1 = 9$

$9 \times 21 = 189$

Exercise 1c

1 Write the first three multiples of
    a 5   **b** 14   **c** 21   **d** 35   **e** 48   **f** 115

2 Write all the factors of
    a 20   **b** 28   **c** 45   **d** 52   **e** 66   **f** 84

3 a Write a multiple of 30 between 100 and 140.
   b Write a multiple of 45 between 100 and 140.

4 Use the divisibility tests to answer each of these questions.
In each case explain your answer.
    a Is 2 a factor of 74?   **b** Is 3 a factor of 72?
    c Is 4 a factor of 102?   **d** Is 5 a factor of 135?
    e Is 6 a factor of 156?   **f** Is 7 a factor of 112?
    g Is 8 a factor of 200?   **h** Is 9 a factor of 178?
    i Is 12 a factor of 168?   **j** Is 11 a factor of 264?

5 Find the missing digit * in each of these numbers.
    a 834 *25 is divisible by 9   **b** 3*4 582 is divisible by 11

6 For each of these questions show your working out and
explain your thinking.
    a The Headteacher wants to divide 248 students into
       9 equal-size groups. Is it possible?
    b Aunt Hilda wants to divide £540 equally between her
       12 nieces and nephews. Can she do it?
    c Mr Ball is a PE teacher. He has a class of 24 students. Sometimes
       he organises his class into 3 groups of 8 students. In how many
       different ways can he organise his class
       into equal-size groups?

7 In these productogons the number in
each square is the product of the numbers
in the circles on each side of it.
Find the missing numbers in each of these
productogons.

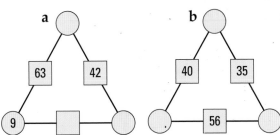

> **investigation**
>
> Jermaine thinks that if a number is divisible by both 3 and 5
> then it will also be divisible by 15.
>
> **a** Investigate to see if Jermaine is correct.
> **b** Invent a divisibility rule of your own for 18.

- Recognise and use primes
- Use tests of divisibility to check for primes
- Find the prime factor decomposition of a number

Keywords
Divisibility
Factor tree
Prime factor
Prime number
Product

- A **prime number** is a number with exactly two factors: the number itself and 1.

Michael uses **divisibility** tests to check if 65 is a prime number. He works through the prime numbers starting with 2.

Is 65 divisible by...		Reason
2	✗	because 65 does not end in 0, 2, 4, 6 or 8
3	✗	because 6 + 5 = 11, which is not a multiple of 3
5	✓	because 65 ends in a 5

1	2	3	4	5	6	7	8	9	10
11	12	13	14	15	16	17	18	19	20
21	22	23	24	25	26	27	28	29	30
31	32	33	34	35	36	37	38	39	40
41	42	43	44	45	46	47	48	49	50
51	52	53	54	55	56	57	58	59	60
61	62	63	64	65	66	67	68	69	70
71	72	73	74	75	76	77	78	79	80
81	82	83	84	85	86	87	88	89	90
91	92	93	94	95	96	97	98	99	100

65 is not a prime number.

Michael uses this method to find the prime numbers from 1 to 100. These numbers are shown in blue in the table.

You can use **factor trees** to break a number down into factors until you reach prime numbers.

example

Write 90 as the **product** of its **prime factors**.

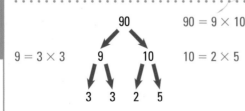

$90 = 9 \times 10$

$9 = 3 \times 3$

$10 = 2 \times 5$

3, 2 and 5 are all prime numbers

90 can be written as $2 \times 3 \times 3 \times 5$.

2, 3 and 5 are the **prime factors** of 90.

Prime numbers are the building blocks of the counting numbers.

- Every whole number can be written as the product of its prime factors. For example, $36 = 2 \times 2 \times 3 \times 3$

Exercise 1d

1 Look at these numbers.

| 3 | 4 | 5 | 6 | 7 | 8 | 9 |
| 10 | 11 | 12 | 13 |

Write which are prime numbers and explain your answers.

2 Write all the factors of

   a 30   **b** 48   **c** 67   **d** 58   **e** 53

Use your results to identify which are prime numbers.

3 Use divisibility tests to answer each of these questions.
In each case explain your answer.

   a Is 5 a factor of 135?   **b** Is 3 a factor of 186?
   c Is 2 a factor of 458?   **d** Is 11 a factor of 143?

> **Did you know?**
>
> The largest known prime number (as of 2008) is 12978189 digits long.

4 Letitia has started trying to check if 59 is a prime number.

   a Complete Letitia's working out to see if 59 is a prime number.

   b Use the same method to check if 67 is a prime number.

2 is not a factor	because 59 does not end in 0, 2, 4, 6 or 8
3 is not a factor	because 5 + 9 = 14, which is not a multiple of 3
5 is not a factor	because 59 does not end in a 0 or a 5 ...

5 Use the divisibility tests for prime numbers to see which of these numbers are prime. In each case explain your answer.

   a 75   **b** 31   **c** 47   **d** 87   **e** 54
   f 79   **g** 85   **h** 89   **i** 96   **j** 105

6 Bob is trying to find the first prime number greater than 200. On the right is his working out so far.

   a What is the first prime number greater than 200?
   b Is 223 a prime number? Explain your method.

200	X Divides by 2
201	X Divides by 3
202	X Divides by 2
203	X Divides by 7
204	X Divides by 2
205	X Divides by 5
206...	

7 Write each of these numbers as the product of its prime factors.

   a 15   **b** 24   **c** 40   **d** 27   **e** 64
   f 56   **g** 48   **h** 72   **i** 80   **j** 96

investigation

The number 20 can be written as $2 \times 2 \times 5$.
So you can say that it has three prime factors (2, 2 and 5).

   a Find four different numbers with exactly three prime factors.
   b Find the smallest number larger than 100 with exactly three prime factors.

- Find the lowest common multiple and highest common factor of two numbers

Keywords
Highest common factor
Lowest common multiple
Prime factor

- The **highest common factor (HCF)** of two numbers is the largest number that will divide into both of them.

8 is the HCF of 16 and 24.

- The **lowest common multiple (LCM)** of two numbers is the smallest number that appears in both times tables.

18 is the LCM of 6 and 9.

- You can find the HCF and LCM by using **prime factors**.

---

example

Find the HCF and LCM of 56 and 70.

. . . .

Write both numbers as the product of their prime factors.

$56 = ② \times 2 \times 2 \times ⑦$
$70 = ② \times 5 \times ⑦$

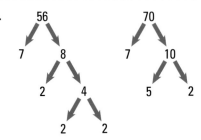

Multiply the prime factors they have in common 2×7
HCF of 56 and 70 = 14

Now take the remaining prime factors:
$56 = 2 \times ② \times ② \times 7$ ⟶ Multiply by the HCF: $2 \times 2 \times 5 \times 14$
$70 = 2 \times ⑤ \times 7$ LCM of 56 and 70 = 280

Alternatively, you can use a **Venn diagram**.

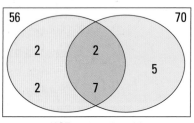

You can check your answers by writing out all the factors and some of the multiples of 56 and 70.

HCF $= 2 \times 7 = 14$
LCM $= 2 \times 2 \times 2 \times 7 \times 5 = 280$

Exercise 1e

1 Copy and complete this table.

Numbers	Factors	HCF	First five multiples	LCM
4	{1, 2, 4}		4 8 12 16 20	
6				

2 Use prime factors to check your answer to question **1**.

3 Use an appropriate method to find the HCF of
   a 8 and 12   **b** 14 and 21   **c** 32 and 40
   d 39 and 52   **e** 56 and 32   **f** 35 and 49

4 Use an appropriate method to find the LCM of
   a 8 and 12   **b** 14 and 21   **c** 32 and 40
   d 39 and 52   **e** 24 and 30   **f** 28 and 49

5 Use an appropriate method to find the HCF and LCM of
   a 28 and 42   **b** 56 and 91   **c** 72 and 108
   d 120 and 144   **e** 225 and 270   **f** 128 and 192

6 In these productogons the number
in each square is the product of
the numbers in the circles
on each side.
Find the missing numbers.

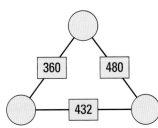

Write each number as the
product of its prime factors.

challenge

Solve these problems.
a Two cars are on a race track. They start at the
same place at the same time. The first car takes
54 seconds to complete a lap, the second car takes
63 seconds to complete a lap. After how many
seconds will the cars be back at the starting place
at exactly the same time?
b Lola is planning to tile the floor of her new kitchen with
square tiles. The kitchen measures 256 cm by 384 cm.
Square tiles come in all sizes from 5 cm by 5 cm up to
20 cm by 20 cm.
Lola wants to use tiles of the same size.
What is the largest size of square tile that can be used
to cover the floor, without needing to break any tiles?

- Recognise and use cube and square numbers
- Use index notation to write squares and cubes

Keywords
Cube number
Index
Square number

Here is a sequence of square patterns on a pegboard.

| $1 \times 1 = 1$ | $2 \times 2 = 4$ | $3 \times 3 = 9$ | $4 \times 4 = 16$ |

p. 158

1, 4, 9 and 16 are the first four **square numbers**.

Here is a sequence of cube patterns.

  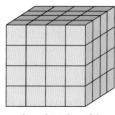

| $1 \times 1 \times 1 = 1$ | $2 \times 2 \times 2 = 8$ | $3 \times 3 \times 3 = 27$ | $4 \times 4 \times 4 = 64$ |

1, 8, 27 and 64 are the first four **cube numbers**.

p. 64

- You can use **index notation** to write squares and cubes.
  $3^2 = 3 \times 3 = 9$
  $4^3 = 4 \times 4 \times 4 = 64$

The small number, or **index**, tells you how many times the number appears in a multiplication.

Work out the value of   **a** 6^3 **b** $(-9)^2$ **c** 3.5^2

. . . .

a $6^3 = 6 \times 6 \times 6 = 216$
b $(-9)^2 = -9 \times -9 = 81$
c $3.5^2 = 3.5 \times 3.5 = 12.25$

The bracket means that you square everything inside the bracket.

Write the square number which is between 750 and 800.

. . . .

$27^2 = 27 \times 27 = 729$
$28^2 = 28 \times 28 = 784$
$29^2 = 29 \times 29 = 841$

28^2 lies between 750 and 800.

Exercise 1f

1 Find

    a the 6th square number   **b** the 9th square number

    c the 12th square number   **d** the 15th square number

    e the 6th cube number   **f** the 10th cube number.

2 **a** Write the cube number nearest to 350.

    b Write the square number which is between 280 and 290.

    c Find three numbers less than 1000 which are both square numbers and cube numbers.

3 Work out these using a calculator where appropriate.

    a 14^2 **b** 18^2 **c** 24^2 **d** 13^3

    e 17^3 **f** $(-7)^2$ **g** 14^3 **h** 2.5^2

    i 10^3 **j** 1.5^3 **k** 7.5^3 **l** $(-5)^3$

4 **a** Match each of these questions to the appropriate estimate.

    b Check your answers using your calculator.

QUESTIONS
A. 3.5^2 B. 7.8^2 C. 11.1^2 D. 5.3^2 E. 13.9^2 F. 3.5^3 G. 5.7^3 H. 2.9^3

ESTIMATES
1. 120   2. 30   3. 40   4. 10   5. 20   6. 180   7. 60   8. 190

5 **a** A square has an area of 121 cm^2. What is the length of side of the square?

    b Karim thinks of a number. He multiplies the number by itself. The answer is 3136. What is Karim's number?

    c Billy wants to build a square house. An architect designs the ground floor of his house in the shape of a square with an area of 1000 m^2.

       What is the length of the ground floor of Billy's house? (Give your answer to the nearest metre.)

6 Find two consecutive numbers with a product of 2070. Explain your method for solving the problem.

Tim thinks that every square number can be written as the sum of two prime numbers.

For example $9^2 = 81 = 2 + 79$

Investigate to see if Tim is correct by seeing which square numbers up to 12^2 can be written as the sum of two prime numbers.

1a

1 Put these numbers in order from smallest to largest.

a -5	4	-3	2	-1
b 1.5	-2.4	-3.1	-0.9	-2
c 3.2	-1.4	-2.6	2.7	-1.1
d -1.5	0.15	-2.1	-1.6	-0.5

2 Calculate

a 8 + -4	**b** 6 + -9	**c** 4 + -8	**d** -3 + -7	**e** -11 + -2
f 9 − -2	**g** 3 − -12	**h** 1 − -5	**i** -8 − -4	**j** -6 − -11
k -9 − -3	**l** -6 − -12	**m** -13 + -21	**n** 12 + -15	**o** 17 − -12
p 11 + -21	**q** 13 − -24	**r** 28 + -23	**s** 35 − -21	**t** -17 + -31

1b

3 Calculate

a 2 × -5	**b** -4 × 3	**c** -6 × -4	**d** -8 × -5	**e** -9 × 6
f -7 × -9	**g** 9 × -9	**h** -12 × -3	**i** -14 × 5	**j** -15 × -6
k -40 ÷ -8	**l** -35 ÷ 7	**m** -36 ÷ -9	**n** -56 ÷ -8	**o** 45 ÷ -9
p -13 × 5	**q** -25 × 4	**r** -11 × -15	**s** -84 ÷ -7	**t** -96 ÷ 8

4 Copy and complete these calculations.

a $8 \times \square = -72$ **b** $-54 \div \square = -6$ **c** $-7 \times \square = 49$

d $-104 \div \square = 8$ **e** $\square \times -12 = -48$ **f** $-6 \times \square = -72$

g $\square \div -4 = 64$ **h** $\square \div -9 = -14$

1c

5 Write all the factors of

a 30	**b** 48	**c** 65	**d** 72	**e** 96	**f** 100
g 130	**h** 108	**i** 120	**j** 132	**k** 144	**l** 150

6 Use the divisibility tests to answer each of these questions. In each case explain your answer.

a Is 2 a factor of 98?   **b** Is 3 a factor of 93?

c Is 4 a factor of 112?   **d** Is 5 a factor of 157?

e Is 6 a factor of 184?   **f** Is 7 a factor of 135?

g Is 8 a factor of 196?   **h** Is 9 a factor of 289?

i Is 12 a factor of 200?   **j** Is 11 a factor of 385?

1d

7 Use the divisibility tests for prime numbers to see which of these numbers are prime. In each case explain your answer.

a 35	**b** 38	**c** 37	**d** 47	**e** 51	**f** 53
g 75	**h** 79	**i** 76	**j** 85	**k** 93	**l** 91

8 Work out the value of

   a $3 \times 3 \times 5$ **b** $2 \times 3 \times 5$ **c** $2 \times 3 \times 3$ **d** $3 \times 3 \times 5 \times 5$

   e $2 \times 3 \times 3 \times 3$ **f** $3 \times 5 \times 5$ **g** $7 \times 7 \times 7$ **h** $3 \times 5 \times 7$

   i $5 \times 5 \times 7$ **j** $3 \times 5 \times 7 \times 11$

9 Write each of these numbers as the product of its prime factors.

   a 18   **b** 28   **c** 45   **d** 57   **e** 63   **f** 76

   g 88   **h** 92   **i** 108   **j** 115   **k** 130   **l** 132

   m 144   **n** 160   **o** 170   **p** 175   **q** 188   **r** 240

10 Use an appropriate method to find the HCF of

   a 6 and 10   **b** 12 and 16   **c** 18 and 27

   d 15 and 20   **e** 24 and 32   **f** 25 and 30

   g 28 and 40   **h** 56 and 80

11 Use an appropriate method to find the LCM of

   a 6 and 10   **b** 12 and 16   **c** 18 and 27

   d 15 and 20   **e** 16 and 24   **f** 24 and 30

   g 28 and 32   **h** 50 and 56

12 In these productogons the number in each square is the product of the numbers in the circles on each side of it. Find the missing numbers in each of these productogons.

> Write each number as the product of its prime factors.

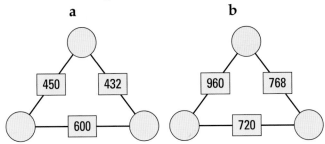

   a   **b**

13 Work out these using a calculator where appropriate.

   a 7^3 **b** 13^2 **c** 21^2 **d** 9^3 **e** 15^3 **f** $(-3)^2$

   g 24^3 **h** 0.5^2 **i** 0.1^2 **j** 0.1^3 **k** $(-2)^2$ **l** $(-2)^3$

Assessment criteria
- Recognise and describe number relationships including multiple and factor and square **Level 4**
- Multiply and divide positive and negative whole numbers **Level 5**

Level 5

1 Write a number in each box to make the calculation correct.

a ☐ + ☐ = -2

b ☐ − ☐ = -2

c ☐ × ☐ = -2

Owas' answer ✔

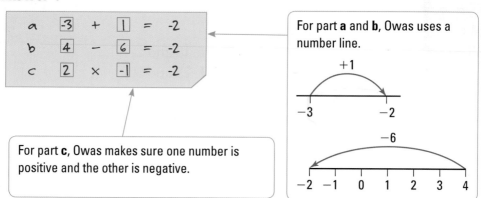

a -3 + 1 = -2

b 4 − 6 = -2

c 2 × -1 = -2

For part **a** and **b**, Owas uses a number line.

+1

−3   −2

−6

−2 −1 0 1 2 3 4

For part **c**, Owas makes sure one number is positive and the other is negative.

Level 5

2 a I am thinking of a number.
   My number is a multiple of 4.

   Tick (√) the true statement below.

   My number   My number   My number could
   must be even   must be odd   be odd or even
      ☐   ☐   ☐

   Explain how you know.

b I am thinking of a different number.
   My number is a factor of 20.

   Tick (√) the true statement below.

   My number   My number   My number could
   must be even   must be odd   be odd or even
      ☐   ☐   ☐

   Explain how you know.

Key Stage 3 2006 4–6 Paper 1

2 Geometry

Measures

How far is it to Somerford Keynes?

Probably 2 miles, but could it be 2 kilometres?

What's the point? Units of measurement are essential in everyday life. You should always give the units when you measure or describe quantities, otherwise people won't know what you mean.

✔ Check in

Level 5

Work out the calculations in questions **1–3**.

1 **a** 30×100 **b** $560 \div 10$ **c** 4.6×10 **d** $8500 \div 1000$

2 **a** 60×2.2 **b** 8×4.5 **c** 5×1.6 **d** 15×0.6

3 **a** $32 \div 1.6$ **b** $20 \div 2.5$ **c** $60 \div 0.6$ **d** $18 \div 4.5$

Level 4

4 Calculate the perimeter and the area of these shapes.
   Each square represents one square centimetre.

   a   **b**   **c**

17

- Use appropriate units to measure length, mass and capacity

Keywords
Capacity   Mass
Length   Metric

You can measure **length** and distance using the **metric** units millimetre (mm), centimetre (cm), metre (m) and kilometre (km).

1 cm = 10 mm
1 m = 1000 mm
1 m = 100 cm
1 km = 1000 m

The **mass** of something is how heavy it is. You can measure mass using grams (g), kilograms (kg) and tonnes (t).

1 kg = 1000 g
1 t = 1000 kg

A paper clip weighs about $\frac{1}{2}$ g

A bag of sugar weighs 1 kg

A small car weighs about 1 tonne

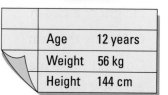

Age	12 years
Weight	56 kg
Height	144 cm

Capacity is the amount of liquid a container holds.

You can measure capacity using millilitres (ml), centilitres (cl) and litres (ℓ).

1 ℓ = 1000 ml
1 ℓ = 100 cl

A teaspoon holds 5 ml

A can of drink holds 33 cl

A carton of fruit juice holds 1 ℓ

example

Convert these measurements into the units indicated in brackets.

a 5 ℓ (into ml)   **b** 450 cm (into m)

. . . .

a   × 1000

1 ℓ = 1000 ml

÷ 1000

5 ℓ = 5 × 1000 ml
    = 5000 ml

b   × 100

1 m = 100 cm

÷ 100

450 cm = 450 ÷ 100 m
     = 4.5 m

Exercise 2a

1 Copy and complete each sentence, using the most appropriate metric unit.

a The amount of liquid in a mug is 25 _____.

b The length of a room is 2.8 _____.

c A bucket holds 9 _____ of water.

d A teabag has a mass of 5 _____.

e The width of my fingernail is 10 _____.

Did you know?

One litre of water weighs one kilogram.

2 Estimate the size of each of these measurements. Use the approximations to help you.

Measurement	Useful approximations
Distance across a road	Height of a door = 2 m
Capacity of a rucksack	Height of a house = 10 m
Mass of an elephant	Mass of 1 bag of sugar = 1 kg
Time to boil an egg	Mass of a small car = 1 tonne
Mass of a small child	Capacity of a bottle of drink = 2 ℓ
Height of a classroom	Time to walk 1 km = 15 mins

3 Calculate the number of metres in a 50 km race.

4 Convert these measurements to the units in the brackets.

a 7500 g (kg)   b 650 mm (cm)   c 850 cl (ℓ)

d 500 m (km)   e 2500 kg (t)   f 8.5 m (cm)

g 7 ℓ (ml)   h 19.5 kg (g)   i 4 km (cm)

5 Type A fence panels have a width 75 cm.
Type B fence panels have a width of 1.25 m.

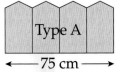

Type A

←—— 75 cm ——→

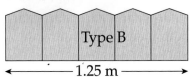

Type B

←———— 1.25 m ————→

Find a combination of fence panels that will fit a 7 metre gap.

6 A 250 ml bottle of hair shampoo costs 99p.
A one-litre bottle of the same shampoo costs £3.99.

Which bottle is better value for money?
Show your working to explain your answer.

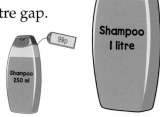

£3.99

Shampoo 1 litre

99p

Shampoo 250 ml

problem

a Which weighs more, you or one million paper clips? Explain your answer.

b How many paper clips could you carry in one go? Explain your answer.

A paper clip weighs about $\frac{1}{2}$ of 1 gram.

- Know rough metric equivalents of imperial units
- Read and interpret scales on a range of measuring instruments

Keywords
Imperial   Metric
Instrument   Scale

Measurements can use **metric** or **imperial** units.

1 foot = 12 inches
1 yard = 3 feet
1 yard = 36 inches

≈ means approximately

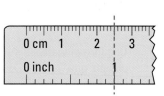

1 inch ≈ 2.5 cm

1 yard is just less than 1 metre

5 miles ≈ 8 km

1 mile ≈ 1.6 kilometres

1 kilogram ≈ 2.2 lb (pounds)

1 pint ≈ 0.6 litre

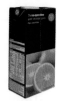

1 gallon ≈ 4.5 litres

example

a Convert 50 kg to pounds (lb).   **b** Convert 100 cm to inches.

a

×2.2

1 kg ≈ 2.2 lb

÷2.2

50 kg ≈ 50 × 2.2 lb ≈ 110 lb

b

×2.5

1 inch ≈ 2.5 cm

÷2.5

100 cm ≈ 100 ÷ 2.5 inches ≈ 40 inches

You use measuring **instruments** to measure quantities.
You need to understand the **scale** to read them.

example

Write down the reading on each of the scales.

a

0   100   200   °C

b

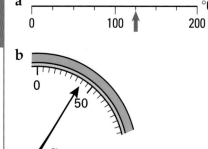

a 125 °C
    4 spaces represent 100 °C
    Each space represents 25 °C

b 40 g
    10 spaces represent 50 g
    Each space represents 5 g

Exercise 2b

1 State the larger unit of measurement.
   a inch or centimetre
   b pound (lb) or kilogram
   c pint or litre
   d mile or kilometre
   e yard or metre

2 Convert these measurements to the units in brackets.
   a 5 kg (lb)
   b 8 pints (litre)
   c 12 inches (cm)
   d 70 kg (lb)
   e 36 inches (cm)
   f 80 kg (lb)
   g 14 pints (litre)
   h 0.5 kg (lb)
   i 2 feet (cm)

3 Convert these measurements to the units in brackets.
   a 15 cm (inches)
   b 99 lb (kg)
   c 12 litres (pints)
   d 300 cl (pints)
   e 40 cm (inches)
   f 132 lb (kg)
   g 50 cm (inches)
   h 24 litres (pints)
   i 125 cm (inches)

4 The sign on the right shows the distances in miles from Preston to other cities.
   Calculate the distances in kilometres.

🛣	
Manchester	30
Stoke	65
Birmingham	110
Bath	200

5 A litre of petrol costs 130 pence.
   What will a gallon cost?

6 Write down the readings on each scale.

a   0   ↑   250   ↑   500   miles

b   0   ↑   10   ↑   20   °C

c   0   ↑   ↑   250   ml

d   0   ↑   100   ↑   200   m

e   0   ↑ 50   ↑   100   cm

---

problem

a Susan eats 40 g of cereal for breakfast every day.
   i How much will she eat in one year?
   ii When will she have eaten 50 kg of cereal?

b Susan puts 125 ml of milk on each helping of her cereal.
   How many pints of milk does she need in a whole year?

2c Perimeter and area of a rectangle   **LEVEL 5**

- Calculate the perimeter and area of a rectangle

Keywords

2-D
Area
Length

Perimeter
Rectangle
Square

In this drawing, the wall goes around the **perimeter** of the lawn. The grass covers the **area** of the lawn.

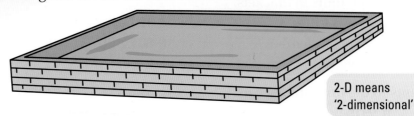

2-D means
'2-dimensional'

- The perimeter is the distance around a **2-D** shape.

You measure perimeter in units of **length**, such as mm, cm, m, km.

- The area of a shape is the amount of surface it covers.

You measure area in **squares**, such as square millimetres (mm^2), square centimetres (cm^2), square metres (m^2) or square kilometres (km^2).

You can find the area of a rectangle using a formula.

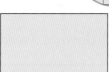

width

- Area of a **rectangle** = length × width

length

---

example

Calculate the perimeter and area of the rectangle.

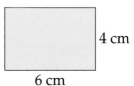

4 cm

6 cm

Perimeter = 6 cm + 4 cm + 6 cm + 4 cm
         = 20 cm
Area = 6 × 4
     = 24 cm^2

There are 4 rows of 6 squares.

---

example

Calculate the perimeter and area of this shape.

First calculate the missing lengths.
7 − 2 = 5 m   5 − 3 = 2 m
Perimeter = 2 m + 5 m + 7 m + 3 m + 5 m + 2 m = 24 m
Area = 3 × 5 + 2 × 5
     = 15 + 10
     = 25 m^2

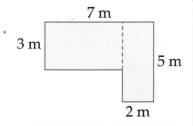

7 m

3 m

5 m

2 m

The shape is made from two rectangles.

Exercise 2c

1 Calculate the perimeter and area of these rectangles.
State the units of your answers.

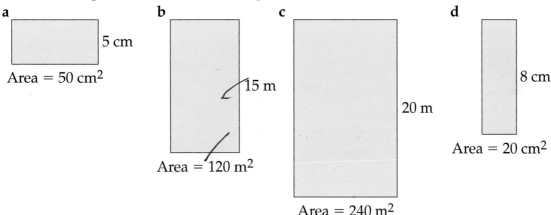

a
15 cm
6 cm

b
5 cm
15 cm

c
6 m
5.5 m

d
4.4 mm
5 mm

2 Calculate the perimeter of these rectangles.

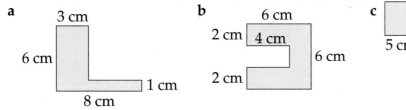

a
5 cm
Area = 50 cm²

b
15 m
Area = 120 m²

c
20 m
Area = 240 m²

d
8 cm
Area = 20 cm²

3 Calculate the perimeter and area of these shapes
made from rectangles.
If necessary, draw the shapes on square grid paper.

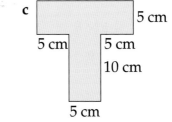

a
3 cm
6 cm
1 cm
8 cm

b
6 cm
2 cm   4 cm
6 cm
2 cm

c
5 cm
5 cm   5 cm
10 cm
5 cm

This is the national flag of Sweden.

Calculate   **a** the area of each blue rectangle
             b the area of the yellow shape.

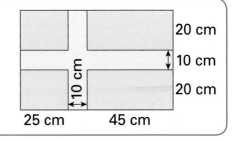

20 cm
10 cm
20 cm
10 cm
25 cm   45 cm

• Calculate the area of a triangle

Keywords
Area   Right angle
Base   Triangle
Perpendicular

The area of this green triangle is also half the area of the surrounding rectangle.

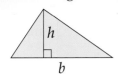 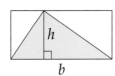 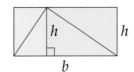

Area of the rectangle = $b \times h$

> • The **area** of any **right-angled triangle** is half the area of the surrounding rectangle.

> • The area of a triangle
>
> $= \frac{1}{2} \times b \times h$
>
> $= \frac{1}{2} \times$ base $\times$ perpendicular height

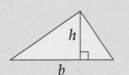

b is the **base**.
h is the perpendicular height.
Perpendicular means 'at right angles to'.

example

Calculate the area of these triangles.

a

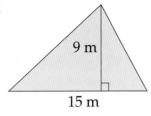

9 m

15 m

b

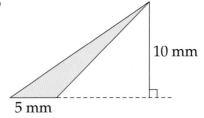

10 mm

5 mm

a Area $= \frac{1}{2} \times b \times h$

$= \frac{1}{2} \times 15 \times 9$

$= 67.5 \text{ m}^2$

b Area $= \frac{1}{2} \times b \times h$

$= \frac{1}{2} \times 5 \times 10$

$= 25 \text{ mm}^2$

example

The area of this triangle is 96 cm².

Calculate the perpendicular height.

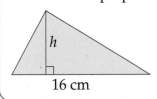

h

16 cm

Area $= \frac{1}{2} \times b \times h$

$96 = \frac{1}{2} \times 16 \times h$

$96 = 8 \times h$

$h = 12 \text{ cm}$

$96 \div 8 = 12$

Exercise 2d

1 Calculate the area of these triangles. Each square represents 1 cm².

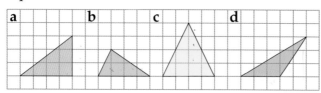

a   b   c   d

2 On square grid paper, draw a triangle with an area of 15 cm².

3 Calculate the area of these triangles. State the units of your answers.

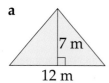
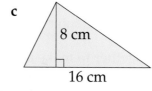

a   7 m   12 m

b   5.5 cm   8 cm

c   8 cm   16 cm

d   5 mm   7 mm

4 Calculate the unknown length in these triangles.

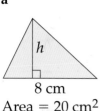
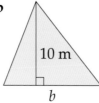
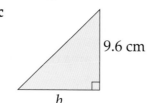

a   h   8 cm   Area = 20 cm²

b   10 m   b   Area = 60 m²

c   9.6 cm   b   Area = 48 cm²

d   h   8 mm   Area = 30 mm²

5 Calculate the area of these shapes. Each square represents 1 cm².

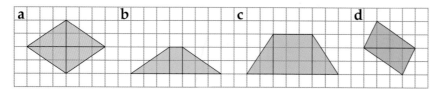

a   b   c   d

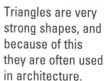

Did you know?

Triangles are very strong shapes, and because of this they are often used in architecture.

challenge

The surrounding rectangle is drawn round a kite.
The rectangle has a length of 20 cm and a width of 10 cm.

Calculate   **a** the area of the rectangle

           b the area of the kite.

Explain your answers.

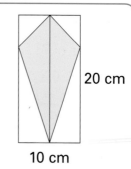

20 cm

10 cm

• Calculate the area of a parallelogram and a trapezium

Keywords

Area   Parallelogram
Base   Perpendicular
Parallel   Trapezium

The **area** of the **parallelogram** is double the area of the triangle.

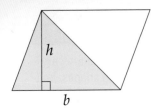 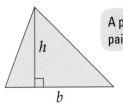

A parallelogram has two pairs of **parallel** sides.

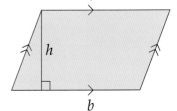

Area of the triangle $= \frac{1}{2} \times b \times h$

b is the **base**.
h is the perpendicular height.
Perpendicular means 'at right angles to'.

• The area of a parallelogram $= b \times h$
$\qquad\qquad\qquad\qquad\qquad = $ base $\times$ perpendicular height

You can fit two **trapeziums** together to make a parallelogram.

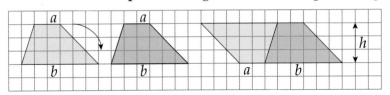

A trapezium has one pair of parallel sides.

The area of the trapezium is half the area of the parallelogram.

Area of the parallelogram $= (a + b) \times h$

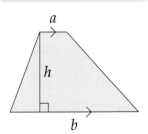

• The area of a trapezium $= \frac{1}{2} \times (a + b) \times h$

a and b are the lengths of the parallel sides.
h is the perpendicular height.

---

example

Calculate the area of the shapes.

a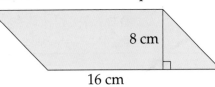

b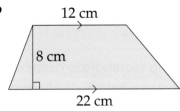

....

a Area $= b \times h$

$\quad = 16 \times 8 = 128$ cm^2

b Area $= \frac{1}{2} \times (a + b) \times h$

$\quad = \frac{1}{2} \times (12 + 22) \times 8$

$\quad = \frac{1}{2} \times 34 \times 8 = 136$ cm^2

$a = 12, b = 22, h = 8$

Exercise 2e

1 Calculate the area of these parallelograms. State the units of your answers.

a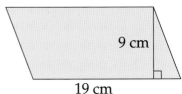

b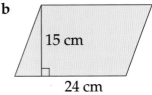

c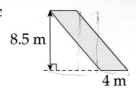

2 Calculate the area of these trapeziums.

a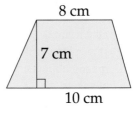

b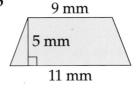

c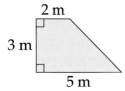

3 Find the lengths b and h in these parallelograms. State the units of your answers.

a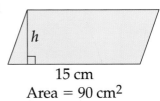

b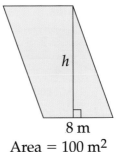

c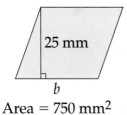

activity

Copy the five-piece tangram on square grid paper.

a Calculate the area of the tangram.
Cut out the five pieces.

b Arrange shapes A, B, D and E to form

  i a rectangle

  ii a parallelogram

  iii an isosceles trapezium.

c Calculate the area of each quadrilateral in part **b** using the appropriate formula. Show your working in each case.

d Calculate the area of shape C using the appropriate formula.

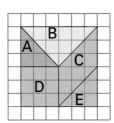

2a

1 Copy and complete each sentence, using the most appropriate metric unit of length.
  a A banana weighs 150 ___.
  b I can walk 1 ___ in 15 minutes.
  c The weight of a football is just over 400 ___.
  d A ruler is 30 ___ long.
  e A small flask holds 300 ___ of liquid.

2 Convert these measurements to the units indicated in brackets.
  a 380 mm (cm)   b 4.5 kg (g)   c 6.5 ℓ (cl)
  d 3500 mm (m)   e 2500 kg (t)

2b

3 Convert these measurements to the units indicated in brackets.
  a 8 inches (cm)   b 132 lbs (kg)   c 40 km (miles)
  d 5 pints (ℓ)   e 10 gallons (ℓ)

4 Write down each reading on the scales.

a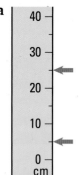

b

gallons

c

2c

5 Copy and complete the table for the rectangles.

	Length	Width	Perimeter	Area
a	15 cm	10 cm		
b	25 cm	20 cm		
c	9 cm			63 cm²
d	4.5 cm			18 cm²
e	5.5 cm		20 cm	
f	7.5 cm		26 cm	
g			28 cm	48 cm²

6 Calculate the perimeter and area of these shapes made from rectangles.

a
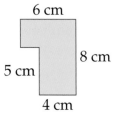
6 cm
8 cm
5 cm
4 cm

b
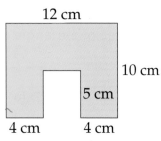
12 cm
10 cm
5 cm
4 cm   4 cm

c
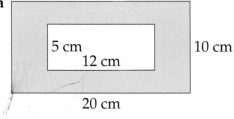
3 cm
2 cm
6 cm

7 Calculate the area of the shaded region.

a
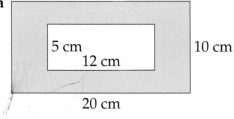
5 cm
12 cm
10 cm
20 cm

b
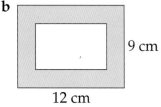
9 cm
12 cm
The shaded border is 2 cm wide.

8 On square grid paper, draw
   a two different rectangles, each with an area of $6\,\text{cm}^2$
   b two different right-angled triangles, each with an area of $6\,\text{cm}^2$
   c two different triangles, neither of them right-angled each with an area of $6\,\text{cm}^2$.

9 Calculate the area of these parallelograms.

a
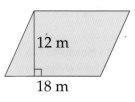
12 m
18 m

b
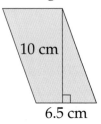
10 cm
6.5 cm

c
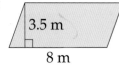
3.5 m
8 m

10 Calculate the area of these trapeziums.

a
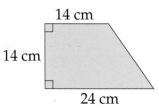
14 cm
14 cm
24 cm

b
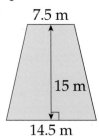
7.5 m
15 m
14.5 m

c
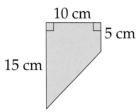
10 cm
5 cm
15 cm

Assessment criteria

- Convert one metric unit to another **Level 5**
- Solve problems involving conversion of units **Level 5**
- Deduce and use formulae for the area of a triangle and a parallelogram **Level 6**

Level 6

1 A parallelogram has a base of 18 cm and a perpendicular height of 8 cm.

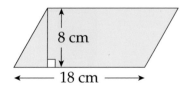

8 cm

18 cm

Four of these parallelograms are placed together to form a quadrilateral.

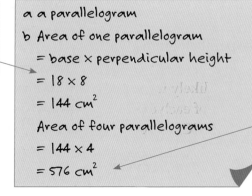

a What is the mathematical name of the quadrilateral?

b Calculate the area of the quadrilateral. State the units of your answer.

Bryony's answer ✔

The quadrilateral has two sets of parallel lines, two sets of equal lengths and no 90° angles.

a a parallelogram

b Area of one parallelogram

= base × perpendicular height

= 18 × 8

= 144 cm²

Area of four parallelograms

= 144 × 4

= 576 cm²

She measures the area in square centimetres.

Level 5

2 Find the missing numbers.

a 120 mm is the same as ☐ cm

b 120 cm is the same as ☐ m

c 120 m is the same as ☐ km

Key Stage 3 2006 4–6 Paper 2

3 Statistics

Probability

Most consumer items, such as cars or electronic devices, have experiments carried out on them to find out their probability of breaking or becoming defective. This probability is often related to the product's warranty – the length of time during which you can have the product repaired or replaced.

What's the point? Products with a longer warranty are likely to outlast those with a shorter one.

Check in

Level 4

1 Think about what the weather is likely to be where you live tomorrow. Describe in words the likelihood of each of these types of weather.
   a Rain   **b** Temperatures over 50°C   **c** Snow   **d** Cloud

Level 5

2 Convert each of these fractions to decimals.
   a $\frac{1}{2}$ **b** $\frac{2}{5}$ **c** $\frac{3}{8}$

3 Convert these percentages to decimals.
   a 35%   **b** 63.5%   **c** 0.7%

- Use diagrams and tables to record mutually exclusive outcomes

Keywords
Event
Outcome
Sample space diagram
Tree diagram
Trial

- A **trial** is a statistical experiment, like throwing a dice.

- An **outcome** is a possible result of a trial, like throwing a 5.

- An **event** is a collection of outcomes, like throwing an odd number (1, 3 or 5).

These two **tree diagrams** show possible outcomes when a normal dice is rolled.

You can record the outcomes for two events using either a **tree diagram** or a **sample space diagram**. Both of these diagrams show the possible outcomes when you spin two coins.

		Second coin	
		Head	Tail
First	**Head**	(H, H)	(H, T)
coin	**Tail**	(T, H)	(T, T)

> In simple cases, a tree diagram is quick and easy to draw.
> If there are lots of different outcomes, a sample space diagram may be more convenient.

You can choose to use a tree diagram or a sample space diagram depending on the problem you are solving.

Exercise 3a

1 Draw tree diagrams to show the results of these experiments.

  a Carole shuffles a set of cards marked 1 to 5, and then picks one at random and records the number on it.

  b Lee rolls an ordinary dice once, and records whether the score is odd or even.

2 The list on the right shows the possible outcomes when Danni chooses a flavour of food to feed her cat.

  Draw a tree diagram to show the possible outcomes.

Flavours available

Chicken

Tuna

Beef

Cod

3 For each of the following situations, draw **i** a two-stage tree diagram, and **ii** a sample space diagram to show the possible outcomes.

  a John throws two darts at a dartboard, aiming at the bull's-eye (centre). Each throw is either a hit or a miss.

  b Karen takes two Spanish tests. For each test, she can either pass or fail.

  c A hockey team plays two matches. Each match results in a win, a draw or a loss.

4 This sample space diagram shows the possible setting of two sets of traffic lights on a road.

  Draw a tree diagram to represent the same set of information.

		Second set		
		Red	**Amber**	**Green**
First set	**Red**	(R, R)	(R, A)	(R, G)
	Amber	(A, R)	(A, A)	(A, G)
	Green	(G, R)	(G, A)	(G, G)

5 This tree diagram shows the possible marks a student can be given in the school register for two days.

  Draw a sample space diagram to represent the same set of information.

```
        Day 1      Day 2
                    P
            P       L
                    A
                    P
            L       L
                    A
                    P
            A       L
                    A
```

P = Present, L = Late, A = Absent

---

discussion

You have used tree diagrams and sample space diagrams to show the possible outcomes of single events, and of two successive events. What sort of diagram would you use if you wanted to show the outcomes of three successive events?

- Understand and use the probability scale from 0 to 1
- Find probabilities based on equally likely outcomes
- Know that if the probability of an event occurring is p, then the probability of it not occurring is $1 - p$

Keywords

Certain	Impossible
Evens chance	Outcome
Event	Probability

Probability describes how likely an **event** is.

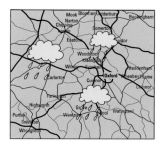

This event is highly unlikely. Its probability is close to zero.

This event is highly likely. Its probability is close to 1!

Probabilities can be shown on a scale of 0 to 1.

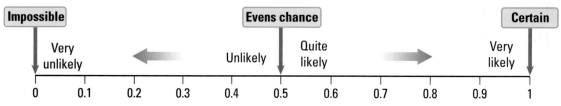

You can work out the probability of a simple event using a formula.

- Probability of an event
$$= \frac{\text{Number of outcomes that belong to the event}}{\text{Total number of possible outcomes}}$$

The formula only works if all the possible **outcomes** are equally likely.

example

Six students in a class of thirty wear glasses. What is the probability that a student chosen at random
a wears glasses   **b** does not wear glasses?

- -

a There are 30 possible outcomes.
There are 6 outcomes of 'the student wears glasses'.
Using the formula, the probability is $\frac{6}{30} = \frac{1}{5}$.

b Probability of wearing glasses $= 0.2$
so probability of not wearing glasses $= 1 - 0.2 = 0.8$.

- If the probability of an event occurring is p, then the probability of it not occurring is $1 - p$.

Exercise 3b

1 Copy this probability scale.

Write each of these words into the appropriate box. The first two are done for you.

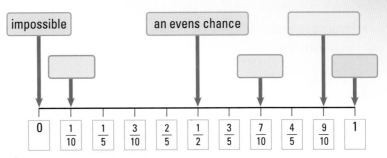

impossible	an evens chance	very unlikely
likely	almost certain	certain

2 Draw a probability scale, labelling it in percentages. Mark every 10% along the scale from 0% to 100%.

Draw boxes and arrows to show where these labels might go.

almost impossible	an evens chance	fairly unlikely
better than evens chance	certain	impossible

3 Explain in words how likely each of these events is. Suggest a possible value for the probability in each case.
  a It will snow at your school tomorrow.
  b A person chosen at random from your class is twelve years old.
  c You will have a maths lesson next week.
  d You get an even score when you roll an ordinary dice.

4 An ordinary dice is rolled once.
Use the formula to work out the probability of the number rolled being
  a exactly 6   **b** a multiple of 3   **c** less than 4   **d** 7

5 a The probability of a football team winning a game is 0.3. What is the probability that they will not win the game?
  b There is a 45% chance of snow tonight. What is the probability that it will not snow?
  c A teacher chooses a student at random from class 8X. If the probability of the chosen student being female is $\frac{7}{16}$, what is the probability that they are male?

Did you know?

In the British national lottery there are 49 balls and six are chosen at random. You have a 1 in 13 983 816 chance of winning the big prize!

discussion

Sarah carried out a survey asking teenagers on which days they preferred to go shopping. Before starting the survey she said, "There are two days in the weekend, so the probability that people pick a Saturday or Sunday should be $\frac{2}{7}$." Is Sarah correct?

- Estimate probabilities by collecting data from an experiment

Keywords
Estimate
Experiment
Trials

Ravi the technician is testing a set of computers.

He wants to know the likelihood of a computer passing the quality tests.

Ravi thinks, 'There are only two possible outcomes – pass or fail. So the probability that the next computer passes is 50%.'

Then he tests 100 computers and finds that 78 pass the test.

Ravi **estimates** the probability of passing as 78 ÷ 100 = 0.78 or 78%.

- An **experiment** is a series of **trials**.

In an experiment, you can estimate the probability of an event using the formula:

$$\text{Experimental probability} = \frac{\text{Number of successful trials}}{\text{Total number of trials}}$$

example

Ravi carries out safety checks on 46 projectors. Two of the projectors fail the test.

a Estimate the probability of a projector failing the test.

b How could Ravi get a better estimate?

· ·

a This is an experiment with 46 trials, and two 'successes'.

Using the formula,

A 'success' is not always a good thing!

$$\text{Experimental probability of failing safety test} = \frac{\text{Number of projectors that fail}}{\text{Total number tested}}$$

$$= \frac{2}{46} = \frac{1}{23} = 0.043 = 4.3\%$$

b Ravi could test more projectors.

Exercise 3c

1 A scientist checks some trees to see whether they are infected with a disease. She checks 28 trees, and 5 of them are infected. Estimate the probability that a tree chosen at random has the disease.

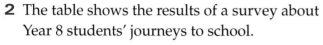

2 The table shows the results of a survey about Year 8 students' journeys to school.

Transport	Cycle	Walk	Bus	Car
Number	18	29	14	8

Estimate the probability that a student chosen at random from Year 8 would have cycled to school.

3 This table shows the number of points scored by twenty competitors in an athletics competition.

15	14	11	8	11	17	7	16	16	8
18	10	4	17	13	6	15	3	9	12

Use the data in the table to estimate the probability that a competitor chosen at random would have scored more than ten points.

4 Andy and Ben both carry out experiments to estimate the probability of a particular kind of seed germinating. The table shows their results.

	Andy	Ben
Germinated	32	58
Failed	18	42

 a Estimate the probability of a seed germinating, using Andy's results.
 b Now estimate the probability using Ben's results.
 c Whose results do you think should be more reliable – Andy's or Ben's?

discussion

Tara wants to estimate the probability of it snowing in London next Christmas Day. Explain how she could do this.

• Compare experimental probabilities with theoretical probabilities

Keywords
Biased
Experiment
Theoretical probability

You can use an **experiment** to estimate a probability.

• If you repeat an experiment you will usually get different results, and different estimates for the probability.

---

example

Karl and Jenny both tested this spinner. The table shows their results.

Estimate the probability of the spinner landing on green using

a Karl's data   **b** Jenny's data.

	Red	Blue	Green	Yellow
Karl	8	14	16	22
Jenny	12	24	28	36

a 16 green, 8 + 14 + 16 + 22 = 60 outcomes altogether
Estimated probability = 16 ÷ 60 = 0.266…

> In this case, the calculated probabilities are quite similar – they might not be!

b 28 green, 12 + 24 + 28 + 36 = 100 outcomes altogether
Estimated probability = 28 ÷ 100 = 0.28

Jenny's results should be more reliable because her experiment had more trials.

• Increasing the number of trials should give more reliable results.

You can use an experiment to check a **theoretical probability**.

---

example

Jim tests a coin by spinning it 20 times. The coin lands on Heads 14 times. Is the coin fair? How can Jim be sure that his results are reliable?

Jim knows that the theoretical probability of getting Heads with a fair coin is 0.5.

Estimated probability = 14 ÷ 20 = 0.7

The difference between the probabilities suggests that the coin might be **biased** towards Heads.

But the number of trials in the experiment is low (only 20).

> An experiment is biased if it does not have equally likely outcomes.

Jim could be more convinced if he spun the coin more times.

Exercise 3d

1 Sam tested a coin to see if it was fair. The table shows his results.

Heads	Tails
31	49

   a How many trials did Sam carry out?
   b Estimate the probabilities of getting heads and tails with this coin, using the results of Sam's experiment.
   c Explain whether you think the coin was fair.
   d Explain what Sam could do to make his results more reliable.

2 A technician tested all of the computers on a network. Each machine either passed or failed the test. The table shows the results of the tests.

Pass	Fail
62	15

   a Use these results to estimate the probability that a computer chosen at random would pass the test.
   b The technician then tested the machines on another network. 28 machines were tested and five of them failed the test. Were the machines on this second network more or less likely to pass the test than those on the first network? Explain your answer.

3 Kelly put these cards into a bag. She then picked one card out of the bag, noted the colour, and put the card back.

   a Work out the theoretical probability of Kelly picking each colour. Kelly carried out an experiment to estimate the probability of picking each colour. The table shows her results.

Colour	Green	Red	Blue	Yellow
Frequency	48	51	19	12

   b Use the results in the table to estimate the experimental probability for each result.
   c Why are the experimental and theoretical probabilities different?

3a

1 Draw a tree diagram for each of these situations.

   a An ordinary dice is rolled, and the score is noted; then a coin is spun, and the result is recorded.

   b An experimenter rolls an ordinary dice, and notes whether the score is odd or even; then a coin is spun, and the result is recorded.

   c A coin is spun, and the result is written down; then the experimenter rolls a dice and records whether or not the result is a multiple of 3.

2 Draw a sample space diagram for each of these situations.

   a A player turns up two cards from a pack of playing cards, and notes the suits.

   b A player picks two letters from a bag of letter tiles. Each tile has a vowel or a consonant.

   c A shopper picks two cans of cat food from a shelf. The flavours available are chicken, beef and fish.

Hearts   Diamonds   Clubs   Spades

3b

3 A computer is used to choose a random whole number between 1 and 100 (inclusive).

Find the probability that the chosen number is

   a exactly 13

   b even

   c a multiple of 10

   d a multiple of 7

3c

4 Here are the scores obtained by a sample of people who carried out a safety test.

| 15 | 17 | 13 | 18 | 19 | 20 | 19 | 13 | 14 | 19 |
| 20 | 11 | 12 | 16 | 18 | 17 | 20 | 14 | 18 | 13 |

   a A score of 15 or more is needed to pass the test. Estimate the experimental probability of passing the test.

   b If 500 people took the test, how many would you expect to pass? Explain your answer.

5 Max put 25 blue counters, 50 red counters and 25 yellow
counters into a bag.
He shook the bag, picked a counter without looking,
recorded the colour and returned the counter to the bag.
He did this 200 times altogether.

  a Calculate the theoretical probability of choosing each
  colour.
  b Max actually obtained 61 blues, 108 reds and 31 yellows.
  Estimate the experimental probability of obtaining each
  colour.
  c Max thought that the theoretical and experimental
  probabilities were different. Give an example of a factor
  that could have caused this difference.

Maths Life

Traditional games and pastimes

It would be very boring if games played the same way each time. Many games include an element of chance so that this doesn't happen. But is it all chance or can you sometimes tip the odds in your favour?

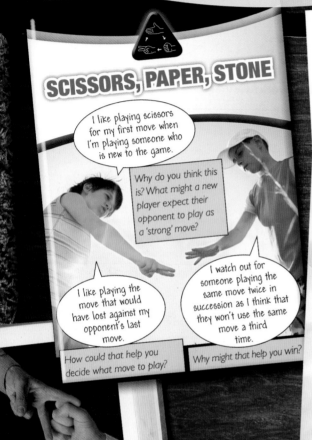

SCISSORS, PAPER, STONE

> I like playing scissors for my first move when I'm playing someone who is new to the game.

> Why do you think this is? What might a new player expect their opponent to play as a 'strong' move?

> I like playing the move that would have lost against my opponent's last move.

How could that help you decide what move to play?

> I watch out for someone playing the same move twice in succession as I think that they won't use the same move a third time.

Why might that help you win?

Play scissors, paper stone against someone who hasn't read any of these ideas.

Do any of the strategies help you to beat your opponent?

Are there any other strategies that you use?

Which strategies would you recommend?

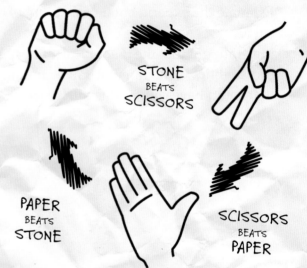

SCISSORS, PAPER, STONE
A traditional school playground game that is sometimes called Rock, Paper Scissors.

STONE BEATS SCISSORS

PAPER BEATS STONE

SCISSORS BEATS PAPER

- What different pairs of moves can happen in a game of scissors, paper, stone?
- How many are winning moves, how many draw and how many lose?
- If you and your opponent both pick moves at random, how likely are you to win?

How likely are you to lose or to draw?

DID YOU KNOW?

Scissors, paper, stone is interesting in that any one of the items can be both stronger and weaker depending on what it is being used against – a stone can beat scissors but is beaten by paper. Paper beats stone but can be beaten by scissors and so on. This is why always playing the same move would not be a winning strategy – there's no one thing that is always stronger than all the others.

The same idea is sometimes used in the programming of combat or strategy video games where, for example, cavalry might overcome archers, archers overcome spearmen and spearmen overcome cavalry. Using 'stronger than this but weaker than that' relationships between elements in the game means that the player can't just play one strategy to win.

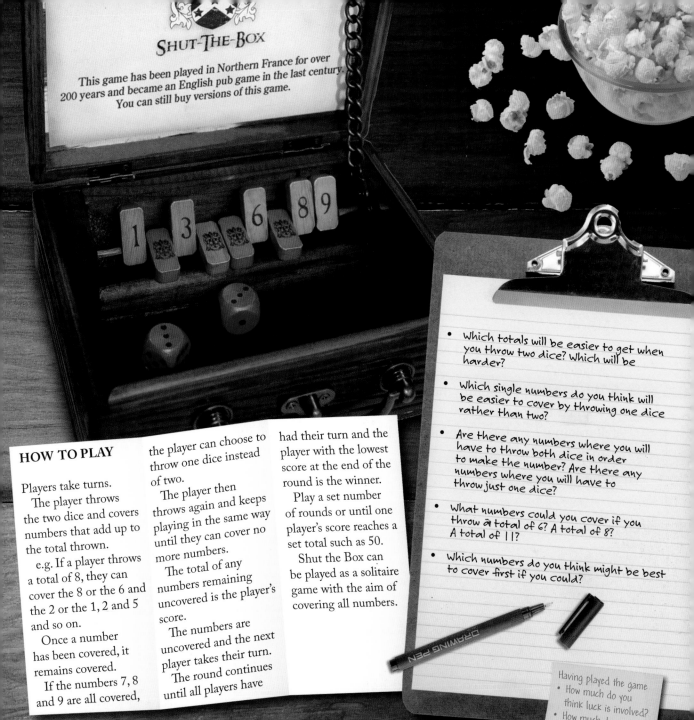

SHUT-THE-BOX

This game has been played in Northern France for over 200 years and became an English pub game in the last century. You can still buy versions of this game.

HOW TO PLAY

Players take turns.

The player throws the two dice and covers numbers that add up to the total thrown.

e.g. If a player throws a total of 8, they can cover the 8 or the 6 and the 2 or the 1, 2 and 5 and so on.

Once a number has been covered, it remains covered.

If the numbers 7, 8 and 9 are all covered, the player can choose to throw one dice instead of two.

The player then throws again and keeps playing in the same way until they can cover no more numbers.

The total of any numbers remaining uncovered is the player's score.

The numbers are uncovered and the next player takes their turn.

The round continues until all players have had their turn and the player with the lowest score at the end of the round is the winner.

Play a set number of rounds or until one player's score reaches a set total such as 50.

Shut the Box can be played as a solitaire game with the aim of covering all numbers.

- Which totals will be easier to get when you throw two dice? Which will be harder?

- Which single numbers do you think will be easier to cover by throwing one dice rather than two?

- Are there any numbers where you will have to throw both dice in order to make the number? Are there any numbers where you will have to throw just one dice?

- What numbers could you cover if you throw a total of 6? A total of 8? A total of 11?

- Which numbers do you think might be best to cover first if you could?

Having played the game
- How much do you think luck is involved?
- How much do you think skill and thinking can help?

Play the game a few times on this board, using counters or coins to cover the numbers.

| 1 | 2 | 3 | 4 | 5 | 6 | 7 | 8 | 9 |

43

Assessment criteria
- Find and record all possible mutually exclusive outcomes for single events and two successive events in a systematic way **Level 6**
- Understand and use the probability scale from 0 to 1 **Level 5**

Level 5

1 Katie and Marcus decide to ask people if they had walked under a ladder in the last month.
The table shows the results.

	Number of people asked	Number who had walked under a ladder	Number who had not walked under a ladder
Katie	50	20	30
Marcus	100		60

a How many people told Marcus they had walked under a ladder?

b What is the probability that Katie was told they had not walked under a ladder?

c Explain why Marcus' results are likely to be more reliable than Katie's.

Brendon's answer ✔

Brendon subtracts 60 from 100.

a 40

b $\frac{30}{50}$ = $\frac{3}{5}$ or 0.6

c Marcus asked more people and so the results are likely to be more reliable

Brendon only uses the 'Katie' row. 30 out of 50 people had not worked under a ladder.

Level 5

2 a Aiden puts 2 white counters and 1 black counter in a bag.
He is going to take one counter without looking.
What is the probability that the counter will be black?

b Aiden puts the counter back into the bag and then puts more black counters in the bag.
He is going to take one counter without looking.
The probability that the counter will be black is now $\frac{2}{3}$
How many more black counters did Aiden put into the bag?

Key Stage 3 2005 4–6 Paper 2

4 Number

Fractions, decimals and percentages

Lots of people rush to the shops after Christmas for the January sales hoping to buy the things they want at a lower price. Shops often advertise reductions in price as a percentage. A larger percentage means a larger saving.

What's the point? If you understand how percentages work, it can save you money!

Check in

Level 3

1 Write these numbers as decimals.

  a 3 tenths   **b** 7 units and 4 tenths   **c** 5 hundredths

Level 4

2 Write these numbers in order starting with the smallest.

  0.4   0.39   0.3   0.23   0.35

3 Calculate these percentages using a mental method.

  a 50% of £60   **b** 10% of 35 kg   **c** 1% of 1800 m

- Understand and use decimal notation and place value
- Compare and order decimals

Keywords
Decimal
Digit
Inequality

- You can write tenths, hundredths and thousandths using **decimals**.

11 seconds 45 hundredths of a second.

= 11 seconds + 4 tenths + 5 hundredths

= 11.45 seconds

Thousands	Hundreds	Tens	Units	.	Tenths	Hundredths	Thousandths
1000	100	10	1	.	$\frac{1}{10}$	$\frac{1}{100}$	$\frac{1}{1000}$
		1	1	•	4	5	

- To compare decimals, **digits** in the same position must be compared, beginning with the first non-zero digit.

example

Which of these numbers is the smallest: 0.047 or 0.0462?

Re-write the numbers vertically, making sure that the decimal points are lined up.

    0.047   has a thousandths digit of 7

    0.0462   has a thousandths digit of 6

    0.0462 < 0.047

> The hundredths digits are the same, so compare the thousandths.

> < means that 0.0462 is smaller than 0.047.

- You can use **inequality** signs to put data involving decimal numbers into groups.

example

Didier records the time it takes ten students to run 100 m.

13.7	16.4	19.8	17.5	21.3
13.9	14.14	18.6	19.3	20.0

Put this data into a frequency table.

> 18 ≤ t < 20 means greater than or equal to 18 seconds but less than 20 seconds. The time 20.0 goes into the next group, 20 ≤ t < 22.

Time t (seconds)	Frequency
12 ≤ t < 14	2
14 ≤ t < 16	1
16 ≤ t < 18	2
18 ≤ t < 20	3
20 ≤ t < 22	2

p. 166

Exercise 4a

1 Write the value of the digit 7 in each of these numbers.
Write your answer in words, in figures and as a fraction
where appropriate.

   a 3730   **b** 17 140   **c** 108 373   **d** 765 283

   e 1 703 018   **f** 37.2   **g** 28.74   **h** 62.057

2 Copy these and place $<$ or $>$ between each pair of numbers
to show which number is the largest.

   a 0.37 ☐ 0.4   **b** 1.52 ☐ 1.51   **c** 5.284 ☐ 5.293

   d 3.35 ☐ 3.3   **e** 4.37 ☐ 4.35   **f** 1.654 ☐ 1.66

3 Write these numbers in order starting with the smallest.

   a 3.4   3.39   3.3   3.23   3

   b 3.74   3.757   3.72   3.88   3.8

   c 0.033   0.035   0.03   0.0362   0.0351

4 Copy these and place $<$ or $>$ between each pair of numbers
to show which number is the largest.

> You will need to change the measurements to the same units.

   a 3.2 m ☐ 325 cm   **b** 25 mm ☐ 2.4 cm

   c 1.95 kg ☐ 1960 g   **d** 4.5 m ☐ 46 cm

5 Haroon records the heights in metres of twenty student in his class.

   1.34   1.56   1.75   1.65   1.39

   1.5   1.67   1.55   1.4   1.31

   1.45   1.62   1.71   1.58   1.52

   1.47   1.61   1.6   1.45   1.7

Height h (metres)	Frequency
$1.3 \leq h < 1.4$	
$1.4 \leq h < 1.5$	
$1.5 \leq h < 1.6$	
$1.6 \leq h < 1.7$	
$1.7 \leq h < 1.8$	

Copy and complete his frequency table.

Which numbers are the most difficult to place in
Haroon's table? Explain your answer.

group work

a Collect some data you can measure on the students in
your class.
For example, the heights of each student in metres; the
distance they live from school in km.

b Put your data into a frequency table using inequalities
for each group.

- Recognise the equivalence of fractions and decimals
- Convert between decimals and fractions
- Order fractions

Keywords

Decimal	Recurring
Denominator	Terminating
Fraction	Unit fraction
Numerator	

The number 0.357 stands for 3 tenths,
5 hundredths and 7 thousandths

$$0.357 = \frac{3}{10} + \frac{5}{100} + \frac{7}{1000}$$

$$= \frac{300}{1000} + \frac{50}{1000} + \frac{7}{1000}$$

$$= \frac{357}{1000}$$

Thousands	Hundreds	Tens	Units	.	Tenths	Hundredths	Thousandths
1000	100	10	1	.	$\frac{1}{10}$	$\frac{1}{100}$	$\frac{1}{1000}$
			0	**•**	**3**	**5**	**7**

- You can use place value to convert a **terminating decimal** into a **fraction**.

A terminating decimal has a fixed number of decimal places.

- You can convert a fraction into a decimal by dividing the **numerator** by the **denominator**.

You can divide using short division...

$$8\overline{)5.000} = 0.625$$

or a calculator.

example

Convert

a 0.8 into a fraction

b 0.64 into a fraction

c $\frac{5}{8}$ into a decimal

- -

a $0.8 = \frac{8}{10}$

$$\frac{8}{10} \overset{\div 2}{\underset{\div 2}{=}} \frac{4}{5}$$

b $0.64 = \frac{64}{100}$

$$\frac{64}{100} \overset{\div 4}{\underset{\div 4}{=}} \frac{16}{25}$$

c $\frac{5}{8} = 5 \div 8$

$$\frac{5}{8} = 0.625$$

- You can order fractions by converting them to decimals.

The decimal 0.333... is called a **recurring** decimal. It can be written as 0.3̇.

example

Put these fractions in order from lowest to highest: $\frac{2}{5}$ $\frac{3}{8}$ $\frac{1}{3}$

- -

$\frac{2}{5} = 2 \div 5 = 0.4$ $\frac{3}{8} = 3 \div 8 = 0.375$ $\frac{1}{3} = 1 \div 3 = 0.333...$

Putting the decimals in order   0.333...   0.375   0.4

Putting the fractions in order $\frac{1}{3}$ $\frac{3}{8}$ $\frac{2}{5}$

Exercise 4b

1 Which of these are terminating decimals?

   a 0.325   **b** 0.666…   **c** 0.1212… **d** 0.4785   **e** 0.999

2 Write these decimals as fractions in their simplest form.

   a 0.3   **b** 0.6   **c** 0.75   **d** 0.28   **e** 0.66

   f 0.05   **g** 0.375   **h** 0.185   **i** 0.095   **j** 0.008

3 Write these fractions as decimals without using a calculator.

   a $\frac{1}{10}$ **b** $\frac{13}{20}$ **c** $\frac{7}{25}$ **d** $\frac{33}{50}$ **e** $\frac{15}{25}$

   f $\frac{3}{5}$ **g** $\frac{19}{20}$ **h** $\frac{3}{4}$ **i** $\frac{7}{10}$ **j** $\frac{11}{50}$

4 Copy these and place < or > between each pair of numbers to show which number is the largest.

   a 0.3 ☐ 0.28   **b** $\frac{7}{8}$ ☐ $\frac{4}{5}$ **c** $\frac{5}{8}$ ☐ $\frac{7}{16}$ **d** 0.37 ☐ $\frac{5}{16}$

   e $\frac{3}{5}$ ☐ $\frac{5}{7}$ **f** 0.54 ☐ $\frac{6}{11}$ **g** $\frac{4}{9}$ ☐ $\frac{3}{7}$ **h** 0.114 ☐ $\frac{1}{9}$

5 Put these fractions in order from lowest to highest.

   a $\frac{3}{7}$ $\frac{4}{5}$ $\frac{7}{8}$ $\frac{3}{4}$

   b $\frac{1}{3}$ $\frac{2}{9}$ $\frac{3}{13}$ $\frac{4}{19}$

   c $\frac{2}{5}$ $\frac{4}{9}$ $\frac{7}{16}$ $\frac{9}{20}$

6 Write these decimals as fractions in their simplest form.

   a 1.5   **b** 2.75   **c** 3.4   **d** 1.35   **e** 1.475

7 Write these fractions as decimals using an appropriate method.

   a $1\frac{7}{10}$ **b** $1\frac{3}{4}$ **c** $1\frac{7}{20}$ **d** $2\frac{5}{16}$ **e** $3\frac{11}{25}$

---

investigation

Calvin thinks that only fractions with a denominator of 2, 4, 5, 10 and 20 will change into terminating decimals. See if he is correct by converting every **unit fraction** from $\frac{1}{2}$ up to $\frac{1}{25}$ into a decimal using your calculator. Try to explain your findings.

A **unit fraction** has a numerator of 1.

- Find equivalent fractions
- Add and subtract fractions with different denominators

- You can add and subtract fractions that have the same denominator.

example

Francis eats $\frac{1}{5}$ of a pizza, and Georgia eats $\frac{3}{5}$ of the pizza.

What fraction of the pizza has been eaten?

Francis and Georgia eat $\frac{1}{5} + \frac{3}{5} = \frac{1+3}{5} = \frac{4}{5}$

They eat $\frac{4}{5}$ of the pizza.

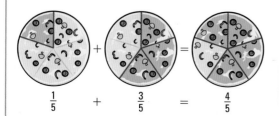

$$\frac{1}{5} \quad + \quad \frac{3}{5} \quad = \quad \frac{4}{5}$$

When the **denominators** are the same you can just add the **numerators**.

- You can add or subtract fractions with different denominators by first writing them as **equivalent fractions** with the same denominator.

example

Calculate   **a** $\frac{2}{3} + \frac{1}{4}$ **b** $\frac{3}{5} - \frac{5}{10}$

Re-write as equivalent fractions with the same denominator.

a
$$\overset{\times 4}{\underset{\times 4}{\frac{2}{3} = \frac{8}{12}}} \quad \overset{\times 3}{\underset{\times 3}{\frac{1}{4} = \frac{3}{12}}}$$

b
$$\overset{\times 2}{\underset{\times 2}{\frac{3}{5} = \frac{6}{10}}}$$

p. 10

The common denominator is 12.
This is the **lowest common multiple** of 3 and 4.

The common denominator is 10.
This is the **lowest common multiple** of 5 and 10.

Add the numerators

$$\frac{8}{12} + \frac{3}{12} = \frac{8+3}{12} = \frac{11}{12}$$

Subtract the numerators

$$\frac{6}{10} - \frac{5}{10} = \frac{6-5}{10} = \frac{1}{10}$$

Exercise 4c

1 Find the missing number in each of these pairs of equivalent fractions.

a $\frac{1}{4} = \frac{\square}{12}$ **b** $\frac{2}{5} = \frac{\square}{25}$ **c** $\frac{3}{7} = \frac{\square}{28}$ **d** $\frac{4}{9} = \frac{\square}{63}$

e $\frac{5}{8} = \frac{45}{\square}$ **f** $\frac{6}{11} = \frac{\square}{88}$ **g** $\frac{7}{12} = \frac{\square}{36}$ **h** $\frac{8}{15} = \frac{\square}{150}$

2 Calculate each of these, giving your answer as a fraction in its simplest form.

a $\frac{2}{7} + \frac{3}{7}$ **b** $\frac{1}{8} + \frac{5}{8}$ **c** $\frac{4}{5} - \frac{1}{5}$ **d** $\frac{7}{8} - \frac{5}{8}$

e $\frac{3}{11} + \frac{5}{11}$ **f** $\frac{9}{13} - \frac{6}{13}$ **g** $\frac{5}{3} - \frac{1}{3}$ **h** $\frac{8}{5} - \frac{4}{5}$

3 Copy the grids and use them to show how to add each of these pairs of fractions.

a $\frac{1}{2} + \frac{1}{5}$

b $\frac{2}{3} + \frac{1}{4}$

c $\frac{2}{5} + \frac{1}{3}$

4 Calculate each of these additions and subtractions, giving your answer as a fraction in its simplest form.

a $\frac{1}{3} + \frac{1}{4}$ **b** $\frac{2}{3} + \frac{1}{5}$ **c** $\frac{1}{6} + \frac{1}{5}$ **d** $\frac{2}{5} + \frac{1}{3}$

e $\frac{5}{8} + \frac{1}{3}$ **f** $\frac{3}{10} + \frac{1}{3}$ **g** $\frac{8}{9} - \frac{3}{5}$ **h** $\frac{9}{11} - \frac{2}{3}$

5 Kyle owns lots of computer games. Exactly $\frac{2}{5}$ of his games are sports games and $\frac{1}{4}$ of his games are action games. The rest of his games are adventure games. What fraction of Kyle's computer games are adventure games?

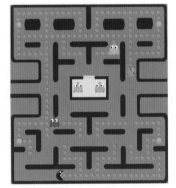

challenge

Jameela and Ursula are working out $\frac{2}{9} + \frac{4}{7}$

Ursula says   'The answer is $\frac{6}{16}$.'

Jameela says   'The answer must be more than a half.'

a Explain what Ursula has done wrong.
b Explain how Jameela knows the answer is more than a half.
c Work out the correct answer.

- Calculate a fraction of a number or quantity
- Begin to multiply a fraction by an integer
- Express one number as a fraction of another number

Keywords
Fraction

You can often find a **fraction** of an amount by using a mental method.

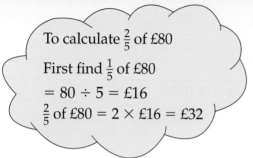

To calculate $\frac{2}{5}$ of £80

First find $\frac{1}{5}$ of £80

$= 80 \div 5 = £16$

$\frac{2}{5}$ of £80 $= 2 \times £16 = £32$

You could use a calculator instead:

2 ÷ 5 × 80

32

Finding $\frac{1}{5}$ of something is the same as dividing by 5.

Alternatively you could use a written method.
Just multiply the fraction by the amount.

example

Find **a** $\frac{3}{4}$ of 60 kg **b** $\frac{3}{8}$ of 10 miles.

. . . .

a

$\frac{3}{4}$ of $60 = \frac{1}{4} \times 3 \times 60$

$= \frac{1 \times 180}{4}$

$= \frac{180}{4}$

$= 45$ kg

b

$\frac{3}{8}$ of $10 = \frac{1}{8} \times 3 \times 10$

$= \frac{1 \times 30}{8}$

$= \frac{30}{8}$

$= 3\frac{6}{8} = 3\frac{3}{4}$ miles

You can write one number as a fraction of another number.

example

John and Gina share £80 between them. John receives £32 and Gina gets the rest.
What fraction of the money does John have?

. . . .

There is £80 altogether.
John receives £32 of the money.

So John has $\frac{32}{80}$ of the money.

$\frac{32}{80}$ can be simplified by cancelling down:

So John has $\frac{2}{5}$ of the money.

$$\overset{\div 16}{\frac{32}{80} = \frac{2}{5}}$$
$$\div 16$$

Exercise 4d

1 Use a mental method to calculate

  a $\frac{1}{3}$ of £15   **b** $\frac{1}{10}$ of 50 MB   **c** $\frac{1}{8}$ of 32 DVDs

  d $\frac{1}{6}$ of 30 pupils   **e** $\frac{4}{5}$ of 25 shops   **f** $\frac{2}{3}$ of 120 g

2 Calculate each of these, leaving your answer in its simplest form and as a mixed number where appropriate.

  a $4 \times \frac{1}{9}$ **b** $6 \times \frac{1}{12}$ **c** $12 \times \frac{1}{18}$

  d $2 \times \frac{2}{3}$ **e** $2 \times \frac{7}{8}$ **f** $\frac{5}{6} \times 4$

3 Calculate these, leaving your answer as a mixed number where appropriate.

  a $\frac{3}{4}$ of 7 feet   **b** $\frac{2}{3}$ of 14 million   **c** $\frac{5}{8}$ of 30 km

  d $\frac{3}{10}$ of 400 kg   **e** $\frac{5}{7}$ of 25 m   **f** $\frac{7}{25}$ of 40 mm

4 Use an appropriate method to calculate these amounts. Where possible give your answer to 2 decimal places.

  a $\frac{3}{5}$ of 148 kg   **b** $\frac{5}{12}$ of £295   **c** $\frac{3}{11}$ of 25 km

  d $\frac{4}{7}$ of 5 kg   **e** $\frac{4}{9}$ of 200 litres   **f** $\frac{3}{20}$ of 360°

5 a A DVD costs £12.95. In a sale all prices are reduced by $\frac{3}{10}$. What is the sale price of the DVD?

  b Isaac earns £28 a week from his paper round. He spends £10 and saves the rest. What fraction of his money does he save?

6 a What fraction of 30 is 12?

  b What fraction of 1 hour is 55 minutes?

  c What fraction of 1 foot is 8 inches?

  d What fraction of July is 1 week?

Did you know?

The average family in the UK spends between $\frac{1}{6}$ and $\frac{1}{10}$ of their income on food. In Sierra Leone the fraction is around $\frac{2}{3}$.

---

challenge

An oak tree is 60 feet tall. Each year the tree increases in height by $\frac{1}{10}$.

  a What is the height of the tree after one year?

  b What is the height of the tree after two years?

  c In how many years will the tree be over 100 feet tall?

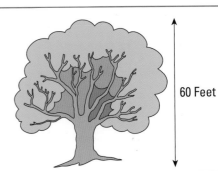

60 Feet

4e Percentages of amounts

LEVEL 5/6

- Recognise the equivalence of fractions and decimals
- Express one number as a percentage of another number
- Calculate a percentage of an amount using mental, written and calculator methods

Keywords
Decimal
Equivalent fraction
Percentage

You can use informal mental methods to calculate **percentages** of amounts.

example

Calculate **a** 65% of 80 kg **b** 35% of £180

a $50\% \text{ of } 80\text{ kg} = \frac{1}{2} \text{ of } 80$
$= 40$

$10\% \text{ of } 80\text{ kg} = \frac{1}{10} \text{ of } 80$
$= 8$

$5\% \text{ of } 80\text{ kg} = \frac{1}{2} \text{ of } 8$
$= 4$

5% = half of 10%

$65\% \text{ of } 80\text{ kg} = 40 + 8 + 4$
$= 52\text{ kg}$

b $25\% \text{ of } 180 = \frac{1}{4} \text{ of } 180$
$= 45$

$10\% \text{ of } 180 = \frac{1}{10} \text{ of } 180$
$= 18$

$35\% \text{ of } £180 = 45 + 18$
$= £63$

You can calculate a percentage of an amount using an **equivalent fraction** or **decimal**.

example

Calculate 12% of £68.

Using an equivalent fraction:

$12\% \text{ of } 68 = \frac{12}{100} \text{ of } 68$
$= \frac{12 \times 68}{100}$
$= \frac{816}{100}$
$= £8.16$

Using an equivalent decimal:

$12\% \text{ of } 68 = \frac{12}{100} \text{ of } 68$
$= 12 \div 100 \times 68$
$= 0.12 \times 68$
$= £8.16$

You could use a calculator to help you with the working

Exercise 4e

1 Calculate these percentages using a mental method.

    a 50% of £70   **b** 10% of 45 kg

    c 1% of 1500 m   **d** 25% of 256 MB

2 Calculate these percentages using a mental method.

    a 20% of £40   **b** 5% of 60 DVDs   **c** 2% of 150 MB

    d 40% of £75   **e** 60% of £700   **f** 15% of 180°

    g 11% of £5500   **h** 30% of 250 N   **i** 8% of 240 ml

    j 35% of £20 000 **k** 65% of 440 yards **l** 95% of 400 kJ

3 Calculate these using a mental, written or calculator method, giving
   your answers to 2 decimal places where appropriate.

    a 18% of £40   **b** 7% of 71 kg   **c** 11% of 58 km

    d 16% of 85 euros **e** 3% of 75 mm   **f** 24% of 55 kB

    g 29% of 18 litres **h** 35% of 92 mph   **i** 46% of 46 m

    j 49% of 90 MB   **k** 63% of 15 cm   **l** 77% of 90°

4 Calculate these using a calculator. Show all the steps of your working
   out, and give your answer to 2 decimal places where appropriate.

    a 12% of £148   **b** 35% of 96 kg   **c** 52% of 512 MB

    d 86% of 355 km   **e** 4% of 185 mm   **f** 55% of 420 ml

    g 2.5% of £800   **h** 47% of 925 g   **i** 12.5% of 48 N

    j 41% of £8000   **k** 73% of 840 kJ   **l** 110% of 5 million

5 a Naheeda scores 45% in her English exam. The maximum score on
     the exam is 120. How many marks did Naheeda score on the exam?

    b Gavin starts to download an 8 GB file from the internet.
     He downloads 65% of the file in 10 minutes. How much
     of the file has he downloaded?

    c The label on the back of a 150 g packet of crisps says that
     the crisps are 6% fat. How much fat is that in grams?

investigation

a Sheena eats 240 g of baked beans. The beans contain

       Sugar   5%

       Fat   0.2%

       Protein   4.9%

       Carbohydrates   13%

   Calculate how much sugar, fat, protein and carbohydrate
   Sheena has eaten.

b Investigate the labels on the back of other things that you eat.

- Convert between percentages, fractions and decimals
- Express one number as a percentage of another.

Keywords
Decimal
Fraction
Percentage

- You can convert between **fractions**, **decimals** and **percentages** using a range of mental methods.

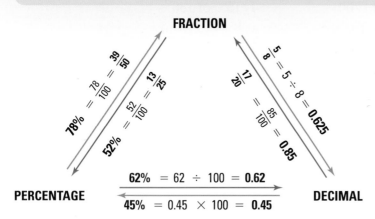

FRACTION

$$78\% = \frac{78}{100} = \frac{39}{50}$$

$$52\% = \frac{52}{100} = \frac{13}{25}$$

$$\frac{5}{8} = 5 \div 8 = 0.625$$

$$\frac{17}{20} = \frac{85}{100} = 0.85$$

$$62\% = 62 \div 100 = 0.62$$

$$45\% = 0.45 \times 100 = 0.45$$

PERCENTAGE   **DECIMAL**

---

example

Convert 0.64 into   **a** a fraction   **b** a percentage.

. . . .

a

$$0.64 = \frac{64}{100} \overset{\div 4}{\underset{\div 4}{=}} \frac{16}{25}$$

b

$$0.64 = \frac{64}{100} = 64\%$$

- You can write one number as a percentage of another number.

---

example

Kira weighs 52 kg. Jack weighs 80 kg.

What percentage of Jack's weight is Kira?

. . . .

Jack weighs 80 kg.

Kira weighs 52 kg.

So Kira is $\frac{52}{80}$ of Jack's weight.

$$\frac{52}{80} = 52 \div 80$$
$$= 0.65$$
$$= 65\%$$

> This fraction can be changed into a decimal using a calculator.

So Kira is 65% of Jack's weight.

Exercise 4f

1 This number line is split into twentieths.

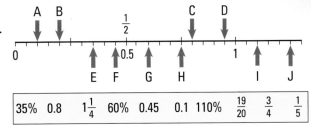

a Match each of the fractions, decimals and percentages to the letters on the number line.

b Write each letter with its percentage, fraction and decimal equivalent.

| 35% | 0.8 | $1\frac{1}{4}$ | 60% | 0.45 | 0.1 | 110% | $\frac{19}{20}$ | $\frac{3}{4}$ | $\frac{1}{5}$ |

2 Write these percentages as fractions in their simplest form.

a 40%   **b** 75%   **c** 85%   **d** 45%   **e** 32%

f 5%   **g** 1%   **h** 125%   **i** 105%   **j** 2.5%

3 Write these percentages as decimals.

a 80%   **b** 25%   **c** 8%   **d** 35%   **e** 99%

f 130%   **g** 23.5%   **h** 7.2%   **i** 4.75%   **j** 145%

4 Write these fractions as percentages without using a calculator.

a $\frac{3}{10}$ **b** $\frac{29}{50}$ **c** $\frac{14}{25}$ **d** $\frac{7}{4}$ **e** $\frac{13}{40}$

f $1\frac{3}{5}$ **g** $1\frac{11}{25}$ **h** $\frac{23}{20}$ **i** $\frac{47}{40}$ **j** $2\frac{3}{8}$

5 Write these fractions as percentages.

a $\frac{9}{16}$ **b** $\frac{27}{40}$ **c** $\frac{17}{25}$ **d** $\frac{5}{4}$ **e** $\frac{13}{25}$

f $\frac{7}{8}$ **g** $\frac{7}{9}$ **h** $\frac{27}{20}$ **i** $\frac{5}{6}$ **j** $\frac{2}{3}$

> Give your answers to 1 decimal place where appropriate.

6 Write these decimals as percentages.

a 0.58   **b** 0.08   **c** 0.8   **d** 1.08   **e** 1.8

f 0.035   **g** 0.415   **h** 1.05   **i** 1.555…   **j** 0.999

7 a Avril scored 48 out of 80 in her maths test. What percentage of the test did she answer correctly?

b In Ken's class there are 12 boys and 18 girls. What percentage of the class are girls?

---

challenge

These are the marks scored by Boris in his recent exams.

a In which subject did he do the best? Explain your answer.

b In which subject did he do the worst? Explain your answer.

c Put the subjects in order from Boris' worst subject to his best.

REPORT CARD

English	14/20
Maths	72%
Science	31/40
French	11/15
History	24/35
Geography	31/45
RE	69%

Consolidation

1 Write these numbers in order starting with the smallest.

a 4.5	4.48	4.4	4.34	4
b 5.96	5.979	5.94	6	5.9
c 0.066	0.068	0.06	0.0695	0.0684
d 2.8	2.771	2.16	2.776	2.77

2 Copy these and place $<$ or $>$ between each pair of numbers to show which number is the larger.

a 0.46 ☐ 0.5   **b** 1.61 ☐ 1.6   **c** 4.375 ☐ 4.384   **d** 5.24 ☐ 5.2

e 7.13 ☐ 7.14   **f** 2.753 ☐ 2.76   **g** 8.0444 ☐ 8.044   **h** 6.999 ☐ 7.1

3 Change these fractions into decimals using division. Use an appropriate method.

a $\frac{7}{8}$ **b** $\frac{7}{16}$ **c** $\frac{7}{20}$ **d** $\frac{1}{6}$ **e** $\frac{5}{9}$

4 Put these fractions in order from lowest to highest.

a $\frac{2}{9}$ $\frac{1}{4}$ $\frac{3}{10}$ $\frac{4}{13}$

b $\frac{2}{3}$ $\frac{3}{4}$ $\frac{13}{18}$ $\frac{11}{15}$

c $\frac{3}{5}$ $\frac{5}{9}$ $\frac{9}{16}$ $\frac{13}{20}$

5 Find the missing number in each of these pairs of equivalent fractions.

a $\frac{2}{3} = \frac{\square}{15}$ **b** $\frac{3}{7} = \frac{\square}{21}$ **c** $\frac{4}{9} = \frac{\square}{36}$ **d** $\frac{5}{7} = \frac{\square}{49}$

e $\frac{4}{11} = \frac{44}{\square}$ **f** $\frac{3}{13} = \frac{\square}{39}$ **g** $\frac{5}{12} = \frac{\square}{72}$ **h** $\frac{7}{16} = \frac{\square}{80}$

6 Calculate each of these additions and subtractions, giving your answer as a fraction in its simplest form.

a $\frac{2}{5} + \frac{1}{4}$ **b** $\frac{3}{7} + \frac{1}{5}$ **c** $\frac{1}{3} + \frac{1}{5}$ **d** $\frac{3}{4} + \frac{1}{9}$

e $\frac{3}{15} + \frac{9}{20}$ **f** $\frac{5}{6} - \frac{4}{9}$ **g** $\frac{5}{8} + \frac{7}{12}$ **h** $\frac{6}{7} - \frac{2}{21}$

4d

7 Use an appropriate method to calculate these amounts. Where appropriate give your answer to 2 decimal places.

    a $\frac{2}{7}$ of 236 g   **b** $\frac{7}{16}$ of £500   **c** $\frac{4}{7}$ of 18 km   **d** $\frac{8}{5}$ of 47 miles

    e $\frac{5}{12}$ of 48 hours   **f** $\frac{3}{5}$ of $25   **g** $\frac{7}{9}$ of 25 tonnes   **h** $\frac{2}{5}$ of 360°

8 **a** In Karla's class there are 14 boys and 21 girls. What fraction of the class are boys?

    b Ronald has 12 music CDs, 10 of which are Country and Western music. What fraction of Ronald's CDs are not Country and Western music?

4e

9 Calculate these using an appropriate method, giving your answers to 2 decimal places where appropriate.

    a 7% of £50   **b** 12% of 45 kg   **c** 31% of 18 km

    d 57% of 39 euros   **e** 29% of £87   **f** 41% of 63 kg

4f

10 Copy and complete this table.

Fraction	Decimal	Percentage
$\frac{17}{25}$		
	0.61	
		42%
$\frac{9}{40}$		

4 Summary

Assessment criteria
- Use the equivalence between fractions, decimals and percentages **Level 5**
- Reduce a fraction to its simplest form by cancelling common factors **Level 5**
- Add and subtract fractions **Level 6**

Level 6

1 Work out, giving your answer in its simplest form.

  a $\frac{1}{2} + \frac{2}{5}$

  b $\frac{5}{7} - \frac{1}{21}$

Kelly's answer ✔

Make equivalent fractions

$$a \quad \overset{\times 5}{\underset{\times 5}{\frac{1}{2} = \frac{5}{10}}} \quad \overset{\times 2}{\underset{\times 2}{\frac{2}{5} = \frac{4}{10}}}$$

$$\frac{1}{2} + \frac{2}{5} = \frac{5}{10} + \frac{4}{10}$$

$$= \frac{5+4}{10}$$

$$= \frac{9}{10}$$

Kelly decides to change both fractions into $\frac{1}{10}$ s.

$$b \quad \overset{\times 3}{\underset{\times 3}{\frac{5}{7} = \frac{15}{21}}} \quad \frac{1}{21} = \frac{1}{21}$$

$$\frac{5}{7} - \frac{1}{21} = \frac{15}{21} - \frac{1}{21}$$

$$= \frac{15-1}{21} = \overset{\div 7}{\underset{\div 7}{\frac{14}{21} = \frac{2}{3}}}$$

She decides to use 21 as the common denominator.

Kelly realises $\frac{14}{21}$ must be cancelled to leave it in its simplest form.

Level 5

2 a Copy and complete the sentences.

  _____ out of 10 is the same as 70%

  10 out of 20 is the same as _____ %

  b Copy and complete the sentence.

  _____ out of _____ is the same as 5%

  Now copy and complete the sentence using different numbers.

  _____ out of _____ is the same as 5%

Key Stage 3 2005 4–6 Paper 1

5 Algebra

Expressions and formulae

Diophantus, who lived in Alexandria, Egypt, is considered by some to be the "father of algebra". Around 200 ＠.c. he wrote Arithmetica, a series of books about solving algebraic equations.

What's the point? Humans have been working with algebra for hundreds of years because it is so important in helping us solve mathematical problems.

✓ Check in

Level 3

1 You have four boxes with twelve pencils in each box. Your also have three packets with six coloured pencils in each packet. How many pencils do you have altogether?

2 Do these multiplications without using a calculator.
a $2 \times 2 \times 2 \times 2$ **b** $2 \times 5 \times 2 \times 5$ **c** $2 \times 2 \times 3 \times 3 \times 5$

Level 4

3 a A minibus can take 8 passengers. A youth club has 36 members. How many trips are needed to take every member by minibus?
b You have 36 eggs and you need 8 eggs to make a large cake. How many of these cakes can you make?
c You have £36 which you share equally amongst 8 friends. How much do they each get?

4 A car travels 20 km on 1 litre of petrol. The distance that it can travel is found from: *Distance (km) = 20 × Litres used*.
Find   **a** how far it travels on a full tank of 40 litres
        b how many litres it uses on a journey of 60 km.

- Use the four basic operations in simple algebraic expressions
- Substitute into simple algebraic expressions

Keywords
Expression
Substitute

- A letter can stand for an unknown number.

You have m sweets in a bag. You put 4 more sweets into the bag.
You now have $m + 4$ sweets in the bag.

gives

m $m + 4$

You have n grapes in a bunch. You eat 6 of them.
You now have $n - 6$ grapes left.

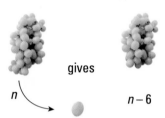

gives

n $n - 6$

If x is a number, four lots of the number is written

$x + x + x + x = 4 \times x = 4x$

and ...

half of the number is written

$x \div 2 = \frac{1}{2}x = \frac{x}{2}$

- An **expression** is formed when letters and numbers are combined by operations, like $+$ and $-$.

You can **substitute** a number for a letter.

If $x = 12$, then $4x = 4 \times 12 = 48$ and $\frac{1}{2}x = \frac{1}{2} \times 12 = 6$

---

example

If $p = 15$, find the values of   **a** $p + 5$ **b** $p - 6$ **c** $2p$ **d** $\frac{1}{3}p$

a $p + 5 = 15 + 5 = 20$ **b** $p - 6 = 15 - 6 = 9$

c $2p = 2 \times p = 2 \times 15 = 30$ **d** $\frac{1}{3}p = \frac{1}{3} \times 15 = 15 \div 3 = 5$

---

example

A car mechanic uses 4 screws weighing x grams each and 5 screws weighing y grams each. The total weight of the screws, T is $4x + 5y$.

Find the value of T when $x = 20$ and $y = 100$.

$T = 4x + 5y = 4 \times 20 + 5 \times 100 = 80 + 500 = 580$

So the total weight of screws is 580 g.

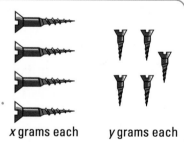

x grams each y grams each

Exercise 5a

1 Write these expressions in a simpler way.
   Here is an example: $a + a + a + a + a = 5a$
   a $x + x + x + x + x$ **b** $y + y + y$ **c** $z + z + z + z$
   d $3 \times z$ **e** $8 \div x$ **f** $y \times 5$
   g $x \div 2$ **h** $y \div 5$ **i** $z \div 3$

   Find the value of each of the expressions if $x = 10$, $y = 5$ and $z = 6$.

2 A bus has x passengers.
   Another four passengers get on.

   a Write an expression for the
      number of passengers on the
      bus now.
   b If $x = 12$, how many passengers are on the bus now?

3 A train has y passengers. At the next station, twelve passengers
   get off and another two passengers get on.
   a Write an expression for the number of passengers on the
      train now.
   b If $y = 50$, how many passengers are on the train after the
      next stop?

4 A box holds n glasses. You have four of these boxes.
   a Write an expression for the total number of glasses
      in the all the boxes.
   b If $n = 6$, how many glasses have you altogether?

5 A square flower bed has sides y metres long.
   a Write an expression for its perimeter.
   b If $y = 12$, how long is its perimeter?

6 A football pitch is r metres long and s metres wide.
   a Write down an expression for its perimeter.
   b If $r = 25$ and $s = 60$, find the length of its perimeter.

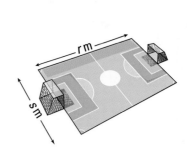

> **Did you know?**
>
> A recent survey
> showed that 2.7 million
> train journeys are made
> on a typical weekday in
> the UK – with London
> alone accounting for
> just under half of this
> amount!

challenge

Here is a street map of part of an American city.
It shows the court house C and the police
department P. Each rectangle of the grid of streets
is x cm by y cm. How long are the shortest routes
from C to P in terms of x and y? How many of
these shortest routes are there?

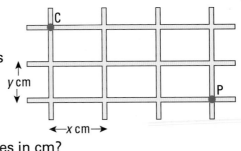

If $x = 5$ and $y = 8$, how long are the shortest routes in cm?

- Know the meaning of an index
- Use indices to simplify expressions

Keywords
Expression   Indices
Index   Power

- Any number or letter multiplied by itself can be written using an **index** or **power**.

$2 \times 2 \times 2 \times 2 \times 2 = 2^5$
This is the index or power.

$2 \times 2 \times 2 = 2^3$

'2 to the power 3' or '2 cubed'.

You can say '2 to the power 5'.

$2 \times 2 \times 2$ is called 2 cubed because you can show it as a cube.

example

Work out the value of $2^4 \times 5^2$.
....
$2^4 \times 5^2 = 2 \times 2 \times 2 \times 2 \times 5 \times 5$
$\qquad = 16 \times 25$
$\qquad = 400$

Indices is the plural of 'index'.

You can simplify an **expression** using **indices**.

example

a Simplify $s \times s \times s \times t \times t \times t \times t \times u$.
b Simplify $6^3 \times 6^4$, giving your answer as a power of 6.
....
a $s \times s \times s \times t \times t \times t \times t \times u = s^3 \times t^4 \times u^1$
$\qquad\qquad\qquad\qquad\qquad = s^3 t^4 u$

Notice that u^1 is just u.

Notice that $3 + 4 = 7$.

b $6^3 \times 6^4 = (6 \times 6 \times 6) \times (6 \times 6 \times 6 \times 6)$
$\qquad\quad = 6^7$

example

Simplify $z^3 \times z^2 \times z^4$.
....
$z^3 \times z^2 \times z^4 = (z \times z \times z) \times (z \times z) \times (z \times z \times z \times z)$
$\qquad\qquad\quad = z^9$

Exercise 5b

1 Simplify these expressions by using indices. Do not work out any values.

Examples: $3 \times 3 \times 3 \times 3 = 3^4$ $a \times a \times a = a^3$

a $2 \times 2 \times 2 \times 2$ **b** $7 \times 7 \times 7 \times 7 \times 7$

c $9 \times 9 \times 9 \times 9 \times 9 \times 9$ **d** $n \times n \times n$

e $y \times y \times y \times y \times y \times y \times y$ **f** $z \times z$

2 Simplify these expressions. Do not work out any values.

a $4 \times 4 \times 4 \times 5 \times 5 \times 5 \times 5$ **b** $8 \times 8 \times 6 \times 6 \times 6 \times 6 \times 6$

c $2 \times 3 \times 2 \times 3 \times 2 \times 3 \times 3$ **d** $5 \times 9 \times 9 \times 5 \times 5$

e $6 \times 4 \times 4 \times 6 \times 6 \times 6$ **f** $3 \times 3 \times 3 \times 3 \times n \times n$

g $r \times s \times s \times s \times s \times r \times s$ **h** $a \times b \times c \times a \times b \times c \times c$

3 Write these out in full and then find their values.

a 2^4 **b** 3^3 **c** 5^2 **d** 2^5 **e** 1^6

f $2^2 \times 3^2$ **g** $2^3 \times 5^2$ **h** $1^4 \times 6^2$ **i** $10^4 \times 3^2$ **j** $0^5 \times 7^3$

4 Simplify each of these. Use indices in your answers. Do not work out the values of any of the expressions.

a $6^4 \times 6^3$ **b** $8^2 \times 8^4$ **c** $2^4 \times 2^5$

d $3^7 \times 3^2$ **e** $5^5 \times 5^3$ **f** $7^4 \times 7^8$

g $10^2 \times 10^4 \times 10^3$ **h** $3^3 \times 3^4 \times 3^2$ **i** $5 \times 5^2 \times 5^4$

j $6 \times 6^5 \times 6^2$ **k** $4 \times 4 \times 4^8$ **l** $10 \times 10^6 \times 10$

5 Find the value of n in each of these statements.

a $2^n = 8$ **b** $3^n = 9$ **c** $10^n = 1000$

d $5^n = 125$ **e** $4^n = 64$ **f** $3^n = 243$

6 A litre of water fills this hollow cube.

a Write the volume of water in cm³ as a power of 10.

b Write how many cm³ there are in 1 litre.

c Find the area of this square and the volume of this cube.

d Can you see why we say 'squared' and 'cubed'?

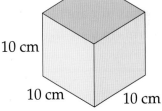

10 cm

10 cm   10 cm

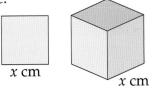

x cm x cm

research

A million is $10 \times 10 \times 10 \times 10 \times 10 \times 10 = 10^6 = 1\,000\,000$.

Find the meaning of *billion*, *trillion* and *quadrillion*.

Can you find any other names for very large numbers?

How did the numbers *googol* and *googolplex* get their names?

- Simplify by collecting 'like terms'

Keywords
Expression   Simplify
Like terms   Term

A **term** is part of an **expression**.

- **Like terms** contain the same letter.

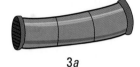
In the expression $5a + 3b$, $5a$ and $3b$ are both terms.

Two pipes of length $5a$ and $3a$ are joined together.
The total length $= 5a + 3a = 8a$
$5a$ and $3a$ are like terms.
They can be combined or collected together.

5a

3a

- You can **simplify** an expression by collecting like terms.

- Terms that use different letters are not like terms.

This necklace is made from two kinds of beads of lengths a cm and b cm.
The total length $= 4a + 3b + 4a = 8a + 3b$.

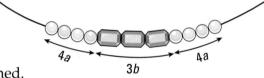

4a

3b

4a

$8a$ and $3b$ are unlike terms and cannot be combined.

example

Simplify this expression by collecting like terms.

$5x + 4y + 2x - 3x + y$

$4a + 4a = 8a$

The terms in x are like terms: $5x + 2x - 3x = 4x$
The terms in y are like terms: $4y + y = 5y$
So, $5x + 4y + 2x - 3x + y = 4x + 5y$

y means $1y$.

$4x$ and $5y$ are not like terms.

- Terms which use different powers are not like terms.
  z and z^2 are not like terms. They cannot be collected together.

example

Simplify this expression.

$3x^2 + 2x - x^2 + x^2 + 4x + 5x^2$

Collect terms in x: $2x + 4x = 6x$
Collect terms in x^2: $3x^2 - x^2 + x^2 + 5x^2 = 8x^2$
So, $3x^2 + 2x - x^2 + x^2 + 4x + 5x^2 = 6x + 8x^2$

Exercise 5c

1 Write the total lengths of these pipes when the two parts are joined together.

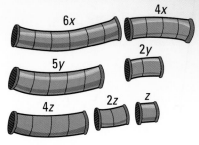

a $6x + 4x = \square$
b $5y + 2y = \square$
c $4z + 2z + z = \square$

2 Simplify these expressions.

a $2n + 3n + n$
b $6m + 4m + 2m$
c $4p + 3p - 2p$
d $8q - 2q - 3q$
e $5t + 3t + 4t$
f $7r + r - 5r$
g $6s - 4s - 2s$
h $8x - 5x - 2x$
i $5x - 6x + 3x$
j $6y - 8y + 9y$
k $z - 3z + 4z$
l $9m - 5m - 4m$

3 Necklaces are made from two kinds of beads of length x cm and y cm.

Write the total lengths of these two necklaces as simply as you can.

a $3x + 2y + 3x = \square$
b $2x + 3y + 2x + 3y = \square$

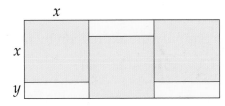

4 Simplify these expressions by collecting like terms.

a $2x + 3x + 6y - 4y$
b $5x + 2y - 3x + 6y$
c $4x + 2y + 3y - 2x$
d $5s + s + 7t - t$
e $u + u + 8v - v$
f $3r + 4r + 5s - 2s$
g $4x + x - 3y + 5y$
h $6a - 2a + a + 3b$
i $3a + 2b + 4a - 5a$

5 Simplify these expressions. Collect terms with the same indices.

a $2x + 4x + 3x^2 + 5x^2$
b $7y + 2y + 6y^2 - 3y^2$
c $4z + 2z^2 + 3z + 2z^2$
d $8u + 5u^2 - 3u - 2u^2$
e $5v + 2v^2 - 3v + v^2$
f $8x + x^2 + 4x^2 - 2x$
g $3z + 2z^3 - z - 2z^3$
h $9h^3 - 2h - h + 5h$
i $j^2 - 3j + j^2 + 4j$

6 This path is laid using square and rectangular slabs.

Write an expression in x and y for
a the area of the path
b the perimeter of the path.

puzzle

A necklace is made up of five beads. Three beads each have a length a cm. The other two each have a length b cm. The beads can be threaded in any order. How many different necklaces of length $3a + 2b$ cm can be made?

• Expand brackets using a simple multiplication

Here are two identical rectangles with sides in cm.

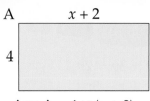

Area A = 4 × (x + 2)
= 4(x + 2) cm²

Area B = 4 × x + 4 × 2
= 4x + 8 cm²

$4(x + 2)$ means you multiply all of $x + 2$ by 4.

So $4(x + 2) = 4x + 8$

The curved lines tell you which terms to multiply.

You don't need to draw rectangles to multiply a term by a **bracket**. Just multiply what's inside the bracket by what's outside.

p. 100

This process is often called **expanding** the brackets.

example

Expand these brackets.
a $3(2x - 4)$
b $x(x + 5)$

a $3(2x - 4) = 3 \times 2x - 3 \times 4$
$= 6x - 12$

b $x(x + 5) = x \times x + x \times 5$
$= x^2 + 5x$

When you expand brackets, you may need to use indices.

• An **expression** can have several pairs of brackets. Expand each pair separately and then collect 'like terms'.

example

Simplify the expression by first expanding brackets.

$2(z + 5) + 4(2z + 3)$

$2(z + 5) + 4(2z + 3) = 2z + 10 + 8z + 12$
$= 10z + 22$

Collect like terms:
$2z + 8z = 10z$ and
$10 + 12 = 22$.

Exercise 5d

1 Expand these brackets using the diagrams to help you.

a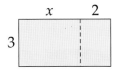

b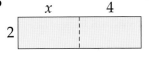

c

$3(x + 2) = \dots$ $2(x + 4) = \dots$ $4(x + 1) = \dots$

2 Expand these brackets.

  a $5(x + 3)$ **b** $5(2x + 5)$ **c** $5(x + 3)$

  d $5(2x - 5)$ **e** $6(3u + 2)$ **f** $3(v - 4)$

  g $5(2a - 3)$ **h** $4(3b - 1)$ **i** $5(3 - 2c)$

3 Expand these brackets. Take care with the powers of x.

  a $x(x + 3)$ **b** $x(5x + 3)$ **c** $x(2x + 4)$

  d $x(3x - 2)$ **e** $x(4x - 5)$ **f** $x(2x - 7)$

  g $x(4 - 5x)$ **h** $x(2 + x)$ **i** $x(7 + 3x)$

4 A metal casting weighing x kg is packed in a crate weighing 8 kg.

Four of these castings are loaded in their crates on a lorry.

  a Use brackets to write an expression for the total mass of the load.

  b Expand the brackets in your expression.

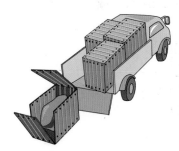

5 A biscuit tin weighs 50 grams. It contains 20 biscuits weighing y grams each. Mrs Hooper buys 3 tins.

  a Use brackets to write an expression for the total mass of her purchase.

  b Expand the brackets.

6 Expand these brackets and collect like terms.

  a $3(2x + 1) + 2(4x + 3)$ **b** $5(3x + 4) + 4(3x - 4)$

  c $5(x + 4) + 6(2x - 3)$ **d** $4(x - 3) + 3(2x + 5)$

  e $5(2x - 1) + 2(3x - 2)$ **f** $4(3x + 1) + 3(x - 4)$

challenge

When you expand $2(6x + 12)$, you get an answer of $12x + 24$.

How many other ways can you use brackets so that you get the answer $12x + 24$ when you expand them?

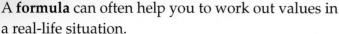

- Substitute numerical values into formulae

Keywords
Formula
Substitute

A **formula** can often help you to work out values in a real-life situation.

p. 200

Claire drives a taxi cab. She calculates the fare £F depending on the length of the journey, M miles where $F = 3 + 2M$.

Claire can **substitute** a value for M to find the fare F.

A journey of 10 miles has $M = 10$.
So, $F = 3 + 2 \times 10 = 3 + 20 = 23$

A journey of 6 miles has $M = 6$.
So, $F = 3 + 2 \times 6 = 3 + 12 = 15$
These two fares cost £23 and £15.

---

example

The amount of sleep that a child needs, H hours, depends on its age, A years, and is given by the formula $H = 16 - \frac{1}{2}A$.

Find the amount of sleep recommended for
a David, aged six
b his sister Jessica, aged twelve.

· ·

a When $A = 6$, $H = 16 - \frac{1}{2} \times 6$
$= 16 - 3$
$= 13$
David needs 13 hours sleep.

b When $A = 12$, $H = 16 - \frac{1}{2} \times 12$
$= 16 - 6$
$= 10$
Jessica needs 10 hours sleep.

- Formulae can involve brackets.

---

example

The cost C pence of using Kieran's radio depends on how long he uses it with batteries, x hours, and how long he uses it with mains electricity, y hours.

If $C = 2(3x + y)$, find C when
a $x = 2$, $y = 8$
b $x = 10$, $y = 0$.

· ·

a When $x = 2$, $y = 8$, $C = 2(3 \times 2 + 8)$
$= 2(6 + 8)$
$= 2 \times 14$
$= 28$
It costs 28 pence.

b When $x = 10$, $y = 0$, $C = 2(3 \times 10 + 0)$
$= 2(30 + 0)$
$= 2 \times 30$
$= 60$
It costs 60 pence.

Exercise 5e

1 A plumber charges £C for a call that lasts h hours where
$C = 20 + 30h$.
Find the value of C when
a $h = 1$ **b** $h = 2$ **c** $h = 5$

2 A car travelling at 20 mph begins to accelerate.
Its speed v after t seconds is given by $v = 20 + 3t$.
Find the value of v when
a $t = 10$ **b** $t = 5$ **c** $t = 1$

3 The time T minutes for a cyclist to ride U km uphill
and then D km downhill is given by $T = 12U + 2D$.

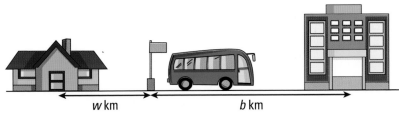

Find T when   **a** $U = 2, D = 5$ **b** $U = 6, D = 8$ **c** $U = 3, D = 12$

4 The time taken, t minutes, to get to school depends on how far you walk,
w km, and how far you go by bus, b km.

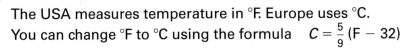

If $t = 5(2w + b)$, find t when
a $w = 1, b = 8$ **b** $w = 2, b = 2$ **c** $w = 3, b = 4$

5 The cost £C of framing a picture depends on its length L cm
and its height H cm, where $C = \dfrac{3L + 2H}{10}$. Find C when
a $L = 50, H = 20$ **b** $L = 30, H = 25$ **c** $L = 40, H = 30$

6 The number of small cakes, n, bought for a child's
birthday party depends on the number of boys B and
the number of girls G who are invited.
If $n = 2(3B + 2G)$, find n when
a $B = 4, G = 2$ **b** $B = 2, G = 3$ **c** $B = 5, G = 0$

The USA measures temperature in °F. Europe uses °C.
You can change °F to °C using the formula $C = \dfrac{5}{9}(F - 32)$

a Change 212 °F and 32 °F to °C. What is special about these two temperatures?

b What do these five surnames of famous scientists have in common?

    Fahrenheit   Celsius   Kelvin   Réaumur   Rankine

- Construct a formula for different situations.
- Use the formula by substituting values into it.

Keywords
Construct
Formula

 The perimeter of this quadrilateral, $P = 6 + 4 + 7 + x$ cm
So, $P = 17 + x$

You can use this **formula** for P if you know the value of x.
If $x = 6$ cm, then $P = 17 + 6 = 23$.
The perimeter is 23 cm.

To **construct** a formula you may need to use mathematical facts that you already know.

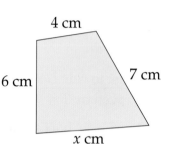

Remember: the perimeter is the distance around a shape.

A quadrilateral is a four-sided shape.

---

example

This isosceles triangle has two equal angles, x.

a Find a formula for the third angle, A.
b Find the value of A when $x = 50°$.

. . . .

a The angles of a triangle add up to 180°.
So, $A = 180 - x - x$
$= 180 - 2x$
The formula is $A = 180 - 2x$.
b When $x = 50$, $A = 180 - 2 \times 50$
$= 180 - 100 = 80$
The third angle, A is 80°.

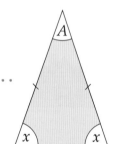

Formulae can also be written for real-life situations.

---

example

A trailer weighs 50 kg. The trailer carries n crates, each weighing 20 kg.

a Write a formula for the total mass of the loaded trailer.
b Find the total load if there are 10 crates.

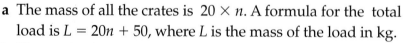

a The mass of all the crates is $20 \times n$. A formula for the total load is $L = 20n + 50$, where L is the mass of the load in kg.
b If $n = 10$, $L = 20 \times 10 + 50$
$= 200 + 50$
$= 250$.
So, with 10 crates, the total load is 250 kg.

n crates

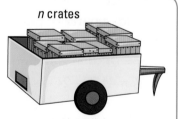

You need to explain what any letters you invent actually mean.

Exercise 5f

1 a Find a formula for the perimeter P of each of these shapes.
The sides are all measured in cm.

i 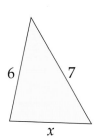   **ii** 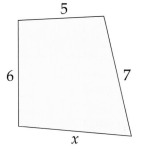   **iii**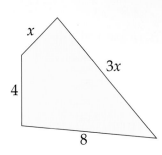

b Find the value of each perimeter P if $x = 4$.

2 The angles x and y make a straight angle of $180°$.
  a Write a formula for y in terms of x.
  b If $x = 60°$, find the value of y.

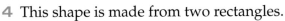

3 These three angles make a full turn of $360°$.
  a Find a formula for the angle A in terms of x.
  b If $x = 100°$, find the value of A.

4 This shape is made from two rectangles.
  a Write the area of each rectangle in cm^2.
  b Write a formula for the total area A of the whole
    shape.
  c Find the value of A when $x = 5$.

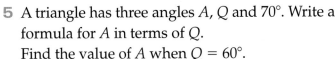

5 A triangle has three angles A, Q and $70°$. Write a
formula for A in terms of Q.
Find the value of A when $Q = 60°$.

6 A school trip to the zoo uses four full coaches, each carrying
p children. Another six children meet the coaches at the zoo.
  a Write a formula for the total number of children C that visit
    the zoo.
  b How many children visit the zoo **i** if $p = 30$ **ii** if $p = 35$?

---

challenge

A rectangular sheet has a square hole cut in it.

a Find a formula for the shaded area A that is left.
b If $x = 6$, find the value of A.

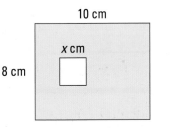

5a

1 Write these in a simpler way.

  a $x + x + x$ **b** $y + y + y + y$ **c** $2 \times 3 \times z$

2 There are x biscuits in a packet. You buy five packets.

  a How many biscuits do you buy?

  b You open one of the packets and eat six biscuits. How many biscuits do you now have altogether?

  c If $x = 10$, how many biscuits are you left with?

3 If $p = 12$ and $q = 4$, find the values of

  a $p + 2q$ **b** $2p - q$ **c** $\dfrac{p}{q}$ **d** $\dfrac{5q + 4}{p}$

5b

4 Find the values of

  a $3 \times 3 \times 3$ **b** 2^4 **c** 10^2 **d** $5^2 \times 10^3$

5 Simplify each of these, using indices in your answers.

  a $a \times a \times a \times b \times b \times c \times c \times c$ **b** $3^4 \times 3^2$ **c** $6^5 \times 6^3$

6 What values of n makes these statements true?

  a $2^n = 16$ **b** $5^3 \times 5^n = 5^7$ **c** $3^6 \times 3^n \times 3^2 = 3^{10}$

5c

7 A necklace is made from two kinds of beads of length x cm and y cm.

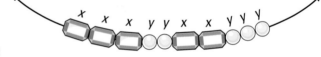

Write the total length of this necklace as simply as you can.

$3x + 2y + 2x + 3y = \square$

8 A patio with this pattern of paving slabs uses four identical hexagons and four identical triangles.

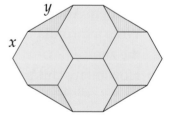

Write an expression for the perimeter of the shape in terms of x and y.

9 Simplify these expressions by collecting like terms.

  a $3p + 2p + 5q - 2q$ **b** $4m + 2n + m - 3n$

  c $3x^2 + 4x + 6x^2 - 5x$ **d** $z^2 + 5z + z^2 - 2z - 2z^2 - 3z$

10 **a** Find the total area of rectangles A and B together.
b Expand this bracket. $5(x + 2)$

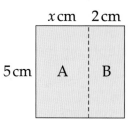

11 **a** Expand these brackets. **i** $4(x + 3)$ **ii** $3(5x + 4)$
b Expand these brackets and simplify your answers by collecting like terms.
i $2(y + 3) + 4(5y + 2)$ **ii** $3(2z + 4) + 2(z - 5)$

12 **a** A box weighing 20 grams contains 10 screws weighing x grams each. Write an expression for the total weight of the box and its contents.
b Mr Sturman buys five of these boxes. Write an expression (using brackets) for the total weight of these five boxes and their contents.
c Expand the brackets.

13 The time T hours to cook a turkey weighing W pounds is given by $T = \dfrac{W}{3} + 1$.

Find T when   **a** $W = 12$ **b** $W = 18$ **c** $W = 20$

14 The charge £C for excess baggage when you fly depends on the weight W kg of your luggage where $C = 5(W - 20)$.
Find C when   **a** $W = 32$ **b** $W = 65$ **c** $W = 20$

15 If $p = 4$, $q = 2$ and $r = 5$, find the values of
a $2p + q$ **b** $4r - 5p$ **c** $3(p + 2q - r)$

16 This trapezium has two sides of 8 cm and 5 cm and two equal unknown sides.
a Write a formula for its perimeter P.
b Find the value of P when $x = 4$ cm.

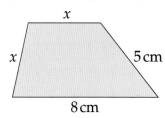

17 A triangle has three angles x, y and A.

a Write a formula for angle A in terms of x and y.
b Find the value of A when $x = 60°$ and $y = 45°$.

18 **a** Expand   **i** $5(x + 2)$ **ii** $3(5x + 4)$
b Expand these and simplify by collecting like terms.

i $2(y + 3) + 4(5y + 2)$ **ii** $3(2z + 4) + 2(z - 5)$

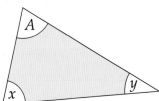

5 Summary

Assessment criteria
- Construct, express in symbolic form, and use simple formulae involving one or two operations **Level 5**

Level 5

1 a Multiply out the brackets
   i $2(x + 3)$
   ii $3(x - 2)$

b Use your answers to simplify
   $2(x + 3) + 3(x - 2)$

Jiger's answer ✔

Jiger knows about the 'invisible' multiplication sign,
$2 \times x = 2x$ and
$2 \times 3 = 6$

a i $2(x + 3) = 2x + 6$
  ii $3(x - 2) = 3x - 6$
b $2(x + 3) + 3(x - 2)$
    $= 2x + 6 + 3x - 6$
    $= 5x$

He adds his answers from part **a**

$2x$ add $3x$ is $5x$
and $6 - 6 = 0$

Level 5

2 Match each statement to the correct expression. The first one is done for you.

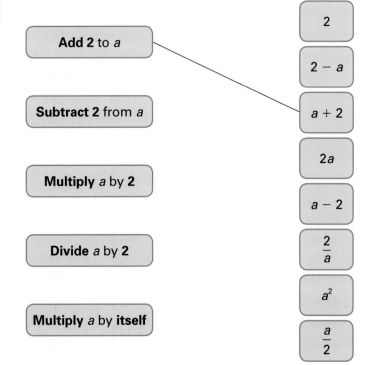

Add **2** to *a*

Subtract **2** from *a*

Multiply *a* by **2**

Divide *a* by **2**

Multiply *a* by **itself**

2

$2 - a$

$a + 2$

$2a$

$a - 2$

$\dfrac{2}{a}$

a^2

$\dfrac{a}{2}$

Key Stage 3 2000 4–6 Paper 2

6 Geometry

Angles and shapes

This pyramid was built in 1989 in front of the Louvre Museum in Paris, France.

The pyramid has a square base measuring 35 metres by 35 metres and is 20.6 metres high. It uses 603 rhombus-shaped and 70 triangular glass pieces.

What's the point? Modern architects often use ideas from history as inspiration for their new work.

 Check in

Level 5

1 Match each angle with the description.

a   b   c   d   e

reflex
straight
right
obtuse
acute

2 Use a protractor to measure these angles.

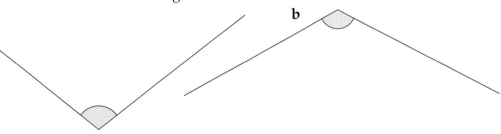

a   b

3 Solve these equations.

  a $2a = 180$ **b** $3b + 30 = 180$ **c** $5c = 360$

- Know facts about angles at a point

Keywords
Angle   Straight line
Degree   Vertically
Point   opposite
Right angle

- An **angle** is a measure of turn. You can measure the turn in degrees. ° is the symbol for **degrees.**

You can describe this angle in different ways:

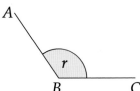

or   angle *ABC*
or   angle *CBA*
or   angle *B*
or   *r*

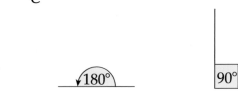

There are 360° in a full turn at a **point**.   There are 180° on a **straight line**.   There are 90° in a **right angle**.

example

Calculate the values of *a* and *b*.

a

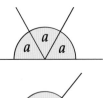

b

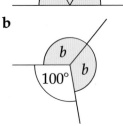

a $a + a + a = 180°$
$$3a = 180°$$
$$3a \div 3 = 180° \div 3$$
$$a = 60°$$

b $b + b + 100 = 360°$
$$2b + 100° = 360°$$
$$2b + 100° - 100° = 360° - 100°$$
$$2b = 260°$$
$$2b \div 2 = 260° \div 2$$
$$b = 130°$$

- **Vertically opposite** angles are equal.

example

Calculate the value of *x*.

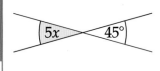

$$5x = 45°$$
$$5x \div 5 = 45° \div 5$$
$$x = 9°$$

Vertically opposite angles are equal.

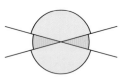

The two red acute angles are equal.
The two green obtuse angles are equal.

Exercise 6a

1 Use the small letters to describe

   a angle *C*   **b** angle *D*

   c angle *ABC*   **d** angle *CBE*

   e angle *DEF*

2 Calculate the value of the letters.

   a 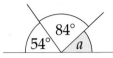   **b** 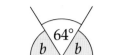   **c**

3 Calculate the value of the unknown angles.

   a 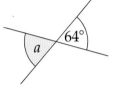   **b**   **c**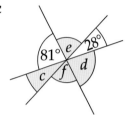

4 Calculate the value of the letters.

   a   **b** 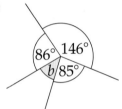   **c**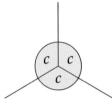

   d 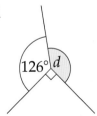   **e** 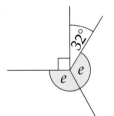   **f**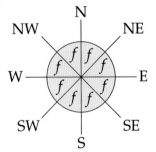

Calculate the smaller angle between the arms on the clocks at

   a three o'clock

   b one o'clock

   c half past nine.

- Know facts about angles in a triangle
- Recognise types of triangles

Keywords
Equilateral   Right-angled
Exterior   Scalene
Interior   Triangle
Isosceles

- A **triangle** is a 2-D shape with 3 sides and 3 angles.

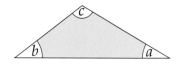

- The **interior** angles of a triangle add to 180°.
  $a + b + c = 180°$

You should know the mathematical name of these triangles.

Equilateral	Isosceles	Scalene	Right-angled
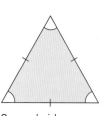	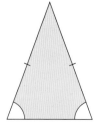		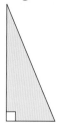
3 equal sides 3 equal angles	2 equal sides 2 equal angles	No equal sides No equal angles	One 90° angle

example

Calculate the values of a and b.

a 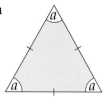   **b**

a $a + a + a = 180°$
$3a = 180°$
$3a \div 3 = 180° \div 3$
$a = 60°$

Check:
$60° + 60° + 60° = 180°$

b $b + b + 44° = 180°$
$2b + 44° = 180°$
$2b + 44° - 44° = 180° - 44°$
$2b = 136°$
$2b \div 2 = 136° \div 2$
$b = 68°$

Check:
$68° + 68° + 44° = 180°$

You find an **exterior** angle of a 2-D shape
by extending a side.

$a + b + c = 180°$ Angles in a triangle add to 180°
$a + d = 180°$ Angles on a straight line add to 180°
So $b + c = d$ By comparing the equations

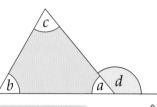

- The exterior angle of a triangle is equal to the sum of
  the two interior opposite angles.

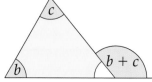

Exercise 6b

1 Calculate the value of the letters.

a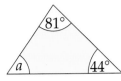

b

c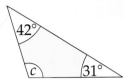

2 Two angles in a triangle are given. Calculate the third angle and state the type of triangle.

    a 60°, 60°   **b** 38°, 71°   **c** 45°, 45°

    d 38°, 64°   **e** 42°, 96°

3 Calculate the size of the unknown angles.

a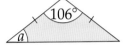

b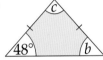

c

4 Some triangles are drawn in this rectangle. Calculate the value of each letter.

5 Calculate the size of the unknown angles.

a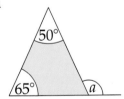

b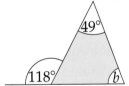

c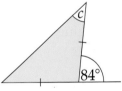

activity

Draw and cut out a triangle.

Find the midpoint of two sides and fold along the dotted line.

Fold along the two further dotted lines.

Explain why this shows that the sum of the interior angles of a triangle is 180°.

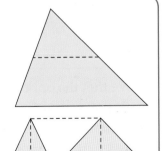

- Know facts about angles on parallel and intersecting lines

Keywords
Alternate
Corresponding
Intersect
Parallel
Perpendicular
Vertically opposite

- **Perpendicular** lines meet at a right angle.

A horizontal and a vertical line are perpendicular.

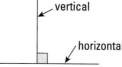

- **Parallel** lines are always the same distance apart.

When a line **intersects** two parallel lines, different types of angle are formed.

Vertically opposite angles are equal.

Alternate angles are equal.

Corresponding angles are equal.

p. 78

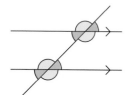

Vertically opposite angles form an X shape.

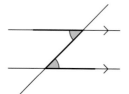

Alternate angles form a Z shape.

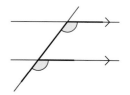

Corresponding angles form an F shape.

example

Calculate the values of angles a and b.

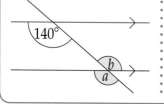

$a = 140°$ Corresponding angles are equal

$b = 140°$ Alternate angles are equal

or $b = 140°$ Vertically opposite angles are equal

a and 140° form an F shape.

b and 140° form a Z shape.

a and b are equal.

example

Prove that the opposite angles of a parallelogram are equal.

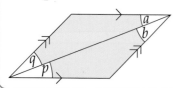

You need to prove $a + b = p + q$

$a = p$ Alternate angles are equal

$b = q$ Alternate angles are equal

So $a + b = p + q$ and the opposite angles of a parallelogram are equal.

a and p form a Z shape.

b and q form a Z shape.

Exercise 6c

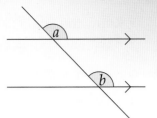

1 Draw a line crossing two parallel lines.
   a Measure the size of *a* and *b* in your diagram.
   b Draw a Z or an F on your diagram to help you decide
   whether the angles *a* and *b* are alternate or corresponding.

2 Copy the diagrams and label the alternate angles to the ones
shown.

a    **b**    **c**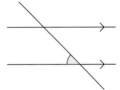

3 Copy the diagrams and label the corresponding angles to the
ones shown.

a    **b**    **c**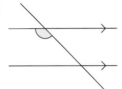

4 Calculate the angles marked by the letters. Give a reason for
your answers.

a 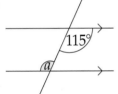   **b** 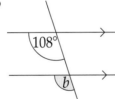   **c**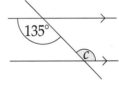

5 Calculate the unknown angles.

a 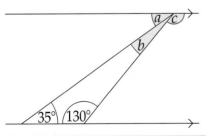   **b**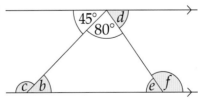

- Know the angle properties of a quadrilateral
- Recognise types of quadrilaterals

Keywords
Interior
Quadrilateral

- A **quadrilateral** is a 2-D shape with four sides and four angles.

You can divide a quadrilateral into two triangles.

$$a + b + c = 180°$$
$$d + e + f = 180°$$

So $a + b + c + d + e + f = 360°$

- The **interior** angles of a quadrilateral add to 360°.
  $$p + q + r + s = 360°$$

You should know the mathematical name of these quadrilaterals.

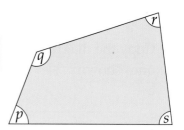

Square	Rectangle	Rhombus	Parallelogram

 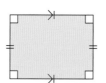 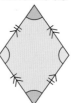 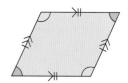

Square	Rectangle	Rhombus	Parallelogram
4 equal sides	2 sets of equal sides	4 equal sides	2 sets of equal sides
4 angles of 90°	4 angles of 90°	2 pairs of equal angles	2 pairs of equal angles
2 sets of parallel sides	2 sets of parallel sides	2 sets of parallel sides	2 sets of parallel sides

Trapezium	Isosceles trapezium	Kite	Arrowhead

Trapezium	Isosceles trapezium	Kite	Arrowhead
1 set of parallel sides	1 set of equal sides	2 sets of equal sides	2 sets of equal sides
	2 pairs of equal angles	1 pair of equal angles	1 pair of equal angles
	1 set of parallel sides	No parallel sides	No parallel sides

Exercise 6d

1 Three angles in a quadrilateral are given. Calculate the fourth angle in each and state the type of quadrilateral.
There could be several answers for each question.

a 90°, 90°, 90°   **b** 60°, 120°, 120°   **c** 90°, 90°, 110°
d 30°, 90°, 210°   **e** 63°, 87°, 110°

2 Copy and complete the table to show the properties of the diagonals of these quadrilaterals. Use Yes or No for each answer.

	The diagonals		
	are equal in length	bisect each other	are perpendicular
Parallelogram			
Kite			
Rhombus			
Square			
Rectangle			

3 Name the different types of quadrilaterals in the regular pentagon on the right.

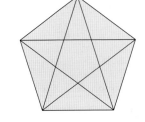

4 Give the names of quadrilaterals that have
a 4 equal angles   **b** only one pair of equal angles
c 4 equal sides.
There may be more than one answer for each question.

Use a protractor and a ruler to draw a regular hexagon.
Draw a circle.
Use a protractor to mark off points at 60° intervals at 0°, 60°, 120°, 180°, 240°, 300° and 360° (same as 0°).
Join up the points with straight lines and cut out the 6 equilateral triangles.

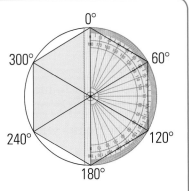

a Rearrange 6 triangles to make a parallelogram.
Show that the opposite angles of this parallelogram are equal.
b Rearrange 5 triangles to make an isosceles trapezium.
Show that this isosceles trapezium has two pairs of equal angles.
c Rearrange 4 triangles to make an equilateral triangle.
Explain why you know the triangle is equilateral.
d Rearrange 3 triangles to make an isosceles trapezium.
Calculate the sum of the interior angles of a trapezium.
e Rearrange 2 triangles to make a rhombus.
Show that the opposite angles of this rhombus are equal.

6d² Properties of a polygon

- Know some properties of polygons

Keywords
Interior   Regular
Polygon   Tessellation

- A **polygon** is a 2-D shape with three or more straight sides.

You should know the names of the polygons in this list.

- A **regular** shape has equal sides and equal angles.

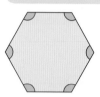

A regular hexagon
has 6 equal sides
and 6 equal angles.

Number of sides	Name
3	Triangle
4	Quadrilateral
5	Pentagon
6	Hexagon
7	Heptagon
8	Octagon
9	Nonagon
10	Decagon

You call the angles inside a shape the **interior** angles.

- The interior angles of a triangle add to 180°.
  $a + b + c = 180°$

- The interior angles of a quadrilateral add to 360°.
  $p + q + r + s = 360°$

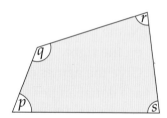

---

example

Draw a regular pentagon.

There are 5 equal angles at the centre.
$360° \div 5 = 72°$
Draw a circle.
Use a protractor to mark off points at 72° intervals
at 0°, 72°, 144°, 216°, 288° and 360° (same as 0°).
Join up the points with straight lines.

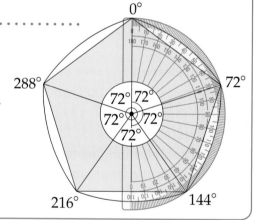

---

p. 136

- A **tessellation** is a tiling pattern with no gaps.

example

Copy this diagram and draw at least five more octagons to show the shape tessellates.

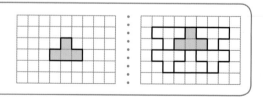

  Geometry Angles and shapes

Exercise 6d²

1 What is the mathematical name for
  a a regular triangle
  b a regular quadrilateral?

2 Calculate the value of the letters.

a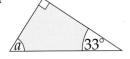

b

c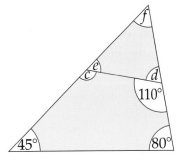

3 a Use a protractor and a ruler to draw a regular nonagon.
   Draw a circle.
   Use a protractor to mark off points at 40° intervals
   at 0°, 40°, 80° etc.
   Join up the points with straight lines.
  b Measure one of the interior angles of the nonagon.
  c Calculate the sum of the interior angles.

4 Tessellate each polygon on square grid paper.

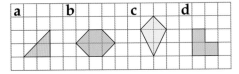

5 Regular octagons do not tessellate as
  squares are needed to fill the gaps.

  Calculate the size of the interior
  angle of a regular octagon.

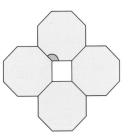

Did you know?

The top surface of
many of the stones
at the Giant's
Causeway in Ireland,
is a hexagon.

Draw a circle.
Use a protractor to mark off points at 60° intervals at
0°, 60°, 120° etc.
Draw a regular hexagon and six of the diagonals.
Cut out the twelve triangles and the smaller hexagon.
Rearrange the pieces to make three congruent
hexagons.

Congruent means
identical.

• Recognise congruent shapes

Keywords
Congruent
Corresponding

These shapes may look different, but they are the same size and the same shape.

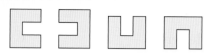

If you cut them out, they would all fit on top of each other. These shapes are **congruent**.

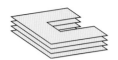

• Congruent shapes are exactly the same size and the same shape.

example

Write down the letters of the congruent shapes.

A   B   C   D   E

A, B and D are congruent as they are the same size and the same shape.

C and E are congruent as they are the same size and the same shape.

 p. 134, 220

• If shapes are congruent, then
  – **corresponding angles** are equal
  – **corresponding sides** are equal.

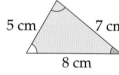

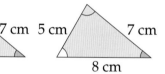

example

The pink triangle and the blue triangle are congruent.

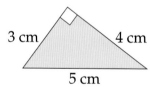

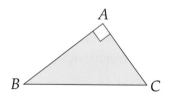

State the lengths of   **a** *AB*   **b** *AC*   **c** *BC*

a *AB* = 4 cm
b *AC* = 3 cm
c *BC* = 5 cm

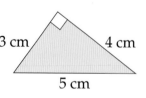

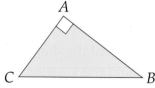

Flip over the blue triangle so it can fit on top of the pink triangle.

Compare the triangles.

Exercise 6e

1 Draw the shape that is not congruent to the others.

a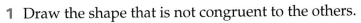

b

c

d

e

2 The blue isosceles trapezium and the green isosceles trapezium are congruent.

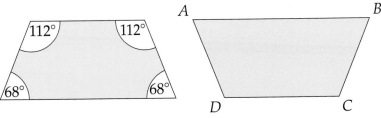

State the values of angles *A*, *B*, *C* and *D*.

3 The brown triangle and the beige triangle are congruent.
State the lengths of
  a *AB*   **b** *AC*   **c** *BC*

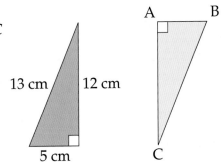

13 cm   12 cm

5 cm

---

activity

a Copy the diagram based on a 3 cm by 9 cm rectangle.

b Use different colours to identify the congruent shapes.

c How many different shapes are in the diagram?

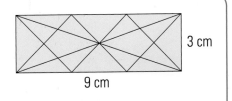

3 cm

9 cm

- Recognise and name 3-D solids
- Recognise the nets of 3-D solids

Keywords

Edge   Net
Cube   Prism
Cuboid Pyramid
Face   Solid
(3-D)   Vertex

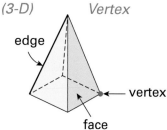

- A **solid** is a shape formed in **three dimensions (3-D)**.
  - A **face** is a flat surface of a solid.
  - An **edge** is the line where two faces meet.
  - A **vertex** is a point at which three or more edges meet.

You should know the names of these solids.

Cube	**Cuboid**	**Prism**	**Pyramid**
All the faces are square	All the faces are rectangles	The cross-section is the same throughout the length	The base tapers to a point

The cross-section decides the name of the prism – this is a triangular prism.

The base decides the name of the pyramid – this is a pentagonal pyramid.

p. 228

- A **net** is a 2-D shape that can be folded to form a solid.

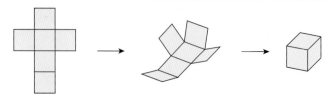

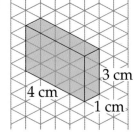
example

The dimensions of a cuboid are 4 cm by 3 cm by 1 cm.
a Draw the cuboid on isometric paper.
b Draw the net of the cuboid.

. . . .

a

3 cm

4 cm

1 cm

b

Exercise 6f

1

A   B   C   D

E   F   G   H

For each solid, state
  a the mathematical name
  b the number of   **i** faces   **ii** vertices   **iii** edges.

> The plural of vertex is **vertices**.

2 The dimensions of a cuboid are 4 cm by 4 cm by 3 cm.
  a Draw the cuboid on isometric paper.
  b Draw the net of the cuboid.
  c Calculate the area of the net.

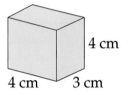

3 Copy this net of a cube.
  a On your diagram, mark the edge that meets the red line when the net is folded.
  b On your diagram, mark the vertices that meet the red dot when the net is folded.

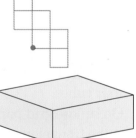

4 A cuboid is made from 4 blue rectangles and 2 green rectangles. The opposite faces are the same colour.
  Find the number of edges where
  a a blue face meets a blue face
  b a blue face meets a green face
  c a green face meets a green face.

5 a Draw a 3-D shape with 5 faces.
  b State the number of vertices and edges on your shape.

- Use isometric paper to draw plans and elevations of 3-D shapes

Keywords
Front elevation
Isometric paper
Plan
Side elevation
Solid

- A **front elevation** (F) is the view from the front.

- A **side elevation** (S) is the view from the side.

- A **plan** (P) shows the view from above.

> The plan is the bird's-eye view.

These are the views of a Police Box.

F

This is the front elevation (F).

S

This is the side elevation (S).

P

This is the plan view (P).

---

example

This **solid** is made from four cubes.
On square grid paper, draw
a the front elevation (F)
b the side elevation (S)
c the plan view (P).

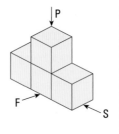

| a | b | c |

Front elevation   Side elevation   Plan view

> The bold lines show when the level of cubes changes.

---

example

Draw a solid on **isometric paper** that has these elevation and plan views.

F   S   P

Front elevation   Side elevation   Plan view

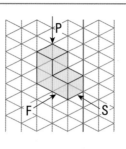

> Notice the vertical lines. The isometric paper must be this way up.

Exercise 6g

1 On square grid paper, draw the front elevation (F), the side elevation (S) and the plan view (P) of these solids.

a b 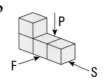 c 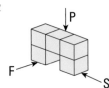 d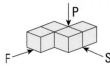

2 i On isometric paper, draw these solids after the shaded cube is removed.

ii On square grid paper, draw the elevations and the plan views of the new solids.

a b 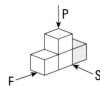 c d

3 A 3-D shape is made from some cubes. The elevations and the plan view are shown.

a Draw the solid on isometric paper.

b How many cubes are needed to make the shape?

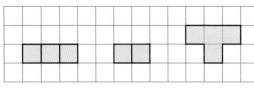

Front elevation   Side elevation   Plan view

4 a Match each solid (A-D) with its plan view (E-F).

b Give the mathematical name of each solid.

A 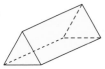 B C D

E F G H

challenge

The front and side elevations and the plan view of this 3-D shape are identical.

a Make this shape using multilink cubes.

b Draw the shape on isometric paper.

c Can you find another solid that has identical elevations and plan view?

F   Front elevation
S   Side elevation
P   Plan view

6 Consolidation

6a

1 Calculate the value of the unknown angles.

a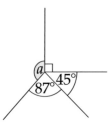

b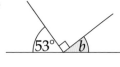

c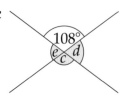

2 Arrange these six angle values so they fit on a straight line and at a point.

14°   22°   24°   124°   142°   214°

6b

3 Two angles in a triangle are given. Calculate the third angle and state the type of triangle.

a 30°, 75°   **b** 43°, 47°   **c** 36°, 108°
d 35°, 64°   **e** 45°, 90°

4 One angle in an isosceles triangle is 70°.
What is the size of the other two angles?

> There are two possible answers to this question.

6c

5 Calculate the unknown angles.
Give a reason in each case.

a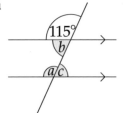

b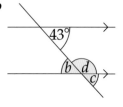

c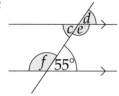

6d

6 Calculate the unknown angles in these quadrilaterals.

a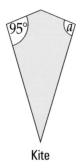

Kite

b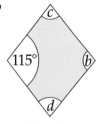

Rhombus

c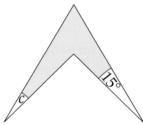

Arrowhead

92   **Geometry** Angles and shapes

7 State which shapes are the same in this regular hexagon and give the mathematical name of each shape.

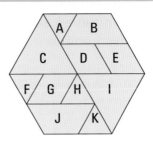

8 The diagram shows five regular pentagons and a rhombus.
One angle in the rhombus is 36°.

Calculate the values of a and b.

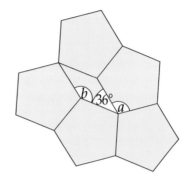

9 Identify the triangles that are congruent to the green triangle.

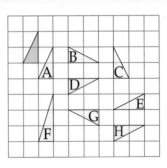

10 A prism is shown.
  a State the number of   **i** faces
                           ii vertices
                           iii edges.
  b Draw the solid on isometric paper.

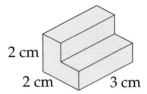

11 Sketch the front elevation (F), the side elevation (S) and the plan view (P) of this dice.

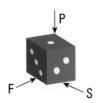

6 Summary

Assessment criteria
- Visualise and use 2-D representations of 3-D objects **Level 6**
- Identify alternate and corresponding angles for parallel lines **Level 6**
- Use angle properties to solve geometrical problems **Level 6**

1 A triangle is formed between two parallel lines.

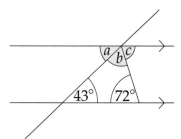

Calculate the value of the angles a, b and c.

Patrick's answer ✔

The Z shape alternate angles are equal

$a = 43°$

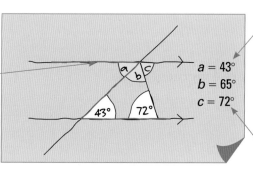

$a = 43°$
$b = 65°$
$c = 72°$

Patrick knows the angles in a triangle add to 180°.

$43° + 72° = 115°$
$180° - 115° = 65°$

$c = 72°$ as alternate angles are equal.

2 a Look at the drawing of a prism on the grid.

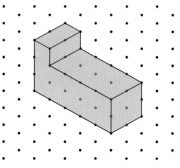

How many faces does the prism have?

b Use isometric grid paper to draw a solid with 6 faces.

Key Stage 3 2007 4–6 Paper 2

7 Algebra

Equations and graphs

Wind tunnels are used to investigate the aerodynamics (motion of air) around objects, for example aircraft or cars.

What's the point? Models of the air movement using algebraic equations help engineers to improve speed and efficiency.

✓ Check in

Level 3

1 What numbers should be placed in these boxes to make the statements correct?

    a $12 + \square = 21$ **b** $15 - \square = 9$ **c** $3 \times \square = 21$ **d** $\dfrac{\square}{4} = 5$

2 The same number can be written in these pairs of boxes. What is the number?

    a $6 \times \square = 42$ and $\dfrac{42}{6} = \square$ **b** $7 \times \square = 56$ and $\dfrac{56}{7} = \square$

Level 4

3 I think of a number, add 6 to it, and get an answer of 14. What number am I thinking of?

4 **a** Write the answer to 7×8.

   b Write two division facts which are based on your answer to **a**.

- Use inverse operations with simple equations

Keywords

Balance   Solution
Equation   Solve
Inverse

Here is a balance containing an unknown weight *x*.

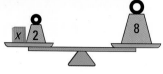

It can be written as an **equation**. $x + 2 = 8$

To find *x*, you need to get it on its own on one side of the equation.

If you subtract 2 from the left, you must also subtract 2 from the right, to keep the **balance**.

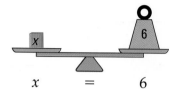

$$x = 6$$

The **solution** of the equation is $x = 6$

---

example

Solve these equations.

a $x + 5 = 9$ **b** $x - 7 = 3$ **c** $3x = 12$ **d** $\frac{1}{2}x = 5$

> 'Solve' means 'Find the solution'.

a

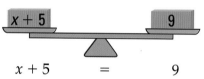

$$x + 5 = 9$$

The **inverse** of $+ 5$ is $- 5$.
Subtract 5 from both sides.
So, $x = 4$

b

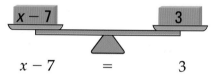

$$x - 7 = 3$$

The **inverse** of $- 7$ is $+ 7$.
Add 7 to both sides.
So, $x = 10$

c

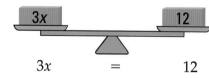

$$3x = 12$$

The inverse of $\times 3$ is $\div 3$.
Divide both sides by 3.
So, $x = 4$

d

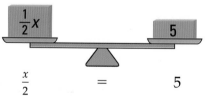

$$\frac{x}{2} = 5$$

The inverse of $\div 2$ is $\times 2$.
Multiply both sides by 2.
So, $x = 10$

Exercise 7a

1 Find the value of x in each of these balances.

a 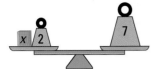   **b** 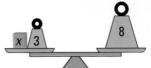   **c**

2 Solve these equations by using inverse operations.

a   **i** $x + 6 = 8$ **ii** $x + 3 = 12$ **iii** $x + 4 = 5$
    iv $x + 7 = 9$ **v** $x + 8 = 12$ **vi** $x + 1 = 10$
    vii $3 + x = 4$ **viii** $5 + x = 7$

b   **i** $x - 8 = 1$ **ii** $x - 2 = 7$ **iii** $x - 4 = 3$
    iv $x - 1 = 9$ **v** $x - 3 = 11$ **vi** $x - \frac{1}{2} = 3$
    vii $9 = x - 2$ **viii** $6 = x - 8$

c   **i** $2x = 10$ **ii** $3x = 12$ **iii** $4x = 8$
    iv $2x = 18$ **v** $5x = 20$ **vi** $7x = 14$
    vii $33 = 3x$ **viii** $20 = 4x$

d   **i** $\frac{x}{2} = 5$ **ii** $\frac{x}{3} = 4$ **iii** $\frac{x}{4} = 2$

    iv $\frac{x}{3} = 6$ **v** $\frac{x}{2} = 7$ **vi** $\frac{x}{5} = 4$

    vii $\frac{x}{10} = 6$ **viii** $\frac{x}{6} = 3$

3 Solve these equations. They need various different operations.

a $x + 7 = 8$ **b** $x - 7 = 8$ **c** $x + 1 = 5$ **d** $x - 1 = 5$

e $2x = 20$ **f** $3x = 12$ **g** $\frac{x}{2} = 9$ **h** $\frac{x}{3} = 6$

i $x + 6 = 17$ **j** $x - 5 = 1$ **k** $\frac{x}{5} = 12$ **l** $6x = 30$

Find the value of x in each of these balances.

a 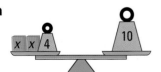   **b**    **c**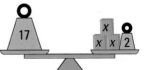

• Solving equations with the unknown on both sides

Keywords
Equation   *Substitution*
Solution   *Unknown*

Solving some **equations** involves more than one step.

example

Solve $2x + 5 = 17$

You can think of this equation as a balance.

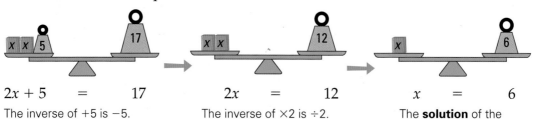

| $2x + 5$ | $=$ | 17 | $2x$ | $=$ | 12 | x | $=$ | 6 |

The inverse of +5 is −5.   The inverse of ×2 is ÷2.   The **solution** of the
Subtract 5 from both sides.   Divide both sides by 2.   equation is $x = 6$.

This balance has the
unknown in both scale pans.

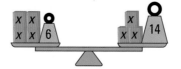

Subtract 3x from both
sides because 3x is smaller
than 4x.

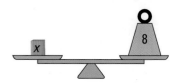

The balance shows the equation $4x + 6 = 3x + 14$
Subtract 3x from both sides. $x + 6 = 14$
Subtract 6 from both sides. $x = 8$

The solution $x = 8$ can be checked by **substitution**:

$4x + 6$ $=$ $3x + 14$

$4 \times 8 + 6 = 38$ $3 \times 8 + 14 = 38$

The check works.   Both sides are equal.

example

Solve the equation $3z + 4 = 9z - 8$

Re-write the equation so that the most zs are on the LHS.

$9z - 8 = 3z + 4$
Subtract 3z from both sides. $6z - 8 = 4$
Add 8 to both sides. $6z = 12$
Divide both sides by 6. $z = 2$

The solution is $z = 2$.

Exercise 7b

1 Solve these equations. Each of them needs two steps.

   a $2x + 4 = 10$ **b** $2x + 3 = 13$ **c** $3x + 1 = 13$

   d $3x + 5 = 11$ **e** $4x + 3 = 19$ **f** $10x + 7 = 57$

   g $2x - 4 = 8$ **h** $2x - 1 = 8$ **i** $3x - 2 = 10$

   j $3x - 5 = 4$ **k** $10x - 7 = 33$ **l** $2x + 3 = 10$

2 Find the value of x in each of these balances.

  a    **b** 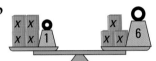   **c**

3 Solve these equations.

   a $4x + 5 = 3x + 8$ **b** $8x + 4 = 7x + 6$ **c** $5x + 3 = 4x + 7$

   d $3x + 1 = 2x + 10$ **e** $7x + 3 = 5x + 9$ **f** $10x + 4 = 8x + 8$

   g $14x + 6 = 7x + 13$ **h** $9x + 4 = x + 24$ **i** $3\frac{1}{2}x + 1 = \frac{1}{2}x + 7$

   j $6x + 1 = 3x + 13$ **k** $12x + 7 = 2x + 27$ **l** $x + 7 = 3x + 1$

4 Solve these equations.

   a $4x - 5 = 3x + 1$ **b** $6x - 2 = 5x + 4$ **c** $7x - 4 = 5x + 2$

   d $9x - 1 = 7x + 7$ **e** $8x - 4 = 5x + 8$ **f** $6x - 7 = x + 3$

   g $10x - 3 = 7x + 3$ **h** $5x - 2 = x + 10$ **i** $4\frac{1}{2}x - 8 = \frac{1}{2}x$

   j $5x - 3 = x + 5$ **k** $3x + 1 = 4x - 6$ **l** $6x = 8x - 4$

5 Solve these equations. They need a mixture of methods.

   a $4x + 3 = 2x + 11$ **b** $4x - 3 = 2x + 11$ **c** $8x + 2 = x + 30$

   d $6x - 7 = x + 3$ **e** $2x + 20 = 8x + 2$ **f** $3x + 1 = 5x - 13$

   g $6x - 8 = 2x$ **h** $7x - 3 = 5x - 3$ **i** $2x = 9x - 28$

   j $8x = 5x + 18$ **k** $2x = 9 - x$ **l** $3x = 21 - 4x$

6 A joiner has seven boxes of screws and four extra
   screws. His workmate has five similar boxes and
   twenty eight extra screws. They have the same total
   number of screws. If there are n screws in each box
   a form an equation involving n **b** find the value of n.

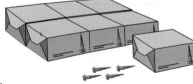

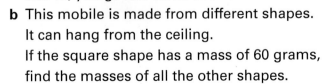

puzzle

  a Think of a number, multiply it by 5 and then
     subtract 3. If you double the same number and
     add 15, you get the same answer. Find the number.

  b This mobile is made from different shapes.
     It can hang from the ceiling.
     If the square shape has a mass of 60 grams,
     find the masses of all the other shapes.

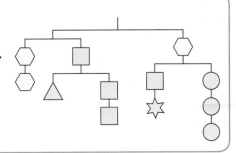

• Solve equations which have brackets

Keywords
Brackets
Expand

This balance shows two identical bags, each holding an unknown mass x and 4 grams.
They are balanced by 18 grams.

The equation is $2(x + 4) = 18$

Expand the **brackets**. $2x + 8 = 18$

p. 68 Subtract 8 from both sides. $2x = 10$

Divide both sides by 2. $x = 5$

> Think $2 \times x = 2x$ and
> $2 \times 4 = 8$

> Check your solution:
> $2 \times (5 + 4) = 2 \times 9 = 18$

Equations can have brackets containing unknowns on both sides.

example

Solve the equation $3(2x - 1) = 5(x + 2)$

$3(2x - 1) = 5(x + 2)$

Expand the brackets $\qquad 6x - 3 = 5x + 10$

Add 3 to both sides. $\qquad 6x = 5x + 13$

Subtract $5x$ from both sides $\qquad x = 13$

The solution is $x = 13$.

> Check:
> $3(2 \times 13 - 1) = 3 \times 25 = 75$
> $5(13 + 2) = 5 \times 15 = 75$

You can solve real-life problems using equations.

example

Katrina is three times older than her sister Siobhan.
In four years' time, Siobhan will be half Katrina's age.
How old are they both now?

Call Siobhan's age n, Katrina's age $= 3n$.

In four years time, $\qquad 3n + 4 = 2(n + 4)$

Expand the brackets $\qquad 3n + 4 = 2n + 8$

$\qquad\qquad 3n = 2n + 4$

$\qquad\qquad n = 4$

So Siobhan is 4, and Katrina is 12.

Exercise 7c

1 Solve these equations by expanding the brackets.

a $2(x + 3) = 16$ **b** $3(x + 3) = 15$

c $2(4x + 5) = 26$ **d** $3(2x + 1) = 21$

e $3(2x - 1) = 21$ **f** $2(2x - 7) = 4$

g $2(x - 4) = 1$ **h** $6(2x - 1) = 18$

i $5(2x - 3) = 10$ **j** $3(3x + 2) = 2(3x + 6)$

k $2(5x + 1) = 4(2x + 3)$ **l** $7(x + 2) = 4(x + 5)$

m $5(2x + 1) = 3(3x + 4)$ **n** $3(6x + 5) = 4(4x + 7)$

o $5(2x - 1) = 3(3x + 2)$ **p** $4(3x - 1) = 2(5x + 7)$

q $3(5x - 2) = 4(3x + 6)$ **r** $9x - 1 = 2(1 + 4x)$

2 Solve these equations.
You will have to collect 'like terms' after expanding the brackets.

a $3(2x + 1) + 2(4x + 2) = 21$ **b** $2(x + 2) + 3(x + 4) = 31$

c $5(2x + 1) + 2(5x + 3) = 91$ **d** $2(4x + 3) + 3(2x + 1) = 23$

e $4(3x + 2) + 8(x + 1) = 56$ **f** $5(2x + 1) + 2(x + 4) = 13$

g $6(x + 2) + 4(x - 3) = 50$ **h** $4(2x + 2) + 2(x - 3) = 12$

i $3(4x + 1) + 2(6x - 1) = 13$ **j** $2(3x - 5) + 3(3x + 4) = 17$

k $4(2x + 1) + 2(3x - 1) = 30$ **l** $5(3x - 1) + 4(2x + 7) = 69$

3 This year, a man is three times older than his son.
In ten years' time, the man will be twice his son's age.
If the son is x years old now, find the value of x.

4 Solve these equations. Use a number line to help with the negatives.

a $x + 2 = 2$ **b** $x + 2 = 1$ **c** $x + 2 = -1$ **d** $x + 2 = -4$

e $2x + 5 = 1$ **f** $2x + 9 = 3$ **g** $3x + 4 = 1$ **h** $3x + 2 = -4$

i $4x + 7 = -1$ **j** $6x + 8 = 8$ **k** $2x + 9 = 5$ **l** $7x + 4 = -10$

m $y - 2 = 3$ **n** $y - 2 = -2$ **o** $y - 2 = -3$ **p** $y - 4 = -2$

5 Solve these equations. The answers have fractions in them.

a $2x + 3 = 10$ **b** $2x + 8 = 13$ **c** $4x + 3 = 8$ **d** $8x - 2 = 23$

e $2(x - 4) = 1$ **f** $4(x - 3) = 5$ **g** $5(2x + 3) = 40$ **h** $4(2x + 5) = 29$

---

challenge

You can convert temperatures in °F to °C using the formula
$$C = \frac{5(F - 32)}{9}.$$

There is a temperature $T°$ which is the same in both Fahrenheit and Celsius.
Use this formula to find the value of T.
Where on Earth might you experience this temperature?

- Use a mapping and a mapping diagram
- Use a function and a function machine

Keywords
Function   Table of
Mapping   values
Rule

This is a **mapping** diagram.

It uses a **rule** of 'add 5' to map X onto Y.

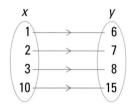

- A mapping uses a rule to link one set of values *X* with another set of values *Y*.

Sometimes the rule can have two stages.

It is often shown in a diagram.

example

Find the rule for this mapping.

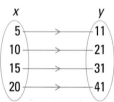

The rule is 'double the X number and add 1'.

A mapping can often be written as a **function**.

In the previous example, the function is $y = 2x + 1$.

- A function uses a rule to link one set of values *x* with another set of values *y*.

p. 206

This two-stage function machine shows how to convert kilometres to miles approximately.

$$x \longrightarrow \boxed{\div 8} \longrightarrow \boxed{\times 5} \longrightarrow y$$

The function connecting kilometres *x* with miles *y* is
    $(x \div 8) \times 5 \approx y$ or $y \approx \frac{x}{8} \times 5$

≈ means approximately

You can complete a **table of values** for this function.

When $x = 16$, $y \approx (16 \div 8) \times 5 = 2 \times 5 = 10$

So $16 \rightarrow 10$ and $16 \, \text{km} = 10 \, \text{miles}$

A table of values works like a mapping diagram – it links pairs of values that are connected by a rule.

Kilometres, *x*	16	24	48
Miles, *y*	10	15	30

Exercise 7d

1 Copy this mapping diagram three times.
Complete your copies for these rules.

   a add 6   **b** subtract 1   **c** multiply by 2 and add 3

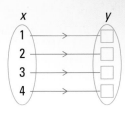

2 Find the rules for these mapping diagrams.

  a 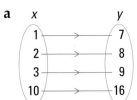   **b**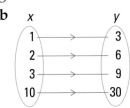

3 Make two copies of this mapping diagram and the table of values.

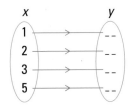

x	1	2	3	5
y	--	--	--	--

Complete your copies using these function machines.

  a $x \longrightarrow \boxed{\times 2} \longrightarrow \boxed{+1} \longrightarrow y$ **b** $x \longrightarrow \boxed{+1} \longrightarrow \boxed{\times 2} \longrightarrow y$

4 During a storm, you can find how far away
the thunder is by counting the seconds
between seeing the lightning and hearing
the thunder and then dividing by 5.

seconds $\longrightarrow \boxed{\div 5} \longrightarrow$ miles

  a How far away is the storm if you count
    10 seconds?

  b Copy this table and use the function machine to complete it.

No. of seconds, x	5	10	15	20	25	30
No. of miles, y						

task

London to Preston in Lancashire is 200 miles by motorway.
The time it takes depends on how fast you go. Draw a
mapping diagram which maps the speed of your car onto
the time taken.
Find the rule in words for the mapping.

- Plot points in all four quadrants
- Draw a straight-line graph of a function

Keywords

Axes
Coordinates
Graph
Equation
Plot

Straight-line
graph
Table of
values

This function machine shows the rule 'subtract 1'.

$$x \longrightarrow \boxed{-1} \longrightarrow y$$

The **equation** of the function is $y = x - 1$.
You can use the equation to find the value of y for different values of x.

When $x = -1$, $y = -1 - 1 = -2$ $x = 2, y = 1$
    $x = 0, y = -1$ $x = 3, y = 2$
    $x = 1, y = 0$ $x = 4, y = 3$

> Use a number line for
> $-1 - 1 = -2$

These results can be placed in a **table of values**.

x	-1	0	1	2	3	4
y	-2	-1	0	1	2	3

You can write **coordinates** from the table of values

(-1, -2), (0, -1), (1, 0), (2, 1), (3, 2), (4, 3)

You can now use these coordinates to plot points on a **graph**.

First draw the **axes**:   Next **plot** the points: Now join the points with a **straight line**:

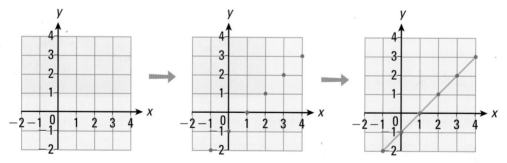

The graph of $y = x - 1$ is a straight line.

- You can draw the graph of a function by first creating a table of values.

Exercise 7e

1 This function machine gives the equation $y = x + 4$.

a Input these x-values into the function machine.
Copy and complete the table.

x	0	1	2	3	4	5
y						

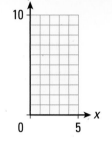

b Use the table to plot six points on axes labelled as here.

c Join the points to draw the graph of the equation $y = x + 4$.

2 For each equation,
  i copy and complete the table from question **1**
  ii plot points on axes labelled as in question **1**
  iii join your points to draw the graph of each equation.

  a $y = x + 2$ **b** $y = x - 1$
  c $y = 2x + 1$ **d** $y = 2x - 3$
  e $y = 10 - x$ **f** $y = 5 - x$

> Remember that $2x + 1$ means 'double x and then add 1'.

3 For each of these equations, copy and complete this table.

x	0	2	4	6	8	10
y						

Draw the graph of each equation. Label your x-axis from 0 to 10 and your y-axis from -4 to 10.

  a $x + y = 10$ **b** $x + y = 6$
  c $x + y = 8$ **d** $y = 9 - x$

4 Lengths of cloth can be bought over the Internet.
Their cost £C depends on their length, x metres, where $C = 4x + 2$.

  a Copy and complete this table.

x	1	2	3	4	5
C					

  b Draw a graph of C against x.
  c Use your graph to find the length of cloth which costs £12.

- Recognise the equations of sloping lines and lines parallel to the axes and draw their graphs
- Use straight-line graphs in real-life contexts

Keywords

Axis   Sloping
Horizontal   Vertical
Parallel

Here is a **horizontal** straight-line graph drawn on axes.

The points $(1, 3)$, $(2, 3)$, $(3, 3)$ and $(4, 3)$ are all on this line. They all have the same y-value of 3.

The equation of this line is $y = 3$.

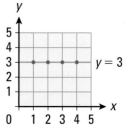

- Lines **parallel** to the x-**axis** have points whose y-values are all the same.

These lines are horizontal.

Now here is a **vertical** straight-line graph.

The points $(4, 1)$, $(4, 2)$, $(4, 3)$ and $(4, 5)$ are all on this line. They all have the same x-value of 4.

The equation of this line is $x = 4$.

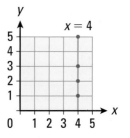

- Lines parallel to the y-axis have points whose x-values are all the same.

These lines are vertical.

Here is a **sloping** straight-line graph.

The points $(1, 2)$, $(2, 4)$, and $(3, 6)$ are all on this line.
The y-value is always double the x-value.

Its equation is $y = 2x$.

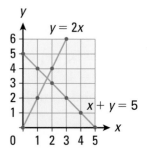

- Sloping lines have equations with both x and y in them.

Sometimes graphs can slope downwards.

Here is the graph of $x + y = 5$.

The x and y values always add up to 5.

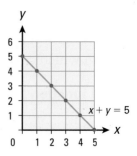

Exercise 7f

1 Here are the equations of some straight lines.
Say whether each line is
  i a line parallel to the x-axis   **ii** a line parallel to the y-axis
  iii a sloping line.
  a $y = 3$ **b** $x = 5$ **c** $y = x - 4$ **d** $y = 2x + 3$
  e $x = 2$ **f** $x + y = 7$ **g** $y = 6$ **h** $y = 4x - 1$

2 Write the equations of these five straight lines A to E.

3 For each set of equations, draw axes, and label both axes
from 0 to 10. Draw all three graphs on the same axes to make
a triangle.
  a $y = x + 1$, $x = 8$, $y = 2$ **b** $y = 2x$, $x = 5$, $y = 4$
  c $y = 2x - 2$, $x = 1$, $y = 8$ **d** $y = 9 - x$, $x = 7$, $y = 8$

> You may need to make
> a table of values for
> the sloping lines.

4 Without drawing any diagrams, find whether
each point lies on the given line.
  a $(1, 5)$ and $y = x + 4$ **b** $(5, 4)$ and $y = x - 1$
  c $(3, 7)$ and $y = 2x + 1$ **d** $(5, 13)$ and $y = 2x - 3$
  e $(0, 8)$ and $y = 6x + 2$ **f** $(3, 6)$ and $y = 9 - x$
  g $(5, \text{-}1)$ and $y = 4 - x$ **h** $(\text{-}1, 3)$ and $y = 4x + 1$

5 On axes labelled from 0 to 10, draw the lines
$x = 4, x = 6$, $y = 1$ and $y = 5$.
Find the area of the shape enclosed by these lines.

6 The average life-span of a man in the UK is eighty years.
A man who is x years old now might expect to live
for another y years, where $y = 80 - x$.

Copy and complete this table.

x	20	30	40	50	60
y					

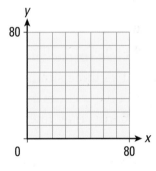

Draw a graph of y against x on axes like these.

investigation

Learn how to use a computer software package to
draw straight-line graphs.
Use a computer to draw the graphs of the two lines with
these equations on the same axes. See if you can find the
point where they cross.

$y = 7 - x$ $y = 2x + 1$

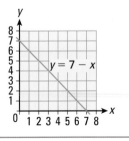

7a

1 Find the value of x in each of these balances.

a

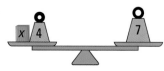

b

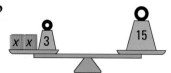

2 Solve these equations by using inverse operations.

a $x + 3 = 7$ b $x - 3 = 7$ c $2x = 8$ d $\frac{x}{2} = 5$

e $4 + x = 6$ f $x - 4 = 1$ g $3x = 18$ h $\frac{x}{4} = 2$

7b

3 Solve these equations. Each of them needs two steps.

a $2x + 4 = 14$ b $3x + 2 = 23$ c $2x - 1 = 11$

d $5x - 6 = 9$ e $\frac{x}{2} + 1 = 6$ f $\frac{x}{3} - 3 = 3$

4 Find the value of x in each of these balances.

a   b

5 Solve these equations. There are unknowns on both sides.

a $4x + 2 = 3x + 7$ b $6x + 1 = 5x + 13$ c $3x + 6 = x + 10$

d $7x + 2 = 4x + 8$ e $6x + 9 = x + 24$ f $7x = 3x + 20$

6 Solve these equations. Take care with the negative signs.

a $3x - 1 = 2x + 4$ b $7x - 2 = 5x + 6$ c $5x - 5 = 3x - 1$

d $8x - 11 = 5x - 2$ e $9x + 8 = 7x + 4$ f $6x + 14 = 3x + 5$

7 Sarah has six packets of Christmas cards and two loose cards. Her sister, Jane, has three similar packets of cards and seventeen loose cards. Each packet has x cards in it. When the sisters open all their boxes and count their cards, they find that they have the same total.
Write an equation and find the value of x.

7c

8 Solve these equations.

a $2(3x + 4) = 20$ b $3(2x - 1) = 21$ c $5(x - 2) = 20$

d $3(4x + 1) = 123$ e $4(2x + 1) = 6(x + 2)$ f $5(3x + 2) = 4(3x + 4)$

9 Solve these equations by expanding the brackets and collecting like terms.

a $3(2x + 4) + 2(3x + 1) = 38$ b $5(2x + 1) + 2(x + 3) = 35$

c $4(x + 3) + 6(x + 1) = 28$ d $2(2x + 3) + 4(2x + 1) = 18$

e $3(5x + 1) + 2(1 - 6x) = 9$ f $5(x + 5) + 2(2x - 3) = 31$

10 Copy this mapping diagram three times.

Complete your copies using these rules.
a add five   **b** subtract two   **c** double then add five
For each mapping diagram, copy and complete this table.

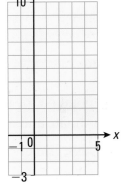

x	1	2	3	10
y				

11 Make two copies of this mapping diagram and the table of values.

x	1	2	3	5	20
y	--	--	--	--	--

Complete your copies using these function machines.

a
$x \longrightarrow \boxed{\times 3} \longrightarrow \boxed{+1} \longrightarrow y$

b
$x \longrightarrow \boxed{+1} \longrightarrow \boxed{\times 3} \longrightarrow y$

12 a Copy and complete this table
for the equation $y = x + 5$.
Plot points on axes labelled
as shown here.
Draw the graph of the
equation $y = x + 5$.

x	−1	0	1	2	3	4
y						

b Repeat for the equations
i $y = x + 2$ **ii** $y = 2x - 1$ **iii** $x + y = 9$

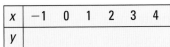

13 Write the equations of these four straight lines A to D.

14 Here are the equations of some straight lines.
Which lines are
i parallel to the x-axis
ii parallel to the y-axis
iii sloping lines?
a $y = 2$ **b** $x = 4$ **c** $y = x + 3$
d $y = 2x + 1$ **e** $x = 5$ **f** $y = -2$

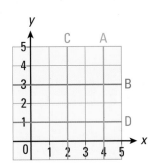

Assessment criteria
- Plot the graphs of simple linear functions **Level 6**
- Construct and solve linear equations **Level 6**
- Construct functions arising from real-life
  problems and plot their corresponding graphs **Level 6**

Level 6

1 Solve the equation $\quad 5x + 4 = x + 12$
Show your working.

Ollie's answer ✔

Ollie decides to subtract 4 from both sides of the equation.

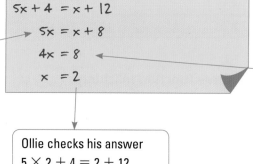

$$5x + 4 = x + 12$$
$$5x = x + 8$$
$$4x = 8$$
$$x = 2$$

He subtracts x from both sides of the equation.

Ollie checks his answer
$5 \times 2 + 4 = 2 + 12$
which is correct.

Level 6

2 Each point on the straight line $x + y = 12$ has an
x-coordinate and a y-coordinate that add together to make 12.

Copy this grid and draw the straight line $x + y = 12$

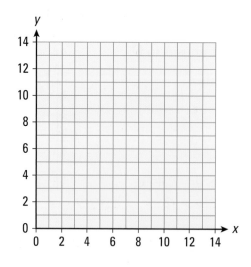

Key Stage 3 2002 4–6 Paper 2

8 Number

Calculations

Wilhelm Schickard (1592–1635) built one of the first calculating machines in 1623 in Germany. It was called a "calculating clock" as it used the same cogs and gears already found in clocks.

What's the point? Calculators can often provide solutions faster than hand-written arithmetic but they couldn't have been invented without understanding the mathematical principles first.

✓ Check in

1 Round each of these numbers to the nearest
   i 1000   **ii** 100   **iii** 10

   a 3462   **b** 5278

2 Calculate these using a mental method. Write the method you have used.
   a 76 + 19   **b** 85 − 29   **c** 3.5 + 8.6   **d** 8.2 − 1.9

3 Calculate these using a written method.
   a 34.6 + 51.5   **b** 87.5 − 19.7

4 Calculate
   a 39 × 10   **b** 4.8 × 100   **c** 58 ÷ 100   **d** 485 ÷ 10

5 Calculate these using mental methods.
   a 17 × 9   **b** 13 × 15   **c** 12 × 19   **d** 11 × 18

6 In each of these questions use an appropriate written method. Remember to do a mental approximation first.
   a 32 × 15   **b** 112 ÷ 7   **c** 18 × 265   **d** 208 ÷ 16

Level 4

Level 5

- Round positive whole numbers to a given power of 10
- Round decimals to the nearest whole number or to 1 or 2 decimal places

Keywords

Digit	Round down
Hundredth	Tenth
Nearest	Thousandth
Round up	

In many real-life situations it is often best to **round** numbers, for example crowd attendances.

- When you round a number to the **nearest** whole number, **nearest tenth** or **nearest hundredth**
  - Look at the next **digit**.
  - If it is 5 or more, then the number is **rounded up**.
  - If it is less than 5, then the number is **rounded down**.

example

Round 3.6476 kg to the
a nearest whole number   b nearest tenth (1 dp)
c nearest hundredth (2 dp)

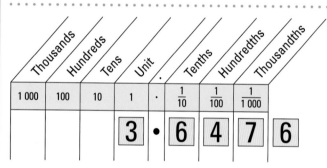

1 000	100	10	1	.	$\frac{1}{10}$	$\frac{1}{100}$	$\frac{1}{1\,000}$
			3	.	6	4	7	6

a Look at the tenths digit–this is 6.
  So round **up**.
  3.6476 kg ≈ 4 kg (nearest whole number)

b Look at the hundredths digit (4).
  So round **down**.
  3.6476 kg ≈ 3.6 kg (1 decimal place)

c Look at the thousandths digit (7).
  So round **up**.
  3.6476 kg ≈ 3.65 kg (nearest hundredth, or 2 decimal places)

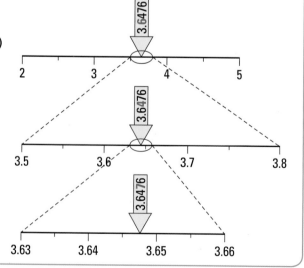

Exercise 8a

1 Round each of these numbers to the nearest

   i 1000   **ii** 100   **iii** 10

a 4072	**b** 7188	**c** 3654	**d** 7528
e 5594	**f** 6573	**g** 4938	**h** 13 394
i 27 593	**j** 31 694	**k** 65 959	**l** 74 999

2 Round each of these numbers to the nearest

   i whole number   **ii** tenth (1 dp)   **iii** hundredth (2 dp).

a 3.736	**b** 4.218	**c** 7.2856	**d** 9.349
e 13.858	**f** 13.036	**g** 4.3061	**h** 7.9384
i 2.0394	**j** 2.6389	**k** 1.318 46	**l** 3.582 23

3 Mona runs 100 m in 17.999 seconds.

Mona decides to round her time to the nearest whole number and also to the nearest tenth. This is what she writes down:

    17.999 ≈ 18 (nearest whole number)

    17.999 ≈ 18 (nearest tenth)

Is Mona correct?

Explain your answer.

4 Work out these using a calculator and giving your answer to an appropriate degree of accuracy.

   a 13% of £25   **b** $\frac{2}{7}$ of £8   **c** 4.75% of £230   **d** $\frac{1}{3}$ of 47p

challenge

Here is some information about a famous event. Write a short article for a newspaper about the event, rounding the numbers you use to an appropriate degree of accuracy.

Date: 16 October 1987

Mini hurricane strikes the south east corner of England.
Duration of winds at high levels 6 hours 43 mins.
Maximum wind speed 115.0779 mph at

Shoreham in Sussex. Average wind speed reached 86.3085 mph for 63 minutes.
14 983 000 trees were lost during the storm.

- Consolidate and extend a range of mental strategies for addition and subtraction

Keywords
Compensation
Partitioning
Strategies

There are lots of mental **strategies** to help you work out additions and subtractions in your head.

- You use the **partitioning** method to split the numbers you are adding or subtracting into easier parts.

- You use the **compensation** method by rounding one of the numbers and then adding or subtracting the extra amount.

example

Calculate **a** $6.6 + 8.7$ **b** $13.4 - 8.9$

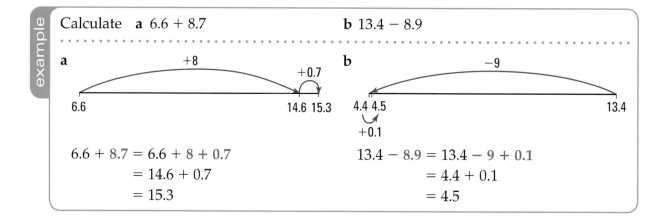

$$6.6 + 8.7 = 6.6 + 8 + 0.7$$
$$= 14.6 + 0.7$$
$$= 15.3$$

$$13.4 - 8.9 = 13.4 - 9 + 0.1$$
$$= 4.4 + 0.1$$
$$= 4.5$$

- You can find the difference between two numbers by counting up from the smallest number to the largest number.

This method is sometimes called shopkeeper's subtraction.

example

Laura attends Heswick High School for Girls. In 2008 she was in Year 8. In a History lesson Laura finds out that the first Viking invasion of Britain took place in the year 793. How many years ago did this event take place?

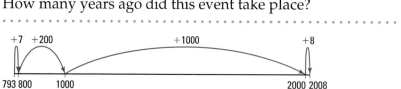

$$2008 - 793 = 7 + 200 + 1000 + 8$$
$$= 1215$$

The invasion was 1215 years ago.

Exercise 8b

1 Calculate these using a mental method.

a 12.7 + 2.4 **b** 15.7 + 4.9 **c** 17.4 − 9.6 **d** 18.8 + 6.6

2 Complete each of these addition pyramids.

a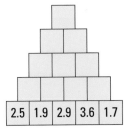

b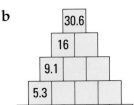

> Each number is the sum of the two numbers below it.

3 Calculate these using a mental method.

a 14.6 + 9.5 **b** 3.57 + 4.9 **c** 3.7 + 6.83 **d** 4.19 + 5.99

4 Find the missing numbers in each of these number sentences.

a 6.43 + □ = 10 **b** 8.95 + □ = 12.1

c □ + 7.3 = 13.25 **d** 6.99 + □ = 20

5 Here are some MP3 music files.

a How much longer is track 02 compared to track 01?

b How much bigger is the file for track 01 compared to track 03?

c What is the total time of the four tracks?

d Norbert can store 11 MB of MP3 music files on his mobile phone. Can he fit all four tracks onto his mobile phone? Explain your answer.

> Track 01
> Hip Hip Hop
> by the Hoppettes
> 3m 28s   3.65MB

> Track 03
> Running up the hill
> by the Fell Runners
> 3m 06s   2.9MB

> Track 02
> Down the other side
> by Friends of the
> Fell Runners
> 4m 15s   3.89MB

> Track 04
> Hop Hop Hip
> by the Hippettes
> 1m 58s   1.59MB

problem

Here are some famous events in British history.

Battle of Hastings	1066
Magna Carta signed	1215
Battle of Bannockburn	1314
Spanish Armada defeated	1588
English Civil War	1642
Battle of Waterloo	1815

a Work out how many years ago each event took place.

b Imagine you live in the year 3542.
How many years in the past would each event be now?

c Imagine you lived in the year 2839 BC.
How many years in the future would each event be?

- Consolidate and develop standard written methods for addition and subtraction

Keywords
Decimal point
Standard written method

When numbers are too difficult to add in your head you can use the **standard written method** for addition.

example

Norris travels on the motorway from Woking to Bristol. What is the total distance he has travelled?

Bristol   Swindon   Reading   Bracknell   Woking
  ○   ○   ○   ○   ○
        64 km   65.05 km   18.76 km   21.4 km

Need to calculate
21.4 km + 18.76 km + 65.05 km + 64 km
Set out the calculation in columns:
Line up the **decimal points**
Fill in with zeros
Total distance travelled = 169.21 km

```
   21.40
   18.76
   65.05
 + 64.00
  169.21
   1 1 1
```

When numbers are too difficult to subtract in your head you should use the standard written method for subtraction.

example

A gritter lorry puts rock salt on roads to stop ice forming on the surface.
At the start of its journey the lorry is loaded with 593.68 kg of rock salt.
After 15 minutes it has released 75.7 kg of rock salt. How much rock salt is left in the lorry?

You must calculate 593.68 kg − 75.7 kg
Set out the calculation in columns:

Total rock salt remaining = 517.98 kg

```
     8 12  1
   593.68
 - 075.70
   517.98
```

Exercise 8c

1 Calculate these using a written or mental method.

    a 54.6 + 41.5   **b** 27.9 + 16.4   **c** 28.3 + 55.4   **d** 47.6 + 75.7

    e 45.9 + 8.3   **f** 84.4 + 19.7   **g** 14.7 − 3.2   **h** 18.6 − 12.1

2 Calculate these using a written method.

    a 5.45 + 9.4   **b** 35.7 − 9.76   **c** 36.42 + 7.7   **d** 38.4 + 19.74

    e 8.7 + 34.96   **f** 38.79 + 34.5   **g** 94.5 − 89.79   **h** 36.7 − 8.68

3 Calculate these using a written method.

    a 534.9 − 51.2   **b** 659.76 + 46.9   **c** 34.68 + 862.9   **d** 1161.7 − 49.36

    e 652.61 − 74.3   **f** 265.73 − 38.9   **g** 673.4 + 9.18   **h** 1357.2 − 89.73

4 Calculate these using a written method.

    a 63.52 + 344.1 + 6.17   **b** 33.6 + 185.8 + 71.47   **c** 5.23 + 6.5 + 8 + 0.37

    d 15.6 + 19.7 + 5.07   **e** 54.6 + 265.3 + 177.9   **f** 348.6 + 137.25 + 18.8

5 Use a mental or written method to solve each of these problems.

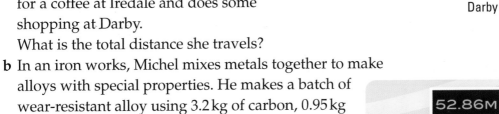

    a Betty uses a route finder to travel from Gorley to Poole. On the way she stops for a coffee at Iredale and does some shopping at Darby.

    What is the total distance she travels?

    b In an iron works, Michel mixes metals together to make alloys with special properties. He makes a batch of wear-resistant alloy using 3.2 kg of carbon, 0.95 kg of manganese, 16.8 kg of chromium, 2.783 kg of molybdenum and 76.5 kg of iron. What is the total weight of the alloy?

    c In the school discus competition, Titus throws the discus 52.86 m. He beats the school record by 9.375 m. What was the old school discus record?

Find the missing amount in each of these number sentences.

a ☐ + 3.78 kg = 12.5 kg

b 16.78 km + 3.8 km + ☐ = 25.27 km

c 89.3 litres + ☐ + 14.06 litres = 164.14 litres

d 3.86 tonnes + 12.7 tonnes + 49.1 tonnes + ☐ = 70.05 tonnes

- Multiply and divide numbers by positive powers of 10
- Multiply and divide by 0.1 and 0.01

Keywords
Digit
Divide
Multiply

- When you **multiply** a number by 10, 100 or 1000, all the **digits** move to the left.

example

Calculate 4.7×100

$4.7 \times 100 = 4.7 \times 100$
$\qquad\qquad\;\; = 470$

H	T	U	•	$\frac{1}{10}$
		4	•	7
4	7	0	•	

When you multiply by 100 the digits move 2 places to the left.

- When you **divide** a number by 10, 100 or 1000, all the digits move to the right.

example

Calculate $28.9 \div 10$

$28.9 \div 10 = 28.9 \div 10$
$\qquad\qquad\;\; = 2.89$

T	U	•	$\frac{1}{10}$	$\frac{1}{100}$
2	8	•	9	
	2	•	8	9

When you divide by 10 the digits move 1 place to the right.

You can also multiply and divide by 0.1 (tenths) and 0.01 (hundredths).

example

Calculate   **a** 9×0.1 **b** 8×0.01

a $9 \times 0.1 = 9 \times \frac{1}{10}$ **b** $8 \times 0.01 = 8 \times \frac{1}{100}$
$\qquad\quad\; = 9 \div 10 = 0.9$ $= 8 \div 100 = 0.08$

$\times \frac{1}{10}$ is the same as $\div 10$

$\times \frac{1}{100}$ is the same as $\div 100$

- Multiplying by 0.1 is the same as dividing by 10.

- Multiplying by 0.01 is the same as dividing by 100.

example

Calculate   **a** $4 \div 0.1$ **b** $8 \div 0.01$

a $4 \div 0.1 = 4 \div \frac{1}{10}$ **b** $8 \div 0.01 = 8 \div \frac{1}{100}$
$\qquad\quad\; = 4 \times 10 = 40$ $= 8 \times 100 = 800$

Think how many …
… tenths are in 4
… hundredths are in 8.

- Dividing by 0.1 is the same as multiplying by 10.

- Dividing by 0.01 is the same as multiplying by 100.

Exercise 8d

1 Calculate

    a 7×10 **b** $40 \div 10$ **c** 49×10 **d** $78 \div 100$

    e 0.3×1000 **f** $4.7 \div 10$ **g** 0.094×10 **h** $59.3 \div 1000$

2 Calculate

    a $\frac{1}{10}$ of £300   **b** $\frac{1}{10}$ of 45 kg   **c** $\frac{1}{100}$ of \$4000   **d** $\frac{1}{100}$ of 385 km

3 **a** Work out $3 \div 0.1$ by finding how many tenths there are in 3.

    b Work out $2 \div 0.01$ by finding how many hundredths there
       are in 2.

4 Calculate

    a 3×0.1 **b** 5×0.1 **c** 9×0.01

    d 7×0.01 **e** $6 \div 0.1$ **f** $9 \div 0.1$

    g $5 \div 0.01$ **h** $3 \div 0.01$

5 Calculate

    a 25×0.1 **b** 29×0.01 **c** $36 \div 0.1$

    d $45 \div 0.01$ **e** 290×0.1 **f** 370×0.01

    g $410 \div 0.1$ **h** $200 \div 0.01$

6 Calculate

    a 39×0.1 **b** $247 \div 0.1$ **c** 2.9×0.1

    d $4.1 \div 0.1$ **e** $17.4 \div 0.01$ **f** $0.93 \div 0.01$

    g 34.5×0.1 **h** 2.7×0.01 **i** 54.8×0.01

    j 0.37×0.1 **k** $27 \div 0.01$ **l** $0.08 \div 0.1$

Did you know?

The decimal system is not the only number system used in the world. The binary system is based on powers of 2 and is what computers rely on to work!

7 Here are six number cards.

 1000   100   10   1   0.1   0.01

Fill in the missing numbers in each of these statements using one
of these cards.

    a $5 \times \square = 50$ **b** $0.2 \times \square = 20$

    c $470 \div \square = 47$ **d** $230 \div \square = 23$

    e $6 \div \square = 60$ **f** $0.3 \div \square = 30$

    g $520 \times \square = 52$ **h** $180 \div \square = 18$

- Consolidate and extend a range of mental strategies for multiplication and division

You can use a range of mental strategies to help you work out multiplications and divisions in your head.

- You can re-write a number as a pair of **factors** and then do two simpler multiplications or divisions.

example

Calculate   **a** 23×0.03 **b** $225 \div 15$

a $23 \times 0.03 = 23 \times 0.01 \times 3$
   $23 \times 0.01 = 0.23$
   $0.23 \times 3 = 0.69$
   $23 \times 0.03 = 0.69$

b $225 \div 15 = 225 \div 5 \div 3$
   $225 \div 5 = 45$
   $45 \div 3 = 15$
   $225 \div 15 = 15$

- You can use **partitioning** to split the numbers you are multiplying or dividing into parts which are easier to work with.

example

Calculate   **a** 12×4.2 **b** $340 \div 16$

a $12 \times 4.2 = (10 \times 4.2) + (2 \times 4.2)$
   $= 42 + 8.4$
   $= 50.4$

b $340 \div 16 = (320 \div 16) + (20 \div 16)$
   $= 20 + 1\,R4$
   $= 21\,R4$

Split 340 into two numbers so that one of the numbers is a multiple of 16 that you can do in your head.

- You can use **compensation** when the number you are multiplying is nearly a multiple of 10 or 100. Round this number up or down and then adjust the answer accordingly.

example

Calculate   **a** 4.1×19 **b** 7.2×21

a $4.1 \times 19 = (4.1 \times 20) - (4.1 \times 1)$
   $= 82 - 4.1$
   $= 77.9$

b $21 \times 7.2 = (20 \times 7.2) + (1 \times 7.2)$
   $= 144 + 7.2$
   $= 151.2$

Exercise 8e

1 Calculate these mentally using factors.

a 8 × 30	**b** 5 × 40	**c** 6 × 300	**d** 7 × 500
e 25 × 20	**f** 17 × 30	**g** 12 × 50	**h** 33 × 200
i 24 × 0.2	**j** 5 × 0.03	**k** 18 × 0.5	**l** 15 × 0.04
m 32 × 0.3	**n** 51 × 0.06	**o** 44 × 0.4	**p** 26 × 0.02
q 156 ÷ 6	**r** 140 ÷ 4	**s** 264 ÷ 12	**t** 360 ÷ 15
u 216 ÷ 8	**v** 126 ÷ 18	**w** 135 ÷ 15	**x** 108 ÷ 12

2 Calculate these using the method of partitioning.

a 3.4 × 12	**b** 2.1 × 15	**c** 13 × 1.4	**d** 16 × 3.5
e 2.8 × 11	**f** 4.3 × 15	**g** 3.9 × 12	**h** 14 × 6.2
i 150 ÷ 7	**j** 190 ÷ 8	**k** 220 ÷ 12	**l** 280 ÷ 13
m 310 ÷ 14	**n** 385 ÷ 15	**o** 410 ÷ 16	**p** 480 ÷ 22

3 Calculate these using the method of compensation.

a 21 × 2.9	**b** 19 × 4.4	**c** 8.1 × 21	**d** 3.6 × 31
e 3.5 × 19	**f** 4.2 × 29	**g** 19 × 1.9	**h** 21 × 5.9
i 3.8 × 19	**j** 2.4 × 22	**k** 18 × 1.6	**l** 49 × 2.5

4 Use an appropriate mental method to solve each of these problems.

a A chocolate bar contains 6.3 g of fat. In a month, Ciaron eats fifteen of the chocolate bars. How much fat does he consume each month by eating the chocolate bars?

b Kiefer drinks 2.3 litres of water a day. How much water does he drink in the month of January?

problem

a Copy and complete the table, clearly showing the mental method you would use to work out each calculation.

b Compare your answers with a partner. Discuss the questions where you used different methods.

Question	Method I would use
8 × 19	Work out 8 × 20 subtract 8
7 × 21	
13 × 15	
156 ÷ 4	
16 × 19	
12 × 34	
31 × 6	
90 ÷ 7	
9 × 30	
11 × 15	

- Extend written methods of multiplication to whole numbers and decimals
- Make and justify estimates and approximations

Keywords
Estimate
Grid method
Standard method
Equivalent

You can use the **standard method** or the **grid method** for multiplying whole numbers and decimals.

---

example

Calculate 31×1.9

$31 \times 1.9 \approx 30 \times 2$
   $= 60$

You should always **estimate** the answer first.

Change to an **equivalent** whole number calculation.
   $31 \times 1.9 \rightarrow 31 \times 19$ Multiply the decimal by 10.

Using the standard method

```
            31
          × 19
10 × 31 =  310
 9 × 31 =  279
           589

31 × 1.9 = 58.9
```

Using the grid method

×	10	9
30	30 × 10 = 300	30 × 9 = 270
1	1 × 10 = 10	1 × 9 = 9

```
300
270
 10
+  9
589
```

Many real-life problems can be solved using written multiplication.

example

Siobhan downloads a 1.87 MB file from the Internet. Unfortunately her computer has a virus and downloads the same file a total of fourteen times. What is the total size of files that her computer has downloaded?

$14 \times 1.87\,\text{MB} \approx 10 \times 2 = 20\,\text{MB}$ Estimate the answer first.

$14 \times 1.87 \rightarrow 14 \times 187$

Using the standard method:

$14 \times 1.87 = 26.18$

```
            187
          ×  14
10 × 187 =  1870
 4 × 187 =   748
            2618
```

Multiply the decimal by 100.

The total size of the files downloaded = $14 \times 1.87\,\text{MB} = 26.18\,\text{MB}$

Remember to divide by 100.

Exercise 8f

Use the standard method to calculate these. Remember to do a mental approximation first.

The standard method is more efficient than the grid method in multiplying harder numbers.

1 **a** 12 × 15 **b** 19 × 24 **c** 18 × 26 **d** 21 × 34
 e 43 × 25 **f** 4 × 122 **g** 136 × 3 **h** 6 × 331

2 **a** 7 × 4.6 **b** 5 × 3.5 **c** 8 × 7.9 **d** 8 × 6.8
 e 9 × 5.3 **f** 8 × 4.6 **g** 31 × 0.9 **h** 26 × 5.4

3 **a** 5 × 2.16 **b** 4 × 2.45 **c** 7 × 6.99 **d** 8 × 9.28
 e 9 × 5.43 **f** 8 × 3.84 **g** 6 × 4.17 **h** 5 × 9.09

4 **a** 13 × 5.4 **b** 24 × 1.6 **c** 19 × 2.1 **d** 37 × 7.6
 e 29 × 7.4 **f** 48 × 5.5 **g** 49 × 8.9 **h** 35 × 3.2

5 **a** 12 × 2.54 **b** 16 × 3.36 **c** 13 × 4.71 **d** 27 × 3.86
 e 39 × 6.74 **f** 42 × 7.25 **g** 68 × 5.49 **h** 95 × 7.99

6 **a** Kayleigh buys 25 boxes of apples. Each box costs £4.24. What is the total cost of the boxes of apples?

 b Petrol costs £1.30 per litre. On a journey Danielle uses 31 litres of petrol. What is the total cost of the petrol for her journey?

 c Megan runs for 55 seconds at 6.8 metres per second.
 Hayden runs for 43 seconds at 7.7 metres per second.
 Who has run the furthest? Explain your answer.

7 **a** At Modeschool there are 37 students who are each 1.56 m tall. If the students lie on the floor in a straight line, from head to toe, how long will the line of students be?

 b At Medianschool the average student's thumb in Jane's class is 5.73 cm long. There are 29 students in Jane's class. Estimate the total length of the students' thumbs in Jane's class.

investigation

Hanif works out 15 × 4.7 = 70.5. Use Hanif's answer to work out these calculations. In each case explain clearly the method you have used.

 a 15 × 47 **b** 15 × 0.47 **c** 15 × 470

 d What other multiplications can you work out using Hanif's calculations?
 Represent your answers on a copy of this spider diagram.

 e Can you use Hanif's calculations to work out any divisions?

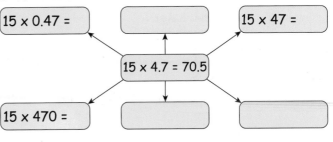

15 × 0.47 =

15 × 47 =

15 × 4.7 = 70.5

15 × 470 =

- Extend written methods of division to decimals with up to 2 places
- Recognise that the remainder from a division can be expressed as a whole number or a decimal
- Make and justify estimates and approximations

Keywords
Estimate
Remainder
Repeated subtraction
Short division

When you divide a number by an integer, the answer often has a decimal **remainder**. You can use the method of **repeated subtraction** to divide decimals by 2-digit numbers.

example

Calculate 88.3 ÷ 15 giving your answer to 1 decimal place.

88.3 ÷ 15 ≈ 90 ÷ 15 = 6

Estimate the answer first.

```
15)88.30
   -75.00      15 × 5 = 75
    13.30
   -12.00      15 × 0.8 = 12.0
     1.30
    -1.20      15 × 0.08 = 1.20
     0.10
        88.3 ÷ 15 = 5.88 R 0.10
        88.3 ÷ 15 ≈ 5.9 (1 dp)
```

Add two zeros to make your calculation easier.

Work out your answer to 2 decimal places so you can round it at the end.

There is another method of division which is very efficient for decimals. This method is called **short division**.

example

Calculate 15 ÷ 8 giving your answer to 2 decimal places.

Estimate the answer first.
15 ÷ 8 ≈ 16 ÷ 8 = 2

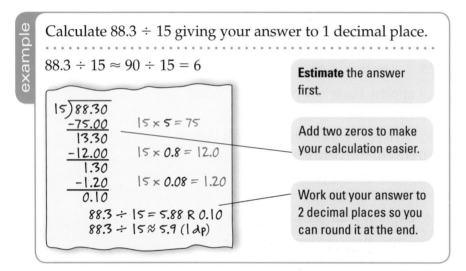

```
        1.875
      8)15.000
         7 6 4
Think  15 ÷ 8 = 1 remainder 7
       70 ÷ 8 = 8 remainder 6
       60 ÷ 8 = 7 remainder 4
       40 ÷ 8 = 5 and no remainder
15 ÷ 8 = 1.875
      ≈ 1.88 (2 dp)
```

Add three zeros to make your calculation easier.

Work out your answer to 3 dp, then you can round it to 2 dp at the end.

Exercise 8g

1 Calculate these using an appropriate method. Give your answer with a remainder where appropriate.

a $161 \div 7$	**b** $156 \div 6$	**c** $279 \div 9$	**d** $272 \div 8$
e $195 \div 13$	**f** $225 \div 14$	**g** $360 \div 15$	**h** $360 \div 17$

2 a What is $729 \div 27$?

   b What is the remainder when 750 is divided by 27?

   c What is the remainder when 720 is divided by 27?

3 Calculate these using an appropriate method.

a $45.6 \div 6$	**b** $63.2 \div 8$	**c** $64.8 \div 9$	**d** $39.2 \div 7$
e $64.8 \div 12$	**f** $81.9 \div 13$	**g** $99.4 \div 14$	**h** $99 \div 15$

4 Calculate these using an appropriate method. Give your answer as a decimal rounded to 1 decimal place where appropriate.

a $55 \div 8$	**b** $20 \div 7$	**c** $35 \div 6$	**d** $46 \div 9$
e $120 \div 11$	**f** $137 \div 12$	**g** $150 \div 16$	**h** $223 \div 18$

Did you know?

5 Calculate these using an appropriate method. Give your answer as a decimal rounded to 1 decimal place where appropriate.

a $25.6 \div 8$	**b** $32.5 \div 7$	**c** $14.5 \div 6$	**d** $24.6 \div 9$
e $34.8 \div 14$	**f** $37.5 \div 15$	**g** $46.3 \div 18$	**h** $55.4 \div 21$

The world's most fuel-efficient car as of 2008 is the Volkswagen 285 MPG. See if you can work out why it's called 285 MPG!

6 In each calculation, decide whether to give your answer either as a remainder or as a decimal to 1 decimal place.

   a Devvon's car uses 27 litres of petrol to travel 400 km. Alec's car uses 25 litres of petrol to travel 365 km. Which car travels further for each litre of petrol? Explain your answer.

   b Farah has been alive for 765 hours. Is she more or less than a month old? Explain and justify your answer.

   c Xan downloads a file at 28 kB per second. The file is 95.2 kB in size. How many seconds does it take to download the file?

puzzle

'Purfect' cat biscuits come in three different sizes.

a Which size of biscuits is the best value for money?

b Explain and justify your answer.

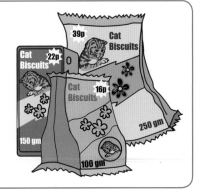

- Know and use the order of operations
- Use the bracket keys on a calculator
- Use the square key on a calculator

Keywords
Brackets
Operation
Power

- When a calculation contains more than one **operation**, you must do the operations in the correct order.

The correct order for working out operations is

Brackets	Work out the contents of any **brackets** first.
Powers	Then work out any **powers**.
Multiply Divide	Then work out any **multiplications** and **divisions**.
Add Subtract	Then work out any **additions** and **subtractions**.

A useful acronym is:
B Brackets
I Indices (or powers)
D Division
M Multiplication
A Addition
S Subtraction

example

Calculate

a $3 + 5 \times 2^2$

b $3 + (5 \times 2)^2$

- -

a $3 + 5 \times 2^2$

There are no brackets   [Bracket]

Work out the power

$= 3 + 5 \times 4$ [Powers]

Work out the
multiplication

$= 3 + 20$ [Multiply] [Divide]

Work out the addition   [Add] [Subtract]

$= 23$

b $3 + (5 \times 2)^2$

Work out the brackets
Inside the brackets there
is a multiplication

$= 3 + (10)^2$

Work out the power

$= 3 + 100$

Work out the addition

$= 103$

It is always a good idea
to show your working out
a line at a time.
On each line, work out
one set of operations.

A fraction can act like a **pair of brackets**. This is useful to know when you are using a calculator.

example

Calculate $\dfrac{8 + 3^2}{32 - 8}$ (give your answer to 2 decimal places)

- -

Re-write using brackets as $\dfrac{(8 + 3^2)}{(32 - 8)} = (8 + 3^2) \div (32 - 8)$

Key in   (8 + 3 x^2) ÷ (3 2 - 8) =

The calculator should display   0.7083…

$= 0.71$ (2 dp)

You can use the x^2 key to
enter the power, or just
know the answer is 9.

Exercise 8h

1 Work out these calculations using the order of operations.

a $5 + 4 \times 6$ **b** $15 - 3 \times 2$ **c** $12 + 2 \times 5$

d $24 - 16 \div 4$ **e** $5 \times 3 - 2 \times 3$ **f** $4 \times 7 + 6 \times 3$

g $18 \div 9 + 15 \div 5$ **h** $7 + 5 \times 3 - 2$

2 Match each question with the correct answer.

Question	Answer X	Answer Y
a $3 + 4^2 \times 5$	83	245
b $20 - 3^2 \times 2$	578	2
c $(19 - 4^2) \times 2$	250	6
d $5 \times (3 + 4)^2$	245	31
e $25 - 3 \times (2^2 - 1)$	87	16
f $3 \times 5^2 + 12 \div 3$	79	29
g $6 \times 7 - 3^2 \times 4$	132	6

Explain your method and reasoning for each answer.

3 Calculate these giving your answer to 1 decimal place where appropriate. You may wish to use a calculator.

a $\dfrac{8 + 4}{5 - 2}$ **b** $\dfrac{5^2 - 1}{3^2 + 4}$ **c** $\dfrac{(28 - 3)}{10 - 3^2}$ **d** $\dfrac{(4 + 3)^2}{4^2 - 1}$

4 Copy and complete each of these by putting brackets in the correct place in the expression.

a $8 + 5 \times 4 - 3 = 49$ **b** $8 + 5 \times 4 - 3 = 13$

c $8 + 5 \times 4 - 3 = 25$

5 Use a calculator to work out these calculations. Give your answers to 2 decimal places where appropriate.

a $(5 + 2.8) \div 7$ **b** $34 - 1.7^2 \times 4$ **c** $6 \times (3.5 - 1.6)^2$

d $(4 + 2.5) \times 7$ **e** $\dfrac{7 + 3^2}{19 - 4^2}$ **f** $\dfrac{13^2 + 6^2}{13^2 - 6^2}$

g $\dfrac{48}{6 \times 8}$ **h** $\dfrac{5 + 2^2}{(18 - 9)}$

investigation

John and Vernon are working out this calculation $\dfrac{60}{3 \times 4}$

John works out $3 \times 4 = 12$, and then $60 \div 12 = 5$

Vernon works out $60 \div 3 = 20$, and then $20 \div 4 = 5$

Explain how and why both methods work.

- Interpret the display on a calculator in different contexts including money
- Convert between units of time by finding whole number remainders after division

Keywords
Convert
Recurring decimal
Remainder

- You can use a calculator to quickly **convert** between units of time.

example

Convert 250 minutes into hours and minutes.

Using a calculator,
$250 \div 60 = 4.1666\ldots$

Divide by 60 because 1 hour = 60 minutes.

Change the remainder from a decimal part of an hour to a whole number of minutes.

This is 4 hours and 0.1666… of an hour.

$0.1666\ldots$ hours $= 0.1666\ldots \times 60$ minutes $= 10$ minutes
250 minutes $= 4$ hours and 10 minutes

Multiply the decimal part of your answer by 60.

As in the previous example, calculators often give you a decimal **remainder**. You must decide how to interpret the remainder.

example

a Aunt Lydia shares £400 between her six grandchildren. How much money does each grandchild receive?
b Bryony needs to do 400 minutes of exercise each week, equally over six days. How much time should she spend exercising each day?

Using a calculator $400 \div 6 = 66.6666\ldots$

a Round it to 2 decimal places. Each grandchild will receive £66.67.
b Give the answer as a whole number (remainder in seconds) 66.6666 mins $= 66$ mins 40 seconds
Bryony should spend 66 mins 40 seconds each day on exercise.

1 minute = 60 seconds, so $0.6666\ldots$ mins $= 0.6666\ldots$ $\times 60 = 40$ seconds

The decimal 0.666… is called a **recurring decimal**. It is equivalent to $2 \div 3 = \frac{2}{3}$

Exercise 8i

1 Calculate these divisions using your calculator, leaving the
remainder part of the answer in the form specified.
   a £200 ÷ 9   (a decimal to 2 dp)
   b 50 cakes ÷ 6   (a whole number remainder)
   c 11 hours ÷ 4   (a fraction)
   d 45 kg ÷ 7   (a decimal to 2 dp)

2 Convert these measurements of time into the units indicated
in brackets.
   a 200 mins   (into hours and mins)
   b 800 hours   (into days and hours)
   c 6450 seconds   (into minutes and seconds)
   d 6220 mins   (into hours and mins)

3 Solve each of these problems. Give each of your answers in a
form appropriate to the question.
   a Samina sells free range eggs. She has 164 eggs. She packs
   them into boxes of 6. How many egg boxes does she need
   to pack the eggs?
   b Avril wins £1 000 000. She decides to share the money
   equally between the 13 people in her family (including
   herself). How much money will each of the relatives receive?
   c 76 pizzas are shared between 40 people. How much pizza does
   each person receive?
   d Cecil is an electrician. He cuts a 25 m length of cable into 7 identical
   pieces. How long is each piece of cable?

Lake Underdale contains 540 000 000 m³ of water.
There are 1000 litres in 1 m³ of water.
An average person should drink 2.5 litres of water per day.
There are 34 652 people living in the town of Underwater.
   a How long would it take one person to drink all the water
   in Lake Underdale?
   b How long would it take all the people of Underwater to
   drink all the water in Lake Underdale?
   c Investigate further problems of your own using these additional facts about
   water consumption.
   One person uses 89.6 litres per day in flushing the toilet.
   A washing machine uses 70.4 litres per wash.
   A shower uses 70.6 litres per use.
   A tap uses 48 litres in a typical day.

investigation

8a

1 Round each of these numbers to the nearest
  i 1000   **ii** 100   **iii** 10

  a 3182   **b** 6273   **c** 4765   **d** 8632   **e** 6713   **f** 7682
  g 5049   **h** 24 505   **i** 38 604   **j** 42 783   **k** 76 060   **l** 39 494

2 Round each of these numbers to the nearest
  i whole number   **ii** tenth (1 dp)   **iii** hundredth (2 dp).

  a 4.847   **b** 3.107   **c** 8.3967   **d** 8.238   **e** 24.969   **f** 22.623
  g 3.4172   **h** 8.0495   **i** 3.1405   **j** 3.0078   **k** 2.429 57   **l** 4.545 45

8b

3 Calculate these using a mental method.
  a 492 − 187   **b** 799 − 203   **c** 2615 − 616   **d** 3639 − 1009
  e 2215 − 1797   **f** 3011 − 1688   **g** 4383 − 3985   **h** 7473 − 4749

4 Calculate these using a mental method.
  a 11.8 + 7.4   **b** 2.68 + 8.9   **c** 4.8 + 5.92   **d** 3.07 + 2.98
  e 13.7 − 8.88   **f** 6.99 − 3.49   **g** 8.71 − 4.8   **h** 9.67 − 3.85

8c

5 Calculate these using a written method.
  a 257.3 − 67.9   **b** 540.87 + 55.9   **c** 45.79 + 753.4
  d 1252.6 − 38.79   **e** 763.72 − 85.4   **f** 376.62 − 49.8
  g 582.5 + 10.36   **h** 2476.2 − 78.67   **i** 1468.4 − 72.56
  j 816.3 − 95.9   **k** 923.28 + 359   **l** 43.5 + 2186.39

8d

6 Calculate
  a 3 × 10   **b** 6 × 100   **c** 90 ÷ 10   **d** 400 ÷ 100
  e 38 × 10   **f** 1.7 × 10   **g** 67 ÷ 100   **h** 497 ÷ 10
  i 0.075 × 10   **j** 6.1 ÷ 100   **k** 48.2 ÷ 1000   **l** 0.0032 × 100

7 Calculate
  a 4 × 0.1   **b** 6 × 0.1   **c** 7 × 0.01   **d** 2 × 0.01
  e 34 × 0.1   **f** 65 × 0.1   **g** 30 × 0.01   **h** 58 × 0.01
  i 85.4 × 0.01   **j** 0.73 × 0.1   **k** 68 ÷ 0.01   **l** 0.03 ÷ 0.1

8e

8 Calculate these using a mental method.
  a 7.3 × 11   **b** 6.4 × 9   **c** 14 × 5.2   **d** 13 × 31
  e 4.7 × 21   **f** 406 ÷ 7   **g** 3.4 × 13   **h** 300 ÷ 9
  i 235 ÷ 4   **j** 16 × 1.9   **k** 576 ÷ 8   **l** 3.7 × 15

9 Calculate these using the standard method.

   a 15×6.5 **b** 35×2.7 **c** 16×4.8 **d** 43×8.5

   e 39×9.2 **f** 57×6.7 **g** 38×7.6 **h** 88×7.7

10 Calculate these using the standard method.

   a 19×3.68 **b** 27×4.18 **c** 46×5.53 **d** 62×7.26

   e 49×5.69 **f** 74×8.57 **g** 79×8.37 **h** 99×9.99

11 Calculate these using an appropriate method. Give your answer as a decimal rounded to 1 decimal place where appropriate.

   a $76 \div 8$ **b** $40 \div 9$ **c** $85 \div 6$ **d** $99 \div 9$

   e $252 \div 18$ **f** $314 \div 19$ **g** $388 \div 21$ **h** $404 \div 25$

12 Calculate these using an appropriate method. Give your answer as a decimal rounded to 1 decimal place where appropriate.

   a $36.7 \div 8$ **b** $43.6 \div 7$ **c** $25.6 \div 6$ **d** $35.7 \div 9$

   e $50.4 \div 24$ **f** $52.7 \div 39$ **g** $91.6 \div 24$ **h** $41.8 \div 17$

13 Calculate

   a $2 \times 8 \div 4$ **b** $40 \div 2 \div 2$ **c** $3 \times 16 - (7 - 3)$

   d $216 \div 18 - (3^2 + 1)$ **e** $9 \times 19 - (14 - 5)$ **f** $90 \div 50 - (5^2 - 4^2)$

14 Use a calculator to work out these calculations. Give your answers to 2 decimal places where appropriate.

   a $(7 + 3.9) \div 5$ **b** $48 - 2.3^2 \times 5$ **c** $9 \times (7.2 - 1.9)^2$ **d** $(3 + 6.7) \times 4$

   e $\dfrac{8 + 5^2}{39 - 5^2}$ **f** $12^2 - 8^2$ **g** $\dfrac{256}{2^2 \times 2^3}$ **h** $\dfrac{11 + 5^2}{(7^2 - 13)}$

15 **a** Giovanni sells hot cross buns.
   He has 183 hot cross buns.
   He puts them into packs of 4.
   How many packs does he need?

   b Alison earns £32 000 per year.
   She shares $\frac{1}{4}$ of her money between her 3 children.
   How much does each child receive?

8 Summary

Assessment criteria
- Know and use the order of operations **Level 5**
- Multiply and divide whole numbers and decimals by 10, 100 and 1000 and explain the effect **Level 5**
- Solve problems with or without a calculater **Level 4**

Level 5

1 Calculate

   a 42×0.6

   b $42 \div 0.6$

Chirag's answer ✔

Chirag estimates $42 \times \frac{1}{2} = 21$

Chirag thinks 'How many $\frac{1}{2}$ s in 42?' About 84.

He decides to multiply by 6 and divide by 10, which is the same as multiplying by 0.6

$$a \quad 42 \times 0.6 = 42 \times 6 \div 10$$
$$= 252 \div 10$$
$$= 25.2$$
$$b \quad 42 \div 0.6 = 42 \div 6 \times 10$$
$$= 7 \times 10$$
$$= 70$$

He decides to divide by 6 and multiply by 10, which is the same as dividing by 0.6

Level 5

2 Use your calculator to work out the answers

   a $(48 + 57) \times (61 - 19)$

   b $\dfrac{48 + 57}{61 - 19}$

Key Stage 3 2005 4–6 Paper 2

9 Geometry

Transformations

This photograph looks like a series of steps in three-dimensions. However it is a floor in two-dimensions from the Church of St Giorgio Maggiore in Venice, Italy.

The floor is made from three different sorts of tiles: a red parallelogram, a white parallelogram and a black rhombus.

What's the point? Artists and architects create striking patterns, often involving optical illusions, by transforming and tessellating shapes.

✓ Check in

Level 5

1 Give the coordinates of the point A after a movement of

   a 2 units to the right and 1 unit down
   b 4 units to the left and 3 units down
   c 2 units to the left and 4 units down.

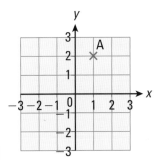

Level 4

2 The photograph of the cup and saucer is rotated.

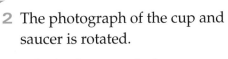

Which photograph shows a rotation of

   a 90° clockwise   **b** 180°
   c 90° anticlockwise **d** 360°?

A B  C D

- Reflect, rotate and translate 2-D shapes

Keywords

Centre of rotation
Congruent
Image
Mirror line

Object
Reflection
Rotation
Transformation
Translation

- A **transformation** moves a shape to a new position.
  The starting shape is called the **object**.
  The **image** is the shape after the transformation.

Here are some different transformations.

- A **reflection** flips an object over a **mirror line**.

You describe a reflection by giving the mirror line.

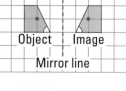

- A **rotation** turns an object about a point, called the
  centre of rotation.

You describe a rotation by giving
  - the centre of rotation
  - the angle of rotation
  - the direction of turn (clockwise or anticlockwise).

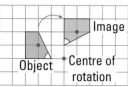

- A **translation** slides an object.

You describe a translation by giving the distance moved left or
right, then the distance moved up or down.

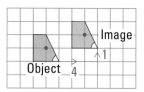

p. 86

The object and the image are **congruent** for reflections,
rotations and translations.

Congruent shapes are
the same size and the
same shape.

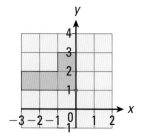

example

Draw the hexagon after a clockwise
rotation of 90° about (0, 1).

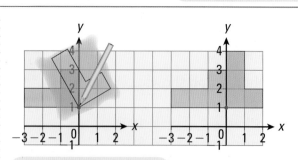

Use tracing paper to rotate
the shape.

Exercise 9a

1 Copy each diagram on square grid paper. Reflect the shape in the mirror line. Give the name of the completed shape and state if it is regular.

> Regular shapes have equal sides and equal angles.

 a   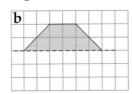 b   c   d

2 Copy this diagram.

   a Rotate the isosceles right-angled triangle through 180° about the midpoint of the longest side.

   b Mark the equal angles and the equal sides on the completed quadrilateral.

   c State the mathematical name of the quadrilateral.

3 On square grid paper, draw the *x*-axis from 0 to 15 and the *y*-axis from 0 to 10.

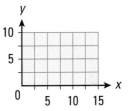

   a Plot each shape on the same grid.

    Shape A (3, 7), (4, 8), (2, 10), (1, 9) and (3, 7)

    Shape B (0, 5), (1, 4), (3, 6), (2, 7) and (0, 5)

    Shape C (5, 6), (4, 7), (3, 6) and (5, 6)

    Shape D (5, 1), (4, 3), (2, 3), (1, 1) and (5, 1)

    Shape E (4, 3), (6, 5), (5, 6), (3, 4) and (4, 3)

    Shape F (6, 7), (7, 8), (5, 10), (4, 9) and (6, 7)

   b Give the mathematical name of each shape.

   c Translate each shape on the same grid.

    Shape A, 6 units to the right and 0 units up

    Shape B, 10 units to the right and 3 units up

    Shape C, 6 units to the right and 3 units up

    Shape D, 7 units to the right and 2 units up

    Shape E, 4 units to the right and 1 unit up

    Shape F, 6 units to the right and 3 units down.

Did you know?

It is thought that many of the 'Old Master' painters used mirrors to paint their pictures and self-portraits.

activity

Draw a rhombus like this on isometric paper. Use a mirror to form these shapes. Draw diagrams to illustrate the position of the mirror in each case.

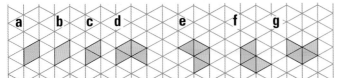

a   b   c   d   e   f   g

- Transform 2-D shapes using combinations of transformations

Keywords
Equivalent   *Tessellation*
Reflection   *Translation*
Rotation

You can transform 2-D shapes using repeated **reflections**, **rotations** and **translations**.

example

a Reflect the pink flag in mirror line 1. Call the image I_1.

b Reflect the image in mirror line 2. Call the image I_2.

c Describe a single transformation that moves the pink flag to I_2.

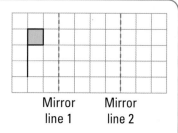

Mirror   Mirror
line 1   line 2

Mirror   Mirror
line 1   line 2

You slide the pink flag 8 units to the right.

c A translation of 8 units to the right.

This means that these two reflections are **equivalent** to one translation.

- A **tessellation** is a tiling pattern with no gaps or overlaps.

 p. 84²

You can tessellate shapes by repeating the same transformation.

This tessellation uses repeated reflections.

This tessellation uses repeated rotations.

This tessellation uses repeated translations.

example

Use repeated rotations of 180° to tessellate this trapezium.

You rotate the trapezium about the midpoint of a side.

Exercise 9b

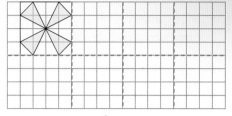

1 This tile design is drawn on a 4 by 4 square. Copy the design and use reflections in vertical and horizontal mirror lines to tessellate the tile shape.

2 **a** Tessellate a scalene right-angled triangle using repeated rotations of 180° about the midpoint of the sides.

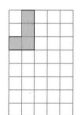

b Colour the equal angles in your tessellation.

3 This pink hexagon is translated 2 units to the right and 1 unit down.

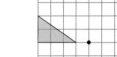

a On a copy of the diagram, draw the image and label it I_1.

b The hexagon I_1 is translated 1 unit to the left and 3 units down.

Draw the new image and call it I_2.

c Describe the single transformation that moves the pink hexagon to I_2.

4 This green triangle is rotated clockwise through 90° about the black dot.

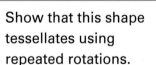

a On a copy of the diagram, draw the image and label it I_1.

b The triangle I_1 is rotated clockwise through 180° about the black dot.

Draw the new image and call it I_2.

c Describe the single transformation that moves the green triangle to I_2.

Draw a 2 by 2 square.	Remove a triangle and rotate it through 180°.	Show that this shape tessellates using repeated rotations.

Colour your tessellation.

- Recognise reflection symmetry and rotation symmetry of 2-D shapes

Keywords
Line of symmetry
Order of symmetry
Reflection symmetry
Rotation symmetry

- A **line of symmetry** divides a shape into two identical halves.

- A shape has **reflection symmetry** if it has at least one line of symmetry.

You can find the line of symmetry by using a mirror or by folding the shape.

- A shape has **rotation symmetry** if it rotates onto itself more than once in a full turn.

- The **order of rotation symmetry** is the number of times a shape looks exactly like itself in a complete turn.

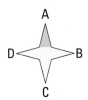

This star has order of rotation symmetry 4.

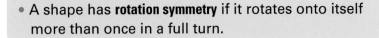

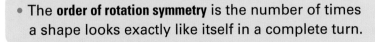

You can use tracing paper to find the order of rotation symmetry.

- A shape with rotation symmetry of order 1 is said to have no rotation symmetry.

A regular shape has equal sides and equal angles.

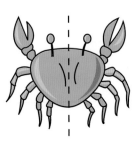

This crab has one vertical line of symmetry, but no rotation symmetry.

example

A regular hexagon is shown.

a Draw the lines of reflection symmetry.
b State the order of rotation symmetry.

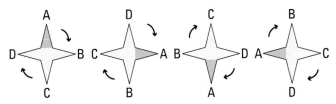

- -

a

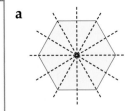

b order 6

There are six positions when the hexagon fits exactly on top of itself during one complete turn.

Exercise 9c

1 These symbols can often be found inside a lift.
Draw each symbol and draw any lines of symmetry.
State the order of rotation symmetry in each case.

a   b   c   d   e

2 This shape has two lines of reflection symmetry and rotation
symmetry of order 2.

Draw these shapes and describe the symmetry in a
similar way.

2 lines of   Rotational
symmetry   symmetry
             of order 2

a   b   c   d

3 The lines of reflection symmetry of a rhombus are along
the diagonals.
The angle shown is 50°.
Calculate the four interior angles of the rhombus.

4 Draw each quadrilateral and give its mathematical name.
On each diagram, draw any lines of symmetry and state the
order of rotation symmetry.

a   b   c   d

e   f   g

---

activity

a Place a mirror on a copy of these two squares to form these shapes.

b Draw these shapes and describe what they all have in common.

---

problem

Can you draw a shape that has:
- rotation symmetry but no reflection symmetry
- reflection symmetry but no rotation symmetry?

Give examples of each case.

- Enlarge a 2-D shape using a positive whole number as the scale factor

Keywords
Enlargement   Scale factor
Image   Similar
Object   Transformation

This **object** has been enlarged to give an **image**.

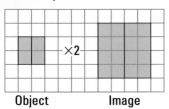

Object   Image

- An **enlargement** is a type of **transformation** that alters the size of a shape.

All the lengths in the object are multiplied by 2. All the angles stay the same.

You enlarge a shape by multiplying the lengths by the **scale factor**.
The angles of the shape do not change.

- The object and the image are **similar**. They are the same shape, but a different size.

You describe an enlargement by giving the scale factor.

example

Calculate the scale factor of the enlargement.

Object   Image

$2 \times$ scale factor $= 4$ and $1 \times$ scale factor $= 2$
So the scale factor is 2.

Each length is multiplied by 2.

example

Draw the enlargement of the pink triangle using a scale factor of 3.

Object

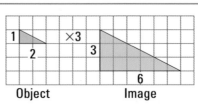

Object   Image

$1 \times 3 = 3$ Each length is multiplied by 3.
$2 \times 3 = 6$

The green triangle is an enlargement by scale factor 3 of the pink triangle.

Exercise 9d

1 Decide whether these diagrams show similar shapes. Explain your reasoning.

a   **b**   **c**

2 The pink shapes are enlarged to give the green shapes. Calculate the scale factor of each enlargement.

a    **b**   **c**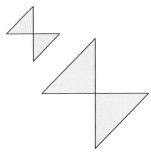

3 Copy the shapes on square grid paper and enlarge each shape by the given scale factor.

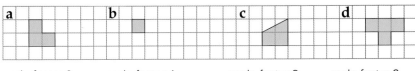

a	b	c	d
scale factor 2	scale factor 4	scale factor 3	scale factor 2

e	f	g	h
scale factor 3	scale factor 2	scale factor 2	scale factor 3

activity

a Draw a scalene triangle *ABC*.

b Mark a point *O* inside the triangle.

c Draw lines from *O* to and beyond the vertices.

d Measure the distance *OA*. Multiply this length by 2. Use this answer to mark a new point measured from *O* on the extended line *OA*.

e Repeat for *OB* and *OC* to form a new triangle.

f Measure the three angles and the three lengths of each triangle.

g Are the triangles similar and what is the scale factor of the enlargement?

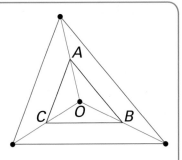

- Enlarge a 2-D shape using a centre of enlargement and a positive whole number scale factor

Keywords
Centre of enlargement
Image
Object
Scale factor
Similar

When you enlarge a shape, the **object** and the **image** are **similar**.
The lengths increase in proportion, but the angles stay the same.

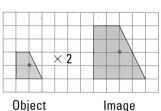

Object   Image

Each length is multiplied by 2.

- The **scale factor** is the multiplier of the enlargement.

The position of the image is fixed, if you use a **centre of enlargement**.

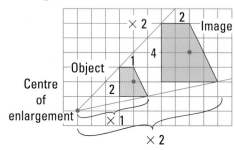

This enlargement is scale factor 2.

- You can describe an enlargement by giving
  - the scale factor
  - the centre of enlargement.

example

Draw the enlargement of this flag using a scale factor of 3 and the marked centre of enlargement.

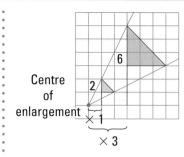

Check the corresponding heights of the flag:
$2 \times 3 = 6$
Each length is multiplied by 3.

Exercise 9e

1 The pink triangle ABC is enlarged to give the green triangle $A_1B_1C_1$.
Copy the diagram on square grid paper.

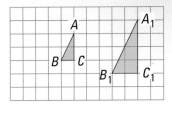

  a Draw and extend the lines from A_1 to A from B_1 to B and from C_1 to C.

  b At the intersection of the lines, mark the centre of enlargement as O.

  c Measure the lines BC, B_1C_1 and AC, A_1C_1.

  d State the scale factor of the enlargement.

  e Measure the lines OA, OA_1 and OB, OB_1 to check the scale factor.

2 Copy these shapes on square grid paper.
Draw the enlargement of each shape using the dot as the centre of enlargement and the given scale factor.

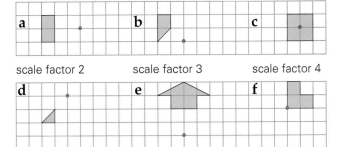

a	b	c
scale factor 2	scale factor 3	scale factor 4
d	e	f
scale factor 2	scale factor 3	scale factor 2

3 The pink triangle is enlarged by scale factor 3 to give the green triangle, which is not all shown here.
The point (1, 4) moves to (3, 0).
Find the other two coordinates of the green triangle.

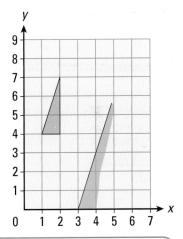

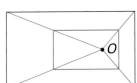

• Use scale drawings to represent real-life objects

Keywords
Represent
Scale
Scale drawing

You can use **scale drawings** to **represent** real-life objects.

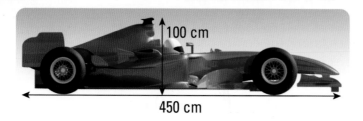

100 cm

450 cm

Real-life lengths are reduced or enlarged in proportion using a **scale**.

The scale allows you to interpret the scale drawing.

The real-life lengths are 50 times larger than in the scale drawing.
$9 \times 50 = 450$
$2 \times 50 = 100$

The real-life lengths are an enlargement scale factor 50 of the scale drawing.

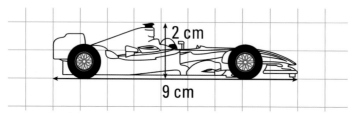

2 cm

9 cm

Scale: 1 cm represents 50 cm

---

example

A mini snooker table measures 180 cm by 100 cm.

a Draw a scale drawing of the table using a scale of 1 cm represents 40 cm.

b Calculate the distance across the diagonal of the table.

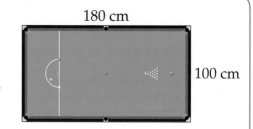

180 cm

100 cm

. . . .

a

4.5 cm

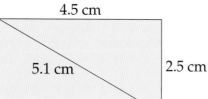

5.1 cm

2.5 cm

$180 \div 40 = 4.5$
$100 \div 40 = 2.5$

b Measuring the diagonal gives 5.1 cm on the scale drawing.

In real life $5.1 \times 40 = 204$ cm

Always put the scale on your diagram.

Exercise 9f

1 A penny-farthing is an old type of bicycle. Parminda wants to draw a scale drawing of the bicycle using a scale of 1 cm to represent 20 cm. Copy and complete the table.

		Real life	Scale drawing
a	Radius of the small wheel		
b	Diameter of the small wheel		
c	Radius of the large wheel		
d	Diameter of the large wheel		
e	Distance between the centres of the wheels		

2 A pentagram is made from five straight lines with angles of 36°.

This scale drawing is used to construct a large pentagram using a scale of 1 cm represents 100 cm.

   a Measure the length of one line in the scale drawing.

   b Calculate the length of this line and the size of one of the marked angles in the large pentagram.

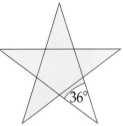

Scale: 1 cm represents 100 cm

3 Grace lives on the next street to Faith.

Grace has to walk 80 metres, turn a corner, then walk another 50 metres if she wants to visit Faith.

   a Draw a scale drawing of this journey using a scale of 1 cm to represent 10 m.

   b Calculate the direct distance between Grace and Faith.

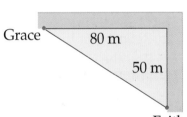

Using a scale of 1 cm represents 50 m, draw scale drawings to represent the heights of these buildings.

Blackpool Tower is done for you.

Building	Height
Blackpool Tower	150 m
HSBC Tower, London	200 m
Chamberlain Clock Tower, Birmingham	100 m
Sutton Coldfield Mast, West Midlands	250 m
Rotunda, Birmingham	80 m

Draw scale drawings for other buildings around the world.

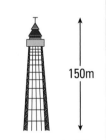

Scale: 1 cm represents 50 m

9a

1 Copy the diagram on square grid paper.
  a Reflect the blue hexagon using the x-axis as the
    mirror line.
    Label the shape A and give the coordinates of
    the vertices.
  b Rotate the blue hexagon through 180° about the
    point $(0, 0)$.
    Label the shape B and give the coordinates of the
    vertices.
  c Translate the blue hexagon by 4 units to the left.
    Label the shape C and give the coordinates of the
    vertices.

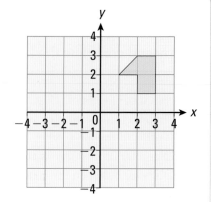

9b

2 a Tessellate a parallelogram using repeated translations.
  b Colour the equal angles in your tessellation.

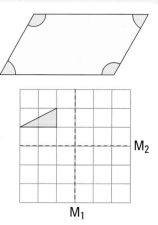

3 Copy the diagram on square grid paper.
  a Reflect the green triangle in the mirror line M_1. Call the
    image I_1.
  b Reflect I_1 in the mirror line M_2.
    Call the image I_2.
  c Describe the single transformation that moves the green
    triangle to I_2.

9c

4 Draw these symbols from Steph's calculator.
  Draw any lines of reflection symmetry and state the order of rotation
  symmetry for each symbol.
  a   b   c 4   d 8   e 0

5 a Draw a polygon with three lines of symmetry and rotational symmetry
    of order 3.
  b Give the mathematical name of this shape.

6

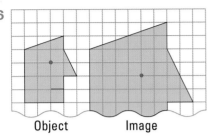

Object   Image

Part of an enlargement of the face is shown.

a Calculate the scale factor of the enlargement.

b Copy and complete the table of measurements.

	Object	Image
Length of the forehead	1 cm	
Slanting length of the nose		
Slanting length of the top of the head		
Thickness of the neck		
Width of the mouth		

c Draw the completed image on square grid paper.

7 a Draw the rectangle on a coordinate grid.

b Enlarge the rectangle by scale factor 2 using (0, 0) as the centre of enlargement.

c Write down the coordinates of the vertices of the object and the image.

d Explain the relationship between these coordinates.

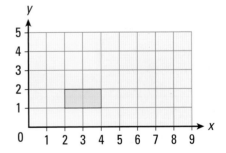

8 A sales brochure shows a scale drawing of a door.
The scale is 1 cm represents 50 cm.

Calculate   **a** the height

               b the width

               c the area of the real door.

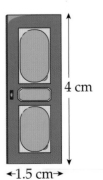

4 cm

←1.5 cm→

Scale: 1 cm represents 50 cm

Maths life

Celtic knots

Knot designs have been used as decoration for many centuries. The designs were adopted by the ancient Celts and nowadays are commonly known as Celtic Knots.

clound

Celtic knot designs are made from interwoven lines. A key element of the design is that each line passes alternately over then under the lines that it crosses, giving a woven effect.

Celtic knots sometimes use a single continuous line, sometimes two or more lines and they often have a lot of symmetry.

A section of a page from an 8th century manuscript known as the Cassiodorus, now found in Durham Cathedral library.

???

Look carefully at the way the knots are made.

Which of the knots could be made with a single continuous string? You might want to trace your finger along the lines to find out.

Which knots would need more than one string? How many strings would they need?

What symmetry can you find in the designs? Describe it as fully as you are able.

Nowadays, the term Celt is usually associated with Celtic speaking areas. The six main Celtic areas are Scotland, Ireland, Wales, Cornwall, Isle of Man and Brittany.

Celtic knots are frequently found on jewellery, t-shirts and souvenirs where they are often used to give a Celtic identity to the items.

N

Follow these instructions to draw a Celtic Knot

1. Draw a grid with 5 pairs of horizontal lines and 5 pairs of vertical lines.

   Draw the lines lightly for now.

2. Rub out the lines at every other junction across the top two horizontal lines, alternating the pattern as shown.

   Continue in the same way for the remaining horizontal lines.

3. Now do the same with the vertical lines to make a woven effect.

   Draw over the remaining lines more heavily.

4. Connect the ends of the lines to form a continuous knot.

???

Does your design have reflective symmetry?

Does it have rotational symmetry?

Could you join the ends of the lines differently so that the knot needs more than one string?

What happens if you start with 4 pairs of horizontal lines and 4 pairs of vertical lines?

Try making a simple Celtic Knot with a piece of string, wool or thin wire.

Assessment criteria
- Recognise and visualise the transformation and symmetry of 2-D shapes **Level 5**
- Enlarge 2-D shapes, given a centre of enlargement and a positive whole number scale factor **Level 6**

Level 5

1 a On square grid paper, show the rhombus after four successive clockwise rotations of 90° using the dot • as the centre of rotation. The first one is done for you.

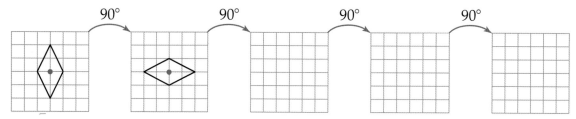

b State the order of rotational symmetry of the rhombus.

Bibin uses tracing paper to find the position after each rotation.

Bibin's answer ✔

a

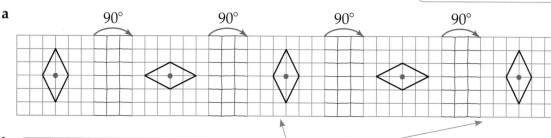

b He notices that there are two positions when the rhombus looks exactly like itself in a complete turn.

The order of rotational symmetry is 2.

Level 6

2 Enlarge the shaded shape by a scale factor of 2, using P as the centre of enlargement.

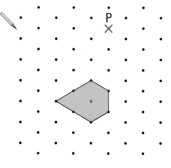

You will need a large sheet of isometric grid paper.

Key Stage 3 2007 4–6 Paper 2

10 Algebra

Sequences and roots

The first electric traffic light was invented in 1912 in Salt Lake City, USA. The simplest control of light changes is based on a timed sequence which is repeated.

What's the point? Traffic lights help to reduce car crashes at junctions!

 **Check in**

Level 4

1 Write the values of 2^2, 3^2 and 10^2.

Level 3

2 **a** Add 4 to each of these numbers.   3   7   11   15
   b What do you notice?
   c What is the next number in the pattern?

Level 4

3 Find the single number that can go in each of the three boxes.
   a $\square \times \square \times \square = 8$ **b** $\square \times \square \times \square = 1000$

> The answer to **b** will be different from **a**.

• Find and use the term-to-term rule in a sequence

Keywords
Rule
Sequence
Term
Term-to-term rule

• A **sequence** is a set of numbers, or **terms**.
Each term can be found using a **rule**.

Julia is laying a path using paving slabs in two colours.
She starts with one slab and then adds more slabs, three at
a time, in alternating colours.

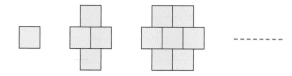

The sequence begins   1   4   7   …   …
The rule is '*start with 1 and add 3 each time*'.
The next two terms are 10 and 13.

• **A term-to-term rule** gives the first term of a
sequence and an instruction telling you how to get
any term from the previous term.

example

Here are two sequences A and B

   A 50   44   38   32 ☐ 20
   B 3   7   15   31 ☐ 127

a Find the term-to-term rule for each sequence.
b Find the two missing numbers.

a For sequence A, each term is 6 less than the previous term.
For sequence B, each term is double the previous term
with 1 more added.

b For A, the rule is '*start with 50 and then subtract 6*'.
The missing number is $32 - 6 = 26$.

Check the next term:
$26 - 6 = 20$

For B, the rule is '*start with 3 and then double and add 1*'.
The missing number is $31 \times 2 + 1 = 62 + 1 = 63$.

Check the next term:
$63 \times 2 + 1 = 126 + 1 = 127$

Exercise 10a

1 These sequences are made using straws. For each sequence,
- draw the next diagram in the sequence
- write the first four terms
- find the term-to-term rule
- write the next three terms.

a

b

c

d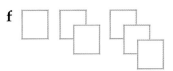

e

f

2 For each of these sequences, find the term-to-term rule and
write the next three terms of the sequence.

a 2 5 8 11 …   **b** 4 9 14 19 …
c 8 12 16 20 …   **d** 50 46 42 38 …
e 30 27 24 21 …   **f** 20 31 42 53 …
g 2 4 8 16 …   **h** 2 5 11 23 …
i 3 7 15 31 …   **j** 3 8 23 68 …

3 Write the first six terms of the sequences with these rules.

a *Start with 6 and add 4*   **b** *Start with 8 and add 2*
c *Start with 60 and subtract 5*   **d** *Start with 5, double and add 1*
e *Start with 2, double and add 4* **f** *Start with 100 and subtract 11*
g *Start with 1, treble and add 1* **h** *Start with 0, treble and add 2*

4 Find the missing terms of these sequences.

a 5 10 20 ☐ 80   **b** 6 11 16 ☐ 26
c 7 11 ☐ 19 23   **d** 30 24 18 ☐ 6
e 10 21 43 87 ☐   **f** 6 11 21 41 ☐
g ☐ 80 60 40   **h** 3 8 18 ☐ 78

Find the 50th term of this sequence.

    8   12   16   20   ….

Is using the term-to-term rule an efficient method?

Can you find a more efficient method?

- Find and use the position-to-term rule in a sequence

Keywords
Position
Position-to-term rule

Julia is exploring different tiling patterns.
This sequence of patterns grows by adding four extra tiles each time.

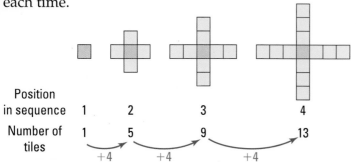

Position in sequence	1	2	3	4
Number of tiles	1	5	9	13

+4   +4   +4

Julia wants to know how many tiles there will be in a particular **position**.

She uses the 4 times table to draw this table ...

Position	1	2	3	4
4 × table	4	8	12	16
No. of tiles (Term)	1	5	9	13

×4

−3

Pattern → ×4 → −3 → Term

... and shows the rule in a function machine.

Julia's rule is '*multiply the position by 4 and then subtract 3*'.
She can now find the number of tiles in any position.

For example, the 50th position has $50 \times 4 - 3 = 200 - 3 = 197$ tiles

- A **position-to-term rule** works out the value of any term from its position in the sequence.

example

The first four terms of a sequence are   5   8   11   14
a Find the position-to-term rule.   **b** Find the 5th term and the 100th term.

. . . .

The sequence grows by adding 3 to the previous term.   5   8   11   14
a Draw a table of values and a function machine:

+3   +3   +3

Position	1	2	3	4
3 × table	3	6	9	12
Term	5	8	11	14

×3

+2

Position → ×3 → +2 → Term

The position-to-term rule is '*multiply the position by 3 and then add 2*'.
b Using the 4th term, the 5th term is $14 + 3 = 17$.
Use the position-to-term rule, the 100th term is
$100 \times 3 + 2 = 300 + 2 = 302$.

You can write the *n*th term as $3n + 2$.

Exercise 10b

1 This sequence of diagrams is formed by squares of circles.

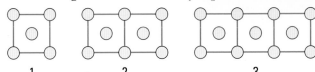

Position   1   2   3

a How many extra circles are added to a position to make the next position?

b Draw the diagram for position 4.

c Copy and complete this table.

Use the correct 'times table' for the middle row.

Position	1	2	3	4
Times table				
Term (Number of circles)				

d Find the position-to-term rule.

e How many circles are there in the 4th diagram of the sequence?

f How many circles are there in the 20th diagram of the sequence?

2 Use the method of question **1** for these sequences of circles. In each case,
- draw the diagram for the next position
- make a table of values
- find the position-to-term rule for the number of circles
- find how many circles are in the 50th term of the sequence.

a
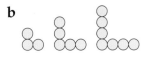

b
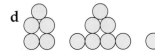

c

d

3 Find the position-to-term rule for each of these sequences.
Also find the next term in the sequence and the 50th term in the sequence.

a 4   7   10   13   16

b 1   3   5   7   9

c 1   5   9   13   17

d 6   10   14   18   22

e 1   4   7   10   13

f 8   15   22   29   36

g 5   13   21   29   37

h 4   5   6   7   8

research

Leonardo Fibonacci was an Italian mathematician who lived about 800 years ago.

He learned about the 'new Arabic numerals' from his father and later travelled in the Middle East to learn more about mathematics.

Find all you can about his life and work and about the **Fibonacci sequence**.

- Find and use both term-to-term and position-to-term rules in context

Keywords
Term-to-term
Position-to-term

Boris the farmer is building a fence. He starts with two posts. Every hour, he adds two more vertical posts with two more supporting posts. Boris wants to know how many posts he can put up in 40 hours.

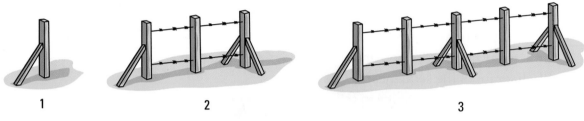

1   2   3

The number of posts for these three positions is given by

The **term-to-term** rule for the sequence is '*add 4*'.

So, the next term is $10 + 4 = 14$. The farmer needs 14 posts for position 4.

From this table the **position-to-term** rule is '*multiply the position by 4 and then subtract 2*'. The 40th term is $40 \times 4 - 2 = 160 - 2 = 158$

Boris can put up 158 posts in 40 hours.

Position	1	2	3	4
4 × table	4	8	12	16
Term (No. of posts)	2	6	10	14

×4
−2

---

example

Here are the first four terms of a sequence.   4 7 10 13 ….
a Find the next term of this sequence   **b** Find the 100th term of the sequence.

. . . .

a The sequence increases in steps of three.   The term-to-term rule is "*add 3*".
The next term is $13 + 3 = 16$.
b A table of values is

Position	1	2	3	4
3 × table	3	6	9	12
Term	4	7	10	13

×3
+1

The position-to-term rule is "*multiply the position by 3 and then add 1*".
So, the 100th term is $100 \times 3 + 1 = 301$.

Exercise 10c

1 Melissa buys a plant with three leaves on it.
Each week, it grows another two leaves.

Week 1   2   3

  a Use a term-to-term rule to find the number of
leaves on Melissa's plant in week 4 and week 5.

  b Copy and complete this table of values to
find the position-to-term rule.

  c How many leaves will be on Melissa's
plant after twelve weeks?

Position (week)	1	2	3	4	5
Times table					
Term (leaves)					

2 Wasim has £20 already saved. He takes a
Saturday job earning £8 a week.
This sequence gives the total amount that he
has saved after each week.

        20 28 36 44 … …

  a Write the term-to-term rule.

  b Write the next two terms in the sequence.

  c Copy and complete this table of values and
find the position-to-term rule.

  d Find the 40th term of the sequence.

  e How much will Wasim have saved after 40 weeks?

Position (week)	1	2	3	4
Times table				
Term (£)				

3 Migrating geese visit a local pond every winter.
On Day 1, fifty geese are living there and then an
average of twenty more geese arrive every day for
a month.

  a Use the term-to-term rule to write the next two
terms of the sequence

        50 70 90 110 … …

  b Find the position-to-term rule.

  c Find the 20th term of the sequence.

  d How many geese are on the pond on Day 30?

---

investigation

Everyone in a group shakes hands with everyone else.
If there are just 2 people in the group, there is just 1 handshake.

  a If there are 3 people in the group, how many handshakes will there be?

  b How many handshakes will there be for a group of 4, 5, 6, … people?

  c Find a sequence for the numbers of handshakes.

  d Can you use a term-to-term rule to find the next term?

  e Can you find a position-to-term rule? If not, why not?

10d Square roots

LEVEL 6

• Find square roots using different methods.

Keywords
Integer
Inverse
Square
Square root
Trial-and-improvement

The area of this **square** is
$6 \times 6 = 36$ cm^2

6 cm

6 cm

You can write   You can say

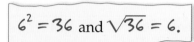

'6 squared is 36' and 'the square root of 36 is 6'.

The sign $\sqrt{}$ comes from the letter r which is the initial of the Latin word 'radix' meaning 'root'. Compare the word 'radish'.

Finding a **square root** is the **inverse** of squaring.

This number line shows the **integer** square roots up to 100.

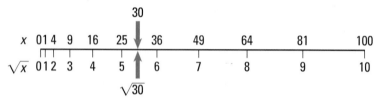

The number line also shows that, for example, $\sqrt{30}$ lies between 5 and 6.

The square root of most numbers is not a whole number.

• You can find square roots by using
• a calculator
• a **trial-and-improvement** method.

example

Find $\sqrt{30}$ correct to 1 decimal place
a by using a trial-and-improvement method   **b** by using a calculator.

a

x	x^2	Comment
5	25	too low
6	36	too high
5.5	30.25	too high
5.4	29.16	too low
5.45	29.7025	too low

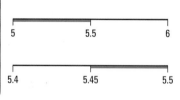

This method is useful if your calculator has no $\sqrt{}$ key.

$\sqrt{}$ of 30 lies between 5.45 and 5.5 so must be 5.5 to 1 dp.

From the table and number line, $\sqrt{30} = 5.5$ correct to 1 decimal place.

b Luckily, almost all calculators have a square root key! $\boxed{\sqrt{}}$

To find $\sqrt{30}$, press $\boxed{\sqrt{}}$ $\boxed{3}$ $\boxed{0}$ $\boxed{=}$ to get the display 5.477225575

So, $\sqrt{30} = 5.5$ to 1 decimal place.

158 **Algebra** Sequences and roots

Exercise 10d

1 Find the length of the sides of these squares.

a
$$16 \text{ cm}^2$$

b
$$25 \text{ cm}^2$$

2 Write the values of these square roots.

a $\sqrt{16}$ **b** $\sqrt{49}$ **c** $\sqrt{81}$ **d** $\sqrt{100}$ **e** $\sqrt{144}$

3 The square roots of these numbers are not integers. Between which two consecutive integers do each of these square roots lie? Use the number line on the opposite page to help you.

a $\sqrt{20}$ **b** $\sqrt{50}$ **c** $\sqrt{28}$ **d** $\sqrt{95}$ **e** $\sqrt{105}$

4 Use a trial-and-improvement method to find the square roots of these numbers to 1 decimal place. The first one is started for you in this table.

a $\sqrt{80}$ **b** $\sqrt{55}$ **c** $\sqrt{38}$

d $\sqrt{70}$ **e** $\sqrt{95}$ **f** $\sqrt{20}$

g $\sqrt{10}$ **h** $\sqrt{105}$ **i** $\sqrt{140}$

x	x^2	
8	64	too low
9	81	just too high

5 A window pane is a square of area 1.5 m².
Find the length of its sides to the nearest whole cm.

$$1.5 \text{ m}^2$$

Did you know?

Before calculators were invented, people used slide rules or mathematical tables to calculate square roots.

When you stand h metres above sea-level, the horizon is x km away from you, where $x = \dfrac{7\sqrt{h}}{2}$.

For example, when you are two metres above sea level

$$h = 2, \quad x = \frac{7 \times \sqrt{2}}{2}$$
$$= 4.95 \ (2 \text{ dp})$$

so you can see 4.95 km to the horizon
Find x when $h = 10$.
Use a computer spreadsheet to find x for many values of h.

- Find cube roots using several different methods

Keywords
Cube
Cube root
Inverse
Trial-and-improvement

The volume of this **cube** is
$5 \times 5 \times 5 = 125 \, \text{cm}^3$.

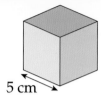

5 cm

p. 12

You can write

$$5^3 = 125 \text{ and } \sqrt[3]{125} = 5$$

You can say

'5 cubed is 125' and 'the cube root of 125 is 5'.

The $\sqrt{}$ sign by itself means square root. With a small ^{3}, the sign $\sqrt[3]{}$ means cube root.

Finding a **cube root** is the **inverse** of finding a cube.

- A calculator can be used to find a cube root if it has a $\boxed{\sqrt[3]{}}$ key.

To find $\sqrt[3]{40}$ correct to 2 decimal places:

Press $\boxed{\sqrt[3]{}}$ $\boxed{4}$ $\boxed{0}$ $\boxed{=}$ to get the display 3.419951893.

So, $\sqrt[3]{40} = 3.42$ to 2 decimal places

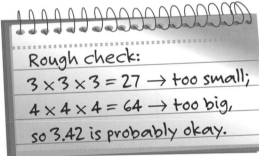

Rough check:
$3 \times 3 \times 3 = 27 \rightarrow$ too small;
$4 \times 4 \times 4 = 64 \rightarrow$ too big,
so 3.42 is probably okay.

- You can also find cube roots by using **trial-and-improvement**.
  This method is useful if your calculator has no $\boxed{\sqrt[3]{}}$ key.

example

Find $\sqrt[3]{40}$ correct to 1 decimal place by using trial-and-improvement.

x	x^3	Comment
3	27	too low
4	64	too high
3.5	42.875	still too high
3.4	39.304	too low
3.45	41.063	too high

3   3.5   4

3.4   3.45   3.5

40 is between 27 and 64, so $\sqrt[3]{40}$ lies between 3 and 4.

$\sqrt[3]{40}$ lies between 3.4 and 3.45

So $\sqrt[3]{40} = 3.4$ to 1 dp.

Exercise 10d²

1 Calculate these cubes and cube roots.

  a 4^3 and $\sqrt[3]{64}$ **b** 2^3 and $\sqrt[3]{8}$ **c** 5^3 and $\sqrt[3]{125}$

  d 3^3 and $\sqrt[3]{27}$ **e** 6^3 and $\sqrt[3]{216}$ **f** 10^3 and $\sqrt[3]{1000}$

2 a Find the volumes of these cubes.   **b** Find the lengths of these cubes.

  i   **ii**   **i** x **ii** y

  4 cm   6 cm $V = 8\ cm^3$ $V = 27\ cm^3$

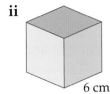
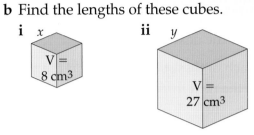

3 If your calculator has a $\sqrt[3]{}$ key, find these cube roots, correct to 2 decimal places.

  a $\sqrt[3]{50}$ **b** $\sqrt[3]{60}$ **c** $\sqrt[3]{63}$ **d** $\sqrt[3]{65}$

  e $\sqrt[3]{124}$ **f** $\sqrt[3]{126}$ **g** $\sqrt[3]{26}$ **h** $\sqrt[3]{100}$

4 Use a trial-and-improvement method to find the cube roots of these numbers to 2 decimal places. The first one is started for you in this table.
Check your answers.

  a $\sqrt[3]{38}$ **b** $\sqrt[3]{80}$ **c** $\sqrt[3]{67}$

  d $\sqrt[3]{70}$ **e** $\sqrt[3]{95}$ **f** $\sqrt[3]{131}$

  g $\sqrt[3]{10}$ **h** $\sqrt[3]{105}$ **i** $\sqrt[3]{140}$

x	x³	
3	27	too low
4	64	too high

5 A child's set of building blocks has cubes of volume of $27\,cm^3$ each.
How long are the edges of these cubes?

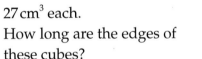

6 The central heating oil for a house is stored in a cubical tank which can hold $9\,m^3$.

To find the length x of the edges of the tank, use a trial-and-improvement method. Give your answer to 1 dp.

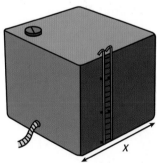

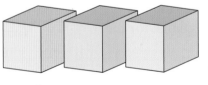

challenge

  a Find two numbers x for which the cube of the number equals the number itself. In other words, find x so that $x^3 = x$.

  b Find another number for which the cube of the number is 10 times the number itself. In other words, find x so that $x^3 = 10x$.

1 This sequence is made using straws. 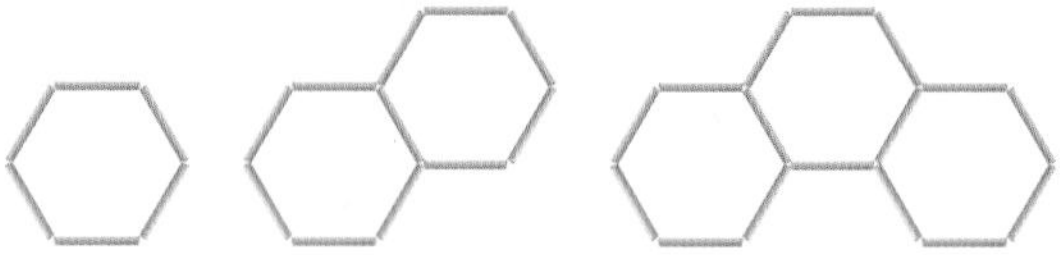
   a Draw the next diagram in the sequence.
   b Write the first four terms.
   c Find the term-to-term rule.
   d Write the next three terms.

2 For each of these sequences, find the term-to-term rule and
   write the next three terms of the sequence.
   a 2   6   10   14   ...   b 3   8   13   18   ...
   c 2   5   11   23   ...   d 30   27   24   21   ...

3 Write the first six terms of each of the sequences with these rules.
   a *Start with 5. Add 4.*   b *Start with 12. Add 6.*
   c *Start with 40. Subtract 6.*   d *Start with 2. Double and add 1.*
   e *Start with 3. Double and subtract 2.*   f *Start with 100 and subtract 21.*

4 This sequence of diagrams is made
   from triangles. 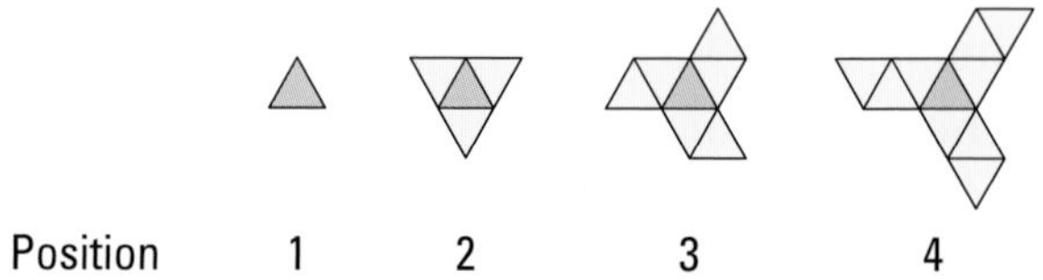
   a How many extra triangles are added
      to each position to make the next
      position?
   b Draw the diagram for position 5.
   c Copy and complete this table.
      Use the correct 'times table' for the
      middle row.
   d Find the position-to-term rule.
   e How many triangles are there in the 10th
      diagram of the sequence?

Position   1   2   3   4

Position	1	2	3	4
Times table				
Term (No. of triangles)				

5 a Find the position-to-term rule for this
      sequence.
      Find the next two terms of the sequence.

Sequence	4	7	10	13	16
Position →	1	2	3	4	5

   b Find the position-to-term rule for each of these sequences.
      Also find the next term and the 20th term in the sequence.
      i   1   3   5   7   9   ii 3   6   9   12   15
      iii 7   12   17   22   27   iv 19   18   17   16   15

6 Jamie bought three tins of cat food on the day he first owned some cats.
He then bought two tins every day after that.
The sequence for the total number of tins bought is 3   5   7   9   ...

Day 1   Day 2   Day 3

a Find the term-to-term rule and the next two terms of this sequence.
b Copy and complete this table and find
  the position-to-term rule.
c Find the 20th term of the sequence.
d How many tins had he bought
  altogether by the 100th day?

Position (day)	1	2	3	4	5
Times-table					
Term (tins)					

7 Write the values of these square roots.
  a $\sqrt{36}$ b $\sqrt{64}$ c $\sqrt{144}$

8 The square roots of these numbers are not integers. Between which two
  consecutive integers does each of these square roots lie?
  a $\sqrt{30}$ b $\sqrt{18}$ c $\sqrt{80}$

9 Use a trial-and-improvement method to find the
  square roots of these numbers to 1 decimal place.
  The first one is started for you in this table.
  a $\sqrt{70}$ b $\sqrt{55}$ c $\sqrt{38}$

$\times$	x^2	
8	64	64<70 Too low
9	81	81>70 Too high

10 Calculate these cubes and cube roots.
   a 10^3 and $\sqrt[3]{1000}$ b 2^3 and $\sqrt[3]{8}$ c 4^3 and $\sqrt[3]{64}$

11 Use a trial-and-improvement method to find
   the cube roots of these numbers to 1 decimal place.
   The first one is started for you in this table.
   Check your answers using a calculator.
   a $\sqrt[3]{40}$ b $\sqrt[3]{98}$ c $\sqrt[3]{50}$

$\times$	x^3	
3	27	27<40 Too low
4	64	64>40 Too high

12 A cube of ice has a volume of 1 litre.
   Find the length of each edge of the cube in centimetres.

10 Summary

Assessment criteria

- Generate terms of a sequence **Level 6**
- Describe the *n*th term of an arithmetic sequence **Level 6**
- Use systematic trial-and-improvement methods to find square roots and cube roots **Level 6**

Level 6

1 The square root button on Tom's calculator is broken.
He wants to find the square root of 70
Use trial-and-improvement to find $\sqrt{70}$ to one decimal place.

Anne's answer ✔

estimate	square	answer	comment
8	8 × 8	64	low
9	9 × 9	81	high
8.5	8.5 × 8.5	72.25	high
8.4	8.4 × 8.4	70.56	high
8.3	8.3 × 8.3	68.89	low
8.35	8.35 × 8.35	69.7225	low

Anne narrows the square root to between 8.3 and 8.4.

Anne narrows the answer further by sketching a number line.

8.3	8.35	8.4
low	low	high

$\sqrt{70} = 8.4$ to 1 decimal place

Level 6

2 Look at these pairs of number sequences.
The second sequence is formed from the first sequence by adding a number or multiplying by a number.
Work out the missing *n*th terms.

  a 5, 9, 13, 17, ...   *n*th term is $4n + 1$
    6, 10, 14, 18, ...   *n*th term is   _____
  b 12, 18, 24, 30, ...   *n*th term is $6n + 6$
    6, 9, 12, 15, ...   *n*th term is   _____
  c 2, 7, 12, 17, ...   *n*th term is $5n - 3$
    4, 14, 24, 34, ...   *n*th term is   _____

Stage 3 2006 4–6 Paper 2

11 Statistics

Collecting and representing data

Data is worth money. Advertisers and manufacturers collect information from many different sources to find out who will buy their goods and services.

What's the point? Sometimes it is obvious when we are providing this data, for example filling in an online survey. Other times it is less overt such as using a store loyalty card.

 Check in

Level 3

1 Karla asked people in her class how many books they had read in the last month.
   a Draw a pictogram for this set of data.
   b Draw a bar chart for the same set of data.

Number of books	Frequency
0	2
1	8
2	12
3 or more	9

Level 4

2 Joe tests a dice by rolling it sixty times. He gets these results.

6	4	3	6	6	5	1	2	3	4	5	4
1	1	2	4	5	1	6	3	3	2	4	4
3	3	5	1	2	4	4	6	3	3	2	4
1	5	5	2	1	4	3	3	3	2	5	6
1	5	4	4	4	3	4	1	5	2	6	1

Draw a table to represent this set of data.

3 Find the mode and the range of each of these sets of numbers.
   a 3, 5, 5, 8   **b** 2, 9, 6, 5, 4, 6, 7, 6, 7   **c** 1, 5, 2, 5, 3, 4, 2, 5,

- Decide which data to collect to answer a question, and the degree of accuracy needed
- Identify possible sources of data, and consider appropriate sample size

Keywords
Primary data
Questionnaire
Sample
Secondary data
Survey

Julie is carrying out a **survey** about use of the Internet. She needs to think carefully about the data that she will need.

- **Primary data** is data that you collect yourself from a survey or experiment.

- **Secondary data** is data that you look up, perhaps in a book or on the Internet.

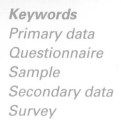

I could use primary data ...or secondary data

Julie chooses primary data, and thinks carefully about how accurate her data needs to be. Instead of asking people exactly how many minutes they spent on the Internet last night, she gives them options on a **questionnaire**.

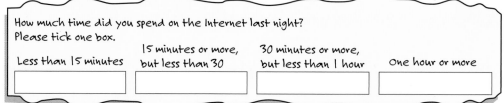

How much time did you spend on the Internet last night? Please tick one box.

Less than 15 minutes	15 minutes or more, but less than 30	30 minutes or more, but less than 1 hour	One hour or more

Julie wants to increase the reliability of her survey by choosing a suitable **sample**. She asks sixteen girls in her class to complete her survey.

Julie wants to make conclusions when she has completed her survey.

If Julie is looking at Internet use by girls of her age, her survey should be fairly reliable.

If she wants to make general conclusions about Internet use, Julie should ask a wider range of people.

Julie's sample size of sixteen is small, and she should consider increasing it.

- Large samples of data generally give more reliable results.

Exercise 11a

1 Explain whether each source of data is primary or secondary data.

 a A chart published in a newspaper

 b The results of a science experiment

 c Data from a class survey

 d A table of data you find on the Internet

 e Data you collect about the lengths of words in a book.

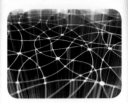
2 Explain whether each of the following topics could be investigated using primary or secondary data. If secondary, suggest where you might find it. If primary, explain how you would collect it.

 a Life expectancy in different countries

 b Favourite lessons of students in Year 8

 c Best deals on mobile phone contracts

 d The most likely scores in football

 e Do teenagers watch too much television?

3 Pete says,

> The Internet is the best place to find data. You can find everything you need without having to leave your seat!

Explain why Pete might not be correct. Give examples of questions that would not be sensible to investigate in this way.

4 Krysia says,

> There is no substitute for collecting your own data. It might take a little time, but you can never really trust data collected by somebody else.

Write a response to Krysia's statement. Include examples of questions that you could not investigate in this way.

discussion

Roisin is investigating the weight of students' school bags.

She decides that she will pick up people's bags, and decide whether each one is light or heavy.

What are the problems with this approach, and how could it be improved?

- Plan how to collect data
- Construct frequency tables with equal class intervals

Keywords
Continuous
Discrete
Frequency table
Two-way table

There are various types of data that you can collect.

Obtained by **describing**

For example, eye colour

Obtained by **measuring**

For example, length of hand

Obtained by **counting**

For example, number of pets

- **Discrete** data is data obtained by counting.

A **two-way table** can be a useful way of displaying discrete data.

example

The table shows information about the cats entered in a show.

How many
a short-haired black cats
b long-haired cats
c tortoiseshell cats were there altogether?

	Black	Tabby	Tortoiseshell
Long-haired	2	2	3
Short-haired	3	8	2

. . . .

a 3   **b** 2 + 2 + 3 = 7   **c** 3 + 2 = 5

- **Continuous** data is data obtained by measuring.

p. 238 You can group continuous data in a **frequency table**.

example

A scientist measured the lengths of some fish. Their lengths (in cm) were

11.7   12.7   9.8   10.1   12.5   11.7   11.5   10.7   11.5   11.5   11.8   10.6   10.4

12.9   11.6   11.9   12.8   10.5   10.8   10.9   13.7   10.5   11.8

Construct a frequency table for this set of continuous data.

. . . .

p. 46

Length, x cm	Tally	Frequency
$9.0 \leq x < 10.0$	I	1
$10.0 \leq x < 11.0$	ЖІ ІІІ	8
$11.0 \leq x < 12.0$	ЖІ ІІІІ	9
$12.0 \leq x < 13.0$	ІІІІ	4
$13.0 \leq x < 14.0$	I	1

$9.0 \leq x < 10.0$ means the length is between 9 and 10 cm, not including 10 cm.

Exercise 11b

1 Here are some examples of data.
Explain whether each one is an example of discrete or
continuous data.

    a Number of children in a family   **b** Weight of piglet

    c Length of a river   **d** Number of people in a car.

2 Jake counted the number of people in cars arriving at his
school for an evening meeting. The data for fifty cars are shown.

```
2  4  2  3  3  4  1  1  2  1  1  1  1
2  2  1  1  3  1  1  1  3  2  1  1  4
2  2  1  4  4  3  3  1  2  1  1  2  2
1  3  1  1  2  3  4  3  2  4  1
```

Copy the table and complete it to find the
frequencies for each number of occupants.

Occupants	Tally	Frequency
1		
2		
3		
4		

3 Here are the heights (in metres) of thirty people.

```
1.69   1.64   1.25   1.37   1.48   1.67   1.37   1.43   1.50   1.59
1.78   1.33   1.45   1.11   1.56   1.52   1.69   1.57   1.87   1.51
1.58   1.44   1.46   1.43   1.37   1.42   1.26   1.76   1.78   1.44
```

Height, h metres	Tally	Frequency
$1.00 \leq h < 1.20$		
$1.20 \leq h < 1.40$		
$1.40 \leq h < 1.60$		
$1.60 \leq h < 1.80$		
$1.80 \leq h < 2.00$		

This is a table for grouped
continuous data.

Copy and complete the table.

4 The diagram represents a set of plates.
There are large and small plates, and
three different colours.
Draw a two-way table to show the
number of plates of each size and colour.

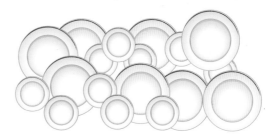

- Construct pie charts for categorical data

Keywords
Categorical
Pie chart
Sector

- **Categorical** data is data obtained by describing. You can show categorical data in a **pie chart**.

- To draw a pie chart, you need to find the angle for each **sector**.

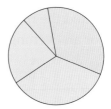

In very simple cases, you can work out the angles mentally.

This table shows how a group of students travelled to school.

Draw a pie chart for this set of data.

Transport	Frequency
Walk	16
Bus	8
Car	8

Half the students walked to school, so the sector for 'Walk' has an angle of 180° (half of 360°). The angles for 'Bus' and 'Car' should both be 90° because they are a quarter each.

○ Walk
○ Bus
○ Car

For most pie charts, you will need a calculator (or a written method) to work out the angles for each sector.

This table shows the eye colours of a group of people.

Eye colour	Frequency
Brown	6
Green	8
Blue	3

Draw a pie chart for this set of data.

○ Brown
○ Green
○ Blue

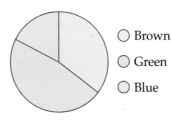

Use a calculator to find the angles to the nearest degree.

6÷17×360

The angles were worked out like this:

Total number of people
= 6 + 8 + 3 = 17
Angle for Brown
= $\frac{6}{17} \times 360° = 127°$
Angle for Green
= $\frac{8}{17} \times 360° = 169°$
Angle for Blue
= $\frac{3}{17} \times 360° = 64°$

Exercise 11c

1 Sketch a pie chart for the data in each of these tables.
You do not need to calculate angles or draw these accurately.

a

Animal	Frequency
Dogs	12
Cats	11
Birds	13

b

Country	Medals won
Spain	19
Cuba	10
USA	11
Japan	41

c

Service	Calls received
Fire	16
Police	14
Ambulance	15
Coast Guard	4

2 Draw the pie charts from question **1** accurately.
You will need to

- calculate the angles (mentally, with a written method or using a calculator), and
- draw the diagram using a protractor, ruler and compasses.

3 Marcus used a spreadsheet to produce this pie chart for the data in the table.

	A	B
1	**Genre**	**Number**
2	**Fiction**	8
3	**History**	12
4	**Reference**	9
5	**Biography**	7

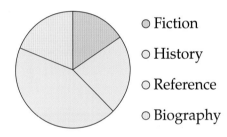

○ Fiction
○ History
○ Reference
○ Biography

a Explain why this pie chart cannot be correct.
b Draw a correct version of the pie chart.

These two pie charts show the types of housing in two towns.

Make a list of some conclusions that you can draw from these pie charts.

What misconceptions might cause someone to draw incorrect conclusions from these pie charts?

○ Terraces   ○ Semi   ○ Detached   ○ Flat

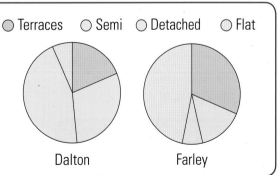

Dalton   Farley

• Construct bar charts and frequency diagrams for discrete and continuous data

Keywords
Bar chart
Frequency diagram

Bar charts are a good way to compare the parts of a set of data.
They are used for categorical or discrete data.

example

The tables show two sets of data for the students in a class.
Draw bar charts to represent the data.

a

Number of siblings	Frequency
0	6
1	4
2	5
3	2
4	1

b

Eye colour	Frequency
Green	4
Blue	11
Brown	3

Siblings are brothers and sisters.

p. 240

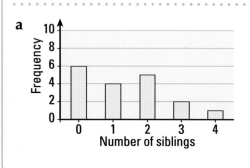

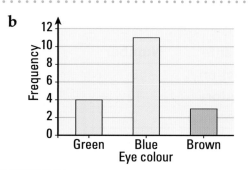

Frequency diagrams can be used to show continuous data.

example

The table shows the heights of students in a class.
Draw a frequency diagram for this data.

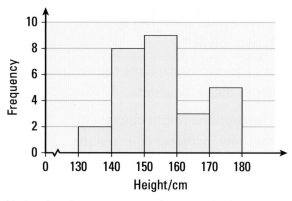

Notice that there are no gaps between the bars.

Height, *h* cm	Frequency
$130 \leq h < 140$	2
$140 \leq h < 150$	8
$150 \leq h < 160$	9
$160 \leq h < 170$	3
$170 \leq h < 180$	5

Exercise 11d

1 This data shows the colours of thirty cars in a survey.

Colours of 30 cars

Green	Grey	Yellow	Grey	Red	Black	Grey	Green	Red	Blue
Red	Blue	Grey	Grey	White	Green	Grey	Grey	Red	Grey
Black	Grey	White	Red	Grey	Grey	Blue	Black	Yellow	Green

Draw a bar chart for this set of data.

2 This data shows the shoe sizes of thirty adults in a survey.

Shoe sizes of 30 people

6	3	6	6	5	8	7	6	9	8
7	5	7	7	4	5	8	5	5	6
6	7	4	6	10	8	4	9	6	8

Draw a bar chart for this set of discrete numerical data.

3 This data shows the weights of thirty adults in a survey.

Draw a frequency diagram for this set of continuous numerical data.

Weight of 30 people

Weight, w kg	Frequency
$50 \leq w < 60$	3
$60 \leq w < 70$	7
$70 \leq w < 80$	15
$80 \leq w < 90$	5

These diagrams show the same two sets of data in different ways.

The data relates to the number of sightings of wildcats in two different regions.

What are the advantages and disadvantages of each type of diagram?

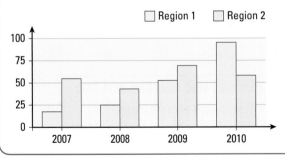

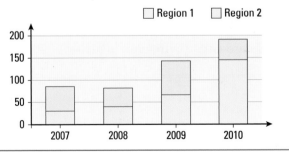

• Construct simple line graphs for time series

Keywords
Time series
Trend

Time series graphs show data changing over time.

p. 242

example

The table shows the temperature at noon each day in June for a town in Wales.
Draw a time series graph for this set of data.

Date	1	2	3	4	5	6	7	8	9	10	11	12	13	14	15
Temp °C	9	10	9	11	10	10	8	12	14	16	17	21	20	15	13

Date	16	17	18	19	20	21	22	23	24	25	26	27	28	29	30
Temp °C	12	14	13	14	15	13	13	12	15	18	19	20	19	18	19

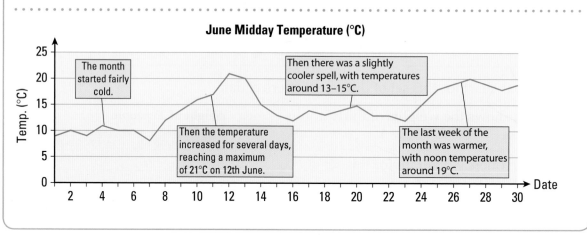

Time series graphs can often show a **trend**.

example

This table shows the change in
world sea level over the last eight
thousand years. Draw a time series
graph for this set of data.

Time (Years before present)	Sea level (Difference in metres)
8000	-15
7000	-4
6000	-2
5000	-1
1000	0
0	0

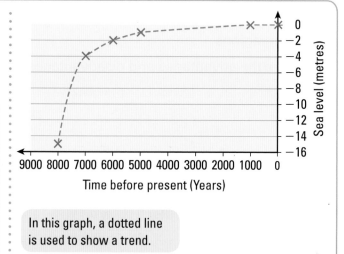

In this graph, a dotted line
is used to show a trend.

Exercise 11 e

1 A researcher used CCTV footage to estimate the number of people on a railway station platform. The table shows the data.

Time	07:00	07:30	08:00	08:30	09:00	09:30	10:00
People	48	145	113	82	45	31	17

Draw a time series graph for this set of data.

2 The table shows the approximate number of miles of track for railway in the UK. Draw a time series graph for this set of data.

Did you know?

Since the early 20th century the government has calculated a Retail Price Index to measure inflation.

Year	Track Miles
1830	0
1840	1000
1850	6000
1860	9000
1870	14000
1880	16000
1890	17000
1900	19000
1910	20000

Year	Track Miles
1920	20000
1930	20000
1940	20000
1950	20000
1960	18000
1970	12000
1980	10000
1990	10000
2000	10000

discussion

The line graph shows how unemployment changed in the UK over a 10-year period.

UNEMPLOYMENT OVER THE LAST 10 YEARS

Million people   April 2008

[Line graph: y-axis from 1.00 to 2.00 in increments of 0.25; x-axis from Jan 98 to Jul 08. Line starts around 1.80, rises slightly, then declines to around 1.50 by 2001, dips to about 1.43 around 2004, then rises to around 1.72 by 2006-07, and rises again to about 1.73 by Jul 08.]

SOURCE: ONS

Discuss the main features of the graph.

Try to suggest reasons for any trends or features that you observe.

* Construct simple scatter diagrams

Keywords
Scatter graph *Variable*
Uniform scale

p. 244

Scatter graphs are used to show patterns in pairs of data.

example

The table shows the number of pages and weights of ten books.
Show this data in a scatter diagram, and describe any patterns.

Book	A	B	C	D	E	F	G	H	I	J
Pages	245	136	128	410	338	237	317	92	602	320
Weight (g)	504	258	855	795	692	451	655	211	1350	700

In general, the scatter diagram shows that
books with more pages are heavier.

There is one book that does not fit this
pattern – this could be a large-format book
with few pages.

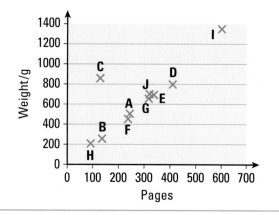

When drawing a scatter diagram, make sure that each axis of the
graph has a **uniform scale**.

example

Colin is looking for a connection between the
weight of a watch and how expensive it is. He
draws a scatter diagram for this table of data.

Weight (g)	49	68	72	86	93	98	104	112
Cost (£)	15	85	45	50	45	29	65	135

Colin says, 'The scatter diagram shows that the
more expensive a watch is, the heavier it is.'
Where has Colin gone wrong?

The graph only looks as if there is a clear connection
between weight and price because incorrect scales
have been used. A corrected version of the graph
shows that there is no such connection between
the two variables.

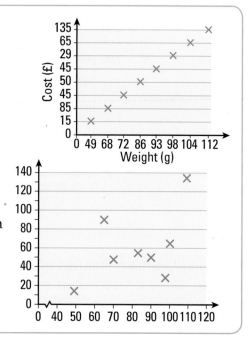

Exercise 11f

1 The data in the table shows the fitness score and the time to complete a 100 m sprint for a group of eight 12-year-olds. Copy and complete the scatter diagram.

Fitness score	8.1	4.8	6.2	3.9	9.8	6.5	7.2	5.9
100 m time (sec)	12.5	19.4	16.3	19.2	12.8	15.8	14.3	17.3

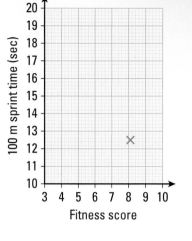

2 This table shows the marks obtained by ten people on three different tests.

Science	64	76	38	58	92	83	42	29	73	51
Maths	58	82	32	63	79	85	49	33	68	44
French	60	71	46	29	58	49	63	40	87	60

Draw scatter graphs to show the connections between
a Science marks and Maths marks   **b** Maths marks and French marks
c French marks and Science marks.
Comment on the patterns in your graphs.

3 The table shows the ages and weights of a group of cats. Simon drew a scatter graph to show this set of data.

Age (years)	8	3	11	7	1	14	2	6
Weight (kg)	2.8	3.5	2.3	4.2	3.7	2.1	3.5	4.2

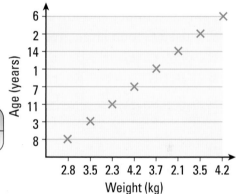

a Explain what Simon did wrong.
b Redraw the scatter diagram correctly.

---

discussion

This graph compares the number of ice creams sold at a beach cafe with the number of people treated for sunburn at the local hospital, for ten days during the summer.

Jason says, 'When more ice creams are sold, more people get sunburnt. So, ice cream causes sunburn.'

Is this a reasonable interpretation of the graph?

11a

1 Give some examples of primary and secondary data that you could use to investigate these topics.
  a Recycling
  b Mobile phone use
  c Exercise and sport

11b

2 Tom asked 30 people in his class how many books they currently had out on loan from the school library. Here are his results.

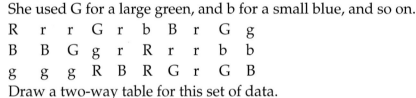

```
3  2  2  2  1  0  3  0  1  4
4  3  1  0  0  1  2  3  3  4
1  3  2  2  2  3  3  4  0  1
```

Organise this data into a frequency table.

3 Sara recorded the size and colour of crayons in a box.
There are three colours of crayon – red, blue and green.
There are two sizes of crayon – large and small.
Sara used upper and lower case letters to represent the crayons.
She used G for a large green, and b for a small blue, and so on.

```
R   r   r   G   r   b   B   r   G   g
B   B   G   g   r   R   r   r   b   b
g   g   g   R   B   R   G   r   G   B
```

Draw a two-way table for this set of data.

11c

4 Here are one season's results for two football teams.
United: Won 14, Drew 8, Lost 8
Wanderers: Won 10, Drew 6, Lost 14
Draw a pie chart for each team's results.

5 This set of data shows the number of phone calls received by a shop each day for 20 days.

4 5 5 3 0 2 7 4 6 5
4 4 1 0 3 2 1 5 5 4

Draw a bar chart to show the data.

6 This set of data shows the length (in minutes and seconds) of 20 phone calls received by a shop.

0:35   1:22   2:47   1:26   3:55   2:50   0:15   1:03   3:35   4:09
3:10   0:59   3:09   2:26   3:11   3:28   2:05   3:54   2:12   1:08

Draw a frequency diagram to show the data.

7 In an experiment, Jackie heated up a beaker of water, and then left it to cool. She recorded the temperature every minute (in degrees Celsius). Here are her results.

95, 79, 67, 57, 49, 43, 38, 34, 31, 28, 26, 25, 23, 22

Draw a time-series graph for this set of data.

8 John recorded the length and weight of 10 earthworms.

Length (cm):   7   8   7   9   11   6   10   5   6   5
Weight (g):   22   24   21   28   30   16   28   17   18   16

Draw a scatter diagram for this set of data.

Assessment criteria

- Construct charts, graphs and diagrams and identify which are most useful in the context of the problem **Level 6**
- Design a survey to capture the necessary data **Level 6**

Level 6

1 Julie wants to find out what percentage of people buy a newspaper.

She goes down to a paper shop at lunchtime and asks the first ten people if they have bought a newspaper.

Give three reasons why her survey may be unreliable.

Ruby's answer ✔

It is more likely that people at the paper shop will buy a paper.

1 Julie has only asked people at the paper shop.

2 The sample is too small.

3 The survey is only done on one occasion.

Asking only 10 people will not give reliable results.

Ruby knows taking the survey at different times of the day and on different days of the week will give more reliable results.

Level 6

2 a A teacher asked her students if they recycled newspapers and glass. The pie chart shows the results.

Five students answered 'Neither'.
How many students answered 'Newspapers only'?
Show your working.

b The teacher asked a different class if they recycled newspapers and glass.
There were twenty four students in the class.
Nine students answered 'Newspapers only'.
On a pie chart, what would the angle be for the sector 'Newspapers only'?
Show your working.

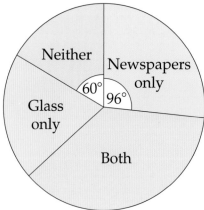

Key Stage 3 2004 4–6 Paper 2

Ratio and proportion

Cements have been used for thousands of years. Primitive "wattle-and-daub" structures used mixtures of mud, animal dung and straw. Modern concrete is made by combining cement, sand and aggregate, then adding water which starts a chemical reaction.

What's the point? The mixture must be made in the correct proportion so the concrete solidifies. Otherwise the building will fall down!

 **Check in**

Level 5

1 Calculate these percentages using a mental or informal written method.
   a 15% of 80   **b** 20% of £60   **c** 40% of 180 g

2 Copy and complete this table using a calculator where appropriate.

Fraction	Decimal	Percentage
$\frac{17}{20}$		
	0.78	
		96%

- Simplify a ratio to an equivalent ratio by cancelling
- Use ratios when interpreting maps

Keywords
Ratio
Scale
Simplify

- You can compare the size of quantities by writing them as a **ratio**.

Brian has 75p, and Esme has £1.25. $\Longrightarrow$ First convert to the same units (pence). $\Longrightarrow$ Now simplify the ratio.

$$75p : £1.25 \Longrightarrow 75p : 125p \Longrightarrow \begin{array}{c} \div 5 \left(\begin{array}{c} 75 : 125 \\ 15 : 25 \\ 3 : 5 \end{array} \right) \div 5 \\ \div 5 \quad\quad \div 5 \end{array}$$

The ratio of Brian's money to Esme's money is 3 : 5.

- To **simplify** a ratio, you divide both parts by the same number.

You must first ensure that the quantities are in the same units.

You can solve ratio problems by multiplying both parts by the same number.

Multiplying is the inverse operation to dividing.

example

The ratio of men to women in a sports club is 7 : 11. There are 175 men. How many women are there?

. . . .

For every 7 men there are 11 women.

For 175 men,

there are 275 women in the sports club.

men : women

$$\times 25 \left(\begin{array}{c} 7 : 11 \\ 175 : 275 \end{array} \right) \times 25$$

Multiply both parts of the ratio by $175 \div 7 = 25$

- You use ratios when you are interpreting maps or drawing to **scale**.

example

A map has a scale of 1 : 200. What distance does 8 cm on the map represent in real life?

. . . .

map : real life

$$\times 8 \left(\begin{array}{c} 1 : 200 \\ 8\,cm : 1600\,cm \end{array} \right) \times 8$$

Multiply both parts of the ratio by 8 cm

The real-life distance = $200 \times 8\,cm = 1600\,cm = 16\,m$

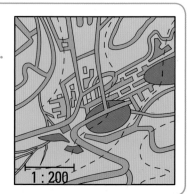

1 : 200

Exercise 12a

1 Write each of these ratios in its simplest form.

   a 4 : 14   **b** 12 : 18   **c** 15 : 25   **d** 14 : 21

   e 40 : 25   **f** 35 : 56   **g** 64 : 40   **h** 72 : 63

2 Write each of these ratios in its simplest form.

   a 40 cm : 1 m   **b** 90p : £2   **c** 25 mm : 4 cm   **d** 300 ml : 1 litre

   e 4 km : 2500 m   **f** 1500 g : 2 kg   **g** 3 hrs : 40 mins   **h** 80p : £1.80

3 Write these as ratios in their simplest form.

   a A cake recipe requires 150 g of sugar for every 100 g of butter.
      What is the ratio of sugar to butter?

   b At Wellbeing 11-18 Comprehensive School there are 1100 students
      in Years 7 to 11 and 250 students in the sixth form. What is the ratio
      of sixth form students to Y7 to Y11 students?

   c A model of a car is 15 cm long. The real car is 3.75 m long.
      What is the ratio of the model to the real car?

4 Solve each of these problems.

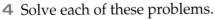

3.75 m   15 cm

   a At a dance club the ratio of boys to girls is 3 : 7. There are
      91 girls at the club. How many boys are there?

   b The main ingredients in a recipe are cauliflower and cheese
      in the ratio 4 : 3 by weight. How many grams of cheese are
      needed if the cauliflower weighs 640 g?

   c A map has a scale of 1 : 250.

     i What is the distance in real life of a measurement of 12 cm
       on the map?

     ii What is the distance on the map of a measurement of 50 m
        in real life?

   d A model of a space shuttle is built to a scale of 1 : 24. The length
      of the real shuttle is 36 m. How long is the model of the shuttle?

---

investigation

Rukshana is 12 and her sister Rowshanara is 4.

a What is the ratio of their ages?

b What will be the ratio of their ages in 10 years' time?

c Investigate what happens to the ratio of their ages as
   Rukshana and Rowshanara get older.

- Divide a quantity into two parts in a given ratio
- Solve simple problems using informal strategies
- Solve simple problems using a unitary method

Keywords
Ratio
Unitary method

- You can divide a quantity in a given **ratio** using **a unitary method**. You find the value of one equal share of the quantity.

example

Stewart and Naomi share a 200 g bar of chocolate in the ratio 2:3. How much chocolate do they each receive?

. . . .

Splitting the chocolate in the ratio 2:3 means that the bar has to be divided into 5 equal parts − 2 parts for Stewart and 3 parts for Naomi.

Each of the parts weighs $200 \div 5 = 40\,g$

Stewart gets 2 parts: $2 \times 40\,g = 80\,g$
Naomi gets 3 parts: $3 \times 40\,g = 120\,g$

You could use an informal method:
2:3 means that in every 5 g, Stewart has 2 g and Naomi has 3 g.
You need 40 lots of 5 g to make 200 g.
× both sides of the ratio by 40:

$$\begin{array}{ccc} 2 & : & 3 \\ 80 & : & 120 \end{array}$$

Stewart gets 80 g and Naomi gets 120 g.

In the example, you can check that Stewart and Naomi's amounts are correct:

By simplifying,

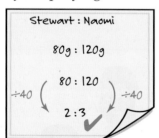

By adding,

80 g + 120 g

= 200 g ✔

Both checks are correct, so the answer is correct.

Exercise 12b

1 Divide these quantities in the ratios given.
   a £50 in the ratio 2:3   **b** 60 cm in the ratio 5:7
   c 72 MB in the ratio 4:5   **d** 90 p in the ratio 1:5
   e 120 seconds in the ratio 3:5 **f** £240 in the ratio 5:3

2 Sian picks some apples.
   She shares out 15 apples between herself and her mum
   in the ratio 2:3.
   a Draw a diagram to show how Sian divides the apples.
   b Write the number of apples she gives to her mum.

3 Morgan wins £40.
   He shares out the £40 between himself and his dad in the ratio 3:5.
   a Draw a diagram to show how Morgan divides the money.
   b Write the amount of money he gives to his dad.

4 Solve each of these problems.
   a At a gym club the ratio of boys to girls is 3:4. There are 63 children
      in total at the club. How many girls are there?
   b Jack and Mona share £84 in the ratio 2:5. How much money does
      Jack receive?

5 For each of these questions, check that the answer is correct.
   Explain your reasoning in each question.
   a At a sports club the ratio of boys to girls is 2:3. There are 25 boys
      and girls in total at the club. How many girls and how many boys
      are there?
      ANSWER: There are 10 boys and 15 girls.
   b Javed and Oprah share £65 in the ratio 4:9. How much money do
      they each receive?
      ANSWER: Javed receives £12 and Oprah receives £30.

Meredith wants to design a flag using two colours – blue and
green. The flag must be coloured blue to green in the ratio 3:5.
a Draw a rectangle 5 cm by 16 cm.
   Colour the flag blue and green in the ratio 3:5.
b Draw a different rectangle 12 cm by 8 cm.
   Colour the flag blue and green in the ratio 3:5.
c How can you tell which sizes of rectangular flags,
   drawn on squared paper, can easily be
   coloured in blue and green in the ratio 3:5?

- Recognise when two quantities are in direct proportion
- Solve simple problems involving direct proportion

Keywords
Approximate
Direct proportion
Unitary method

Here is an **approximate** conversion table for miles and kilometres.

If you double the number of miles, you double the number of kilometres.
If you halve the number of miles, you halve the number of kilometres.
The number of miles is **directly proportional** to the number of kilometres.

Miles	Kilometres
10	16
20	32
5	8

×2 ... ×2

- When two quantities are in direct proportion, if one of them increases the other one increases by the same proportion.

You can use direct proportion to solve simple problems.

example

Three litres of water cost £2.09.
What is the cost of six litres of water?

×2 (3 litres   £2.09 / 6 litres   £4.18) ×2

The number of litres has been multiplied by 2. Multiply the cost by 2.

Six litres of water costs £4.18.

- You can use the **unitary method** to solve problems involving direct proportion.

In this method you always find the value of one unit of a quantity.

example

a 20 text messages cost 48p. What is the cost of 15 text messages?

b There are 140 calories in a 40 g piece of cheese. How many calories are there in a 70 g piece of cheese?

a
÷20 (20 texts   48p / 1 text   2.4p) ÷20
×15 (1 text   2.4p / 15 texts   36p) ×15

15 text messages cost 36p.

b
÷40 (40 g   140 calories / 1 g   3.5 calories) ÷40
×70 (1 g   3.5 calories / 70 g   245 calories) ×70

70 g of cheese contains 245 calories.

Exercise 12c

1 48 bags of crisps cost £11.04. Work out the cost of
  a 24 bags of crisps   **b** 12 bags of crisps   **c** 1 bag of crisps
  d 5 bags of crisps   **e** 50 bags of crisps   **f** 6 bags of crisps.

2 Here are three offers for text messages on a mobile phone.
  In which of these offers are the numbers in direct proportion?
  In each case explain and justify your answers.

D-Mobile

Text messages	Cost (£)
10	£0.40
20	£0.80
40	£1.60

Yellow

Text messages	Cost (£)
5	£0.19
20	£0.72
45	£1.56

Codaphone

Text messages	Cost (£)
20	£0.68
50	£1.70
120	£4.08

3 Use direct proportion to solve each of these problems.
  a 4 apples cost 92p. What is the cost of 12 apples?
  b 28 g of cashew nuts contain 14 g of fat.
     How many grams of fat are there in 42 g of cashew nuts?
  c 200 g of chips contain 500 calories.
     How many calories are there in 40 g of chips?
  d A recipe for 4 people uses 500 g of mushrooms.
     i What weight of mushrooms is needed for 7 people?
     ii How many grams of mushrooms are needed for 13 people?

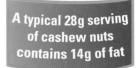

A typical 28g serving of cashew nuts contains 14g of fat

4 Solve each of these problems.
  a 3 litres of lemonade costs £1.11.
     What is the cost of   **i** 9 litres of lemonade   **ii** 8 litres of lemonade?
  b 4 identical pans have a capacity of 14 litres. What is the
     capacity of 7 of these pans?
  c 16 pencils cost £1.92. What is the cost of 7 pencils?
  d £3 is worth 42 Chinese Yuan. How much is £25 worth in
     Chinese Yuan?
  e 35 litres of petrol costs £38.15. What is the cost of 40 litres of petrol?
  f A recipe for 4 people needs 300 g of pasta. How much pasta is
     needed to make the recipe for 7 people?

---

challenge

Use direct proportion to copy and complete
this approximate conversion table for converting
between kilograms and pounds.

How many pounds make 1 kg?
How many kilograms make 1 lb?

Kilograms (kg)	Pounds (lb)
1	
	4
5	11
10	
23	
	110

- Understand the relationship between ratio and proportion
- Solve problems involving ratio and proportion

Keywords
Proportion
Ratio

- **Ratio** compares the size of the parts.

- **Proportion** compares the size of a part with the whole.

example

Wendy has a music collection of 9 CDs and 6 DVDs.

a What proportion of Wendy's collection is CDs and what proportion is DVDs?

b What is the ratio of CDs to DVDs in Wendy's collection?

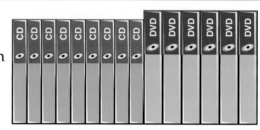

a There are $9 + 6 = 15$ items in Wendy's music collection.

Proportion of CDs $= \frac{9}{15} = \frac{3}{5}$ $\div 3$

Proportion of DVDs $= \frac{6}{15} = \frac{2}{5}$ $\div 3$

This means that $\frac{3}{5}$ of Wendy's collection is CDs and $\frac{2}{5}$ of her collection is DVDs.

b The ratio compares how many CDs there are to how many DVDs there are.

The ratio of CDs to DVDs is $3:2$.

CDs : DVDs

$\div 3 \left(\begin{array}{c} 9 : 6 \\ 3 : 2 \end{array} \right) \div 3$

- You can divide a quantity in a given ratio by using the relationship between ratio and proportion.

example

Jermaine and Gina share £150 in the ratio $3:2$. How much money do they each receive?

Use the ratio to tell you what proportion of the money each person receives.

Jermaine receives $\frac{3}{5}$ of £150 = £90

Gina receives $\frac{2}{5}$ of £150 = £60

This is a similar method to the one on page 188. You have divided by 5 to find the size of each part, and then, for Jermaine, multiplied by 3.

Jermaine : Gina

Ratio $3:2$

Proportion $\frac{3}{5}$ $\frac{2}{5}$

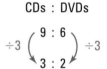

This means that there are 5 equal parts

Exercise 12d

1 For each of these diagrams
   i find the ratio of red sections to yellow sections (in its simplest form)
   ii find the proportion of the shape shaded red (as a fraction in its simplest form)
   iii copy and complete these two sentences for each shape:

   red section = $\dfrac{\square}{\square}$ × yellow section

   yellow section = $\dfrac{\square}{\square}$ × red section

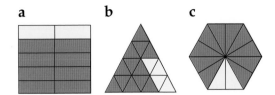

a   b   c

2 In a class of 32 students, there are 20 girls.
   a Write the ratio of boys to girls in the class.
   b Write the proportion of the class that are girls.

3 In a fish tank, there are 20 goldfish and 25 angelfish.
   a Write the ratio of goldfish to angelfish in the tank.
   b Write the proportion of the fish that are goldfish.

4 Use a suitable method to work out these.
   a Divide 40 kg in the ratio 3:2.   b Divide £120 in the ratio 1:5.
   c Divide 360 degrees in the ratio 4:5.   d Divide 180 cats in the ratio 5:7.
   e Divide £4 in the ratio 3:5.   f Divide 6 m in the ratio 7:5.

5 a Amy has 28 plates in her cupboard.
     The ratio of large plates to small plates is 3:4.
     How many small plates does Amy have in her cupboard?
   b Keiley has 54 files stored on her phone.
     The ratio of music to video files is 7:2.
     i How many music files does Keiley have on her phone?
     ii What proportion of the files on her phone are video files?

6 a $\dfrac{3}{5}$ of the people at a pop concert are women.
     What is the ratio of men to women at the pop concert?
   b Harry and Posy shared some money in the ratio 3:4.
     Harry received £36. How much money did Harry and Posy share?

challenge

A sponge cake is made from flour, sugar and margarine in the ratio 4:5:3 by weight. How many grams of margarine and sugar are needed to mix with 280 g of flour?

- Calculate a percentage of an amount using a written method and by using a calculator
- Calculate a percentage increase or decrease

Keywords
Equivalent
Percentage

- You can calculate a **percentage of an amount** by using an **equivalent** fraction or decimal.

For example, 23% of £75

Using an equivalent fraction

$23\% \text{ of } 75 = \frac{23}{100} \text{ of } 75$

$= \frac{23 \times 75}{100}$

$= \frac{1725}{100}$

$= £17.25$

Using an equivalent decimal

$23\% \text{ of } 75 = \frac{23}{100} \text{ of } 75$

$= 23 \div 100 \times 75$

$= 0.23 \times 75$

$= £17.25$

Percentage increases and decreases occur often in real life.

example

A packet of crisps normally weighs 125 g.
The packet is increased in weight by 20%.

What is the new weight of the packet of crisps?

First find the size of the increase.
20% of 125 g

Using a mental method.

$10\% \text{ of } 125\,\text{g} = \frac{1}{10} \text{ of } 125$

$= 12.5$

$20\% = 2 \times 10\%$

$20\% \text{ of } 125\,\text{g} = 2 \times 12.5$

$= 25\,\text{g}$

Then add the increase to the original weight.
New weight $= 125 + 25 = 150\,\text{g}$

example

Harry weighs 80 kg. After a diet he reduces his weight by 12%. What is his new weight?

First find the size of the weight reduction.

$12\% \text{ of } 80\,\text{kg} = 0.12 \times 80$

$= 9.6\,\text{kg}$

Using a calculator method.

Subtract the reduction from Harry's original weight.

$= 80 - 9.6$

$= 70.4\,\text{kg}$

Exercise 12e

1 Calculate these percentages using a mental or informal written method.

   a 10% of 80   **b** 20% of £60   **c** 5% of 180 g

   d 15% of £300   **e** 40% of 320 N   **f** 25% of 160 mm

   g 55% of £2800   **h** 65% of £88

2 Calculate these using a suitable method.

   a 13% of £50   **b** 42% of 67   **c** 50% of 86 kg

   d 16% of $24   **e** 37% of £45   **f** 17.5% of 80 km

   g 65% of £230   **h** 95% of 19.2 kg

3 **a** Increase £50 by 15%.   **b** Decrease £50 by 15%.

   c Increase 160 m by 25%.   **d** Decrease 360° by 10%.

   e Increase 60 kg by 5%.   **f** Decrease £1700 by 13%.

   g Increase £240 by 45%.   **h** Decrease 240 J by 36%.

4 **a** Archenal football stadium has 43 400 seats.
It is rebuilt with an increased seating of 45%.
How many seats are there at the new stadium?

   b A top secret file of size 208 kB is saved on
a computer.
After some information is stolen and deleted
from the file, it is decreased in size by 5%.
What is the new size of the file?

   c A bottle of olive oil holds 560 ml.
It is increased in capacity by 15%.
What is the new capacity of the bottle?

investigation

Here are five items for sale in Cheapos shop with their original prices.

In a 21-day sale, Cheapos reduce all their prices by 21%.

a Calculate the sale price of each of the items.

b How could the sales assistants work out the sale price of an item after a 21% reduction using just a single multiplication?

c Investigate increasing and decreasing the prices by different percentages. Try to find a single multiplication which works out the

- Use the equivalence of percentages, fractions and decimals to compare simple proportions and solve problems

Keywords
Decimal
Fraction
Percentage
Proportion

You can use **percentages**, **fractions** or **decimals** to describe **proportions**.

example

What proportion of this shape is shaded yellow?

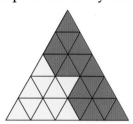

The proportion can be written as a fraction.
Proportion shaded yellow

$$= \frac{10}{25} \overset{\div 5}{\underset{\div 5}{=}} \frac{2}{5}$$

The proportion can also be written as a percentage.
Proportion shaded yellow

$$= \frac{10}{25} \overset{\times 4}{\underset{\times 4}{=}} \frac{40}{100} = 40\%$$

- You can compare proportions by converting them to percentages.

example

Leroy asked some students in Year 8 which subject they liked best.

a i What proportion of the boys chose Maths?
   ii What proportion of the boys chose Science?
b Compare the proportions of boys and girls that chose Maths or Science.

Subject	Boys	Girls
Maths	8	2
English	2	10
Science	7	9
French	1	1
Geography	2	2
History	1	3
Total	21	27

- -

a Proportion of boys

who chose Maths

$$= \frac{8}{21}$$
$$= 0.380\ 95$$
$$= 38.1\% \text{ (1 dp)}$$

who chose Science

$$= \frac{7}{21}$$
$$= 0.333\ 33$$
$$= 33.3\% \text{ (1 dp)}$$

b Proportion of girls

who chose Maths

$$= \frac{2}{27}$$
$$= 0.074\ 074$$
$$= 7.4\% \text{ (1 dp)}$$

who chose Science

$$= \frac{9}{27}$$
$$= 0.333\ 33$$
$$= 33.3\% \text{ (1 dp)}$$

Write the proportion as a fraction.
Convert the fraction into a decimal using division.
Convert the decimal into a percentage.

A greater proportion of boys than girls chose Maths as their favourite subject.
The same proportion of boys and girls chose Science.

Exercise 12f

1 Convert these fractions into percentages using a calculator where appropriate.

a $\frac{7}{10}$ **b** $\frac{23}{50}$ **c** $\frac{14}{25}$ **d** $\frac{5}{4}$ **e** $\frac{17}{40}$

f $\frac{5}{12}$ **g** $\frac{33}{35}$ **h** $\frac{5}{7}$ **i** $\frac{4}{5}$ **j** $\frac{13}{20}$

2 Write the proportion of each of these shapes that is shaded red. Write each of your answers as
  i a fraction in its simplest form
  ii a percentage (to 1 dp where appropriate).

a    **b**   **c**

3 Express each of your answers to these problems
  i as a fraction in its simplest form
  ii as a percentage (to 1 dp where appropriate).
  a Morton scores 49 out of 70 in his English test. What proportion of the test did he answer correctly?
  b Class 8X3 has 33 students. 21 of these students are boys. What proportion of the class are girls?

4 a Hilary McGoalmachine has scored 23 goals in 35 games for her club.
Jodie Goalpoacher has scored 20 goals in 29 games for the same club. Who is the better goal scorer? Explain and justify your answer.
  b Tina put £120 into a savings account. After one year the interest was £8. Harriet put £90 into a savings account. After one year the interest was £7. Who had the better deal?

> **Did you know?**
>
>
>
> As of 2008, the top goalscorer in the football Premier League since it started in 1992 is Alan Shearer with 260 goals in 441 appearances. However that doesn't give him the top scoring rate!

problem solving

Here are the Summer exam results of some students in History, Geography and Religious Studies.
For each student, show clearly in which subject they did the best.
Explain and justify your answers.

Name	History (60 marks)	Geography (70 marks)	Religious Studies (80 marks)
Zak	24	30	33
Wilson	20	14	16
Yvonne	45	50	52
Ulf	55	64	73
Veronica	30	38	33

12a

1 Write each of these ratios in its simplest form.

a 6 : 18	**b** 5 : 15	**c** 8 : 12	**d** 6 : 15
e 35 : 28	**f** 32 : 56	**g** 63 : 90	**h** 70 : 60
i 24 : 100	**j** 24 : 104	**k** 128 : 256	**l** 64 : 176

2 Write each of these ratios in its simplest form.

a 20 cm : 3 m	**b** 50 p : £4	**c** 65 mm : 8 cm	**d** 70 cl : 2 litres
e 7 km : 700 m	**f** 1900 g : 4 kg	**g** 1 hr 20 mins : 80 mins	**h** 70p : £1.70

3 Solve these problems.

a In a fishing club the ratio of men to women is 7 : 2. There are 84 men in the club. How many women are there?

b In a school the ratio of boys to girls is 8 : 9. If there are 624 boys at the school, how many girls are there?

c A map has a scale of 1 : 10 000.

  i What is the distance in real life of a measurement of 3 cm on the map?

  ii What is the distance on the map of a measurement of 5 km in real life?

12b

4 Divide these quantities in the ratios given.

a Divide 65 km in the ratio 6 : 7.   **b** Divide £225 in the ratio 8 : 7.

c Divide 256 MB in the ratio 3 : 5.   **d** Divide 4500 N in the ratio 4 : 5.

e Divide 3 minutes in the ratio 4 : 5.   **f** Divide £2 in the ratio 7 : 13.

5 Solve these problems.

a In a running club the ratio of boys to girls is 5 : 3. There are 96 children in total at the club. How many girls are there?

b Sam and Siobhan share £2400 in the ratio 7 : 5. How much money does Sam receive?

c A pizza is made with dough and vegetables in the ratio 3 : 5. The total weight of the pizza is 320 g. What weight of dough has been used to make the pizza?

12c

6 Here are three offers for different types of bread. In which of these offers are the numbers in direct proportion? In each case explain and justify your answers.

a Wholemeal loaves

Weight of bread	Cost
300 g	£0.45
400 g	£0.60
800 g	£1.20

b Croissants

Weight of bread	Cost
50 g	£0.32
125 g	£0.75
200 g	£1.25

c Currant teacakes

Weight of bread	Cost
40 g	£0.24
100 g	£0.60
240 g	£1.44

7 Use direct proportion to solve each of these problems.

   a 5 pears cost 82p. What is the cost of 15 pears?

   b 150 g of crisps contain 240 calories. How many calories are there in 50 g of crisps?

   c A recipe for 6 people uses 420 g of flour.

      i What weight of flour is needed for 7 people?

      ii How much flour is needed for 3 people?

   d 5 litres of water costs £1.45.

      i What is the cost of 7 litres of water?

      ii What is the cost of 17 litres of water?

8 **a** Steve and Jenny break a 120 g chocolate bar into two pieces. Steve has $\frac{3}{8}$ of the bar and Jenny has the rest. What is the ratio of Jenny's piece of the bar to Steve's piece of the bar?

   b $\frac{8}{9}$ of the people who attended a football match were men. What was the ratio of men to women at the football match?

   c Shirley and Hanif share some money. Shirley receives $\frac{2}{5}$ of the money and Hanif receives £66. How much money did Shirley and Hanif share?

9 **a** Increase £30 by 10%.   **b** Decrease 700 euros by 5%.

   c Increase 8 miles by 20%.   **d** Decrease 180° by 15%.

   e Increase 280 kg by 25%.   **f** Decrease £100 000 by 3%.

   g Increase 250 rabbits by 30%. **h** Decrease 2500 kJ by 22%.

   i Increase 70 g by 9%.   **j** Decrease £1.80 by 35%.

10 **a** Chelski football stadium has 71 440 seats. It is rebuilt with an increased seating of 15%. How many seats are there at the new stadium?

   b A jar of jam holds 370 g. It is increased in capacity by 23%. What is the new capacity of the jar? (Give your answer to the nearest gram.)

   c A memory stick normally cost £36. It is reduced in price in a sale by 17.5%. What is the sale price of the memory stick?

11 **a** Dan scores 62% in his Maths exam, $\frac{37}{60}$ in his Science exam and $\frac{29}{50}$ in his English exam. In which subject did Dan do the best?

   b Megan and Jane play tennis. Last week Megan played 7 matches and won 5 of them. Last month Jane played 20 matches and won 14 of them. Who is the better tennis player? Explain and justify your answer.

Maths Life

Daily bread

There are lots of things to think about when running a business. Here are just some of the things to consider when running a small bakery.

THE BAKERY
01234 123 456, 123 THIS ROAD

OPENING TIMES
Mon - Fri: 9:00am to 5:30pm, Sat: 9:30am to 4:00pm
Sun: Closed

PRICES
White loaf: 98p, Wholemeal: £1.20

You need to think about your sales and income

Total number of loaves sold each day

115.

Day	White	Wholemeal
Mon	78	42
Tues	84	38
Weds	102	66
Thurs	72	48
Fri	90	54
Sat	186	66
Weekly total		

Percentage of white and wholemeal loaves sold

white 66%

wholemeal 34%

Why does the pie chart show wholemeal as about 1/3?

Roughly how many white loaves are sold for every wholemeal loaf?

- How much money do the sales of the white loaf raise in the week?
- How much money do the wholemeal loaves raise in the week?
- Roughly what percentage of the income is from wholemeal bread? Why is this higher than 34%?

WHOLEMEAL LOAF:
550g wholemeal flour
200g strong white flour
2 teaspoons of yeast
2 teaspoons of salt
1.5 teaspoons of sugar
40g butter
540ml water

1. Measure and mix ingredients 5 minutes
2. Knead dough for 10 minutes
3. Leave dough to prove until dough has doubled in size – approx 60-80 minutes
4. Bake for 25-30 minutes

Complete the ready reckoner to help the trainee baker get the right quantities.

WHITE LOAF – READY RECKONER

No. of loaves	Flour (g)	Yeast (tsp)	salt (tsp)	sugar (tsp)	butter (g)	water (ml)
1	750					960
2		3		7.5		
5			20			
10						
15					600	
20						
30						

You need to think about the hours that you will need to employ people

- When should the bakers start making their first batch of wholemeal bread on Saturday in order to be ready for the shop opening?
- What is the earliest time that they could finish baking their last batch of wholemeal bread on Saturday?

REMEMBER:
Maximum capacity
= 30 loaves!!

You need to buy the ingredients

The Supermarket
SALE!!

32 KG
flour!!

- How many bags of each type of flour will the bakery use for the week's baking?

- Would the amount used be likely to change at different times of the year?

What else would you need to think about to run a bakery successfully?

12 Summary

Assessment criteria
- Use the equivalence of fractions, decimals and percentages to compare proportions **Level 6**
- Solve simple problems involving ratio and direct proportion **Level 6**
- Calculate percentages and find the outcome of a given percentage increase or decrease **Level 6**

Level 6

1 A DVD costs £12.
In the sale, the price is reduced by 18%.
Calculate the new price.

DVD
was £12
MASSIVE 18%
reduction.
You pay £

Jack's answer ✔

Jack subtracts as the price is reduced.

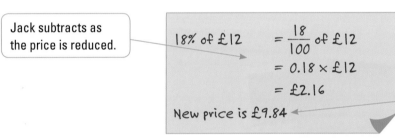

$$18\% \text{ of } £12 = \frac{18}{100} \text{ of } £12$$
$$= 0.18 \times £12$$
$$= £2.16$$
New price is £9.84

Jack could find 82% of £12 to calculate the new price.
$$82\% \text{ of } £12 = \frac{82}{100} \text{ of } £12$$
$$= 0.82 \times £12$$
$$= £9.84$$

Level 6

2 Two parts of this square design are shaded dark grey.
Two parts are shaded grey.

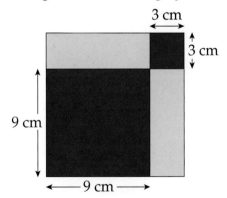

3 cm

3 cm

9 cm

9 cm

Show that the ratio of dark grey to grey is 5 : 3

Key Stage 3 2001 4–6 Paper 1

13 Algebra

Algebra

Ohm's Law is a formula describing the link between voltage, current and resistance:

V = IR

What's the point? This simple formula is used to design the electrical circuits in your house. Without it, you'd have no lights, telly, computer…

✔ Check in

1 What number should be placed in this box to make the statement correct?

   a $2 \times \square + 1 = 7$ **b** $3 \times \square - 1 = 11$

2 You get 10 euros for £7 when you go to Spain on holiday.
   How many euros will you get for
   a £14   **b** £35?

3 I think of a number, double it and add 1. My answer is 21.
   What number am I thinking of?

- Use the four basic operations and brackets
- Collect 'like terms'

Keywords

Brackets   Expression
Expand   Like terms

Five beads on a necklace each have a length x.

The total length is $x + x + x + x + x = 5 \times x = 5x$

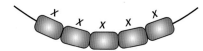

p. 66

- When **expressions** are added or subtracted, you can collect **like terms**.

Alan has x songs on his MP3 player.

Ben has 6 more than Alan.
Cerys has 2 fewer than Alan.
Altogether they have
$x + x + 6 + x - 2 = 3x + 4$ songs.

x $x + 6$ $x - 2$

Alan   Ben   Cerys

$x + x + x = 3x$ and
$6 - 2 = 4$

- Expressions can be divided by a number.

Zahir has $6x + 8$ texts on his mobile.
He deletes half of them.
He has deleted $\frac{1}{2}$ of $(6x + 8) = \dfrac{6x + 8}{2} = 3x + 4$ texts.

You **divide** each term by **2**.

p. 68

- **Brackets** can be used to multiply expressions. When you do the multiplication, you are **expanding** the brackets.

$6x + 8$

Jim has 3 bags with $x + 2$ coins in each bag.

Altogether, he has $3(x + 2) = 3x + 6$ coins.

$x + 2$ $x + 2$ $x + 2$

You **multiply** each term by **3**.

Sometimes expressions can contain more than one pair of brackets.

example

In each expression, expand the brackets and simplify.

a $4(p - 2)$ **b** $3(3n + 2m) + 2(n - 4m)$

....

a $4(p - 2) = 4 \times p - 4 \times 2$
$\qquad = 4p - 8$

b Expand the brackets first.

$3(3n + 2m) + 2(n - 4m) = 9n + 6m + 2n - 8m$
$\qquad\qquad\qquad\qquad\qquad = 11n - 2m$

Draw the curved lines to help expand the brackets.

Collect like terms so
$9n + 2n = 11n$ and
$6m - 8m = -2m$

Exercise 13a

1 Simplify these expressions.

a $x + x + x + x$ **b** $y + y + y$ **c** $z + z + z + z + z$

d $2 \times 5 \times y$ **e** $3 \times n \times 2$ **f** $3 \times 4 \times z \times z$

2 Collect like terms to simplify these expressions.

a $3x + 2y + 5x + 3y$ **b** $8m + 2n - 6m + 4n$

c $2p + 4q + 6p - q$ **d** $7y + 5z - 2y + 3z$

e $8s + 2t - 5t + 2s$ **f** $6x + 2y - 4y - 3x$

g $7c + 8 + 2c - 3$ **h** $5s + 1 - 2s - 3$

i $4x + 2y + 3 + 2x - 4y - 5$ **j** $2x - 3y + 4 + x - 2y - 5$

3 Expand these brackets.

a $3(2x + 3)$ **b** $4(3n - 2)$ **c** $2(3a - 1)$

d $7(x + 2)$ **e** $6(p - 2)$ **f** $5(3 + 2q)$

4 Expand these brackets and then simplify.
Use a number line to help you with negative signs.

a $5(3x + 2) + 2(2x + 3)$ **b** $3(2x + 4) + 2(x - 5)$

c $4(n + 3) + 3(2n - 3)$ **d** $2(3m - 4) + 3(m + 3)$

e $5(y - 2) + 2(2y + 4)$ **f** $6(2z + 1) + 2(z - 4)$

5 Divide these expressions and simplify where necessary.

a $\dfrac{4x + 6}{2}$ **b** $\dfrac{2x + 8}{2}$ **c** $\dfrac{6x + 9}{3}$

> In **e** and **f**, divide the fractions separately, then add the results.

d $\dfrac{5x - 10}{5}$ **e** $\dfrac{2x - 6}{2} + \dfrac{9 + 3x}{3}$ **f** $\dfrac{6x - 3}{3} + \dfrac{8 - 4x}{4}$

---

challenge

This pile of six bricks has expressions written on the bottom layer.

The expression to be written on a blank brick is the sum of the two bricks below it. For example, brick A has $2x + 4$ and $3x - 1$ added together.

Copy the pile and fill in all the missing expressions.

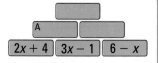

The same rules apply for this pile of bricks.

Find the three missing expressions on the blank bricks.

- Substitute integers into formulae
- Derive a formula

Keywords
Formula
Derive
Substitute

A **formula** is useful for working out quantities in real life.

example

A package holiday for A adults and C children costs £P where
$$P = 150(2A + C).$$
Find the cost of the holiday for 3 adults and 2 children.

• •

Substitute the values $A = 3$ and $C = 2$ into the formula.
$$P = 150(2 \times 3 + 2)$$
$$= 150(6 + 2)$$
$$= 150 \times 8 = 1200$$
The total cost of the holiday is £1200.

p. 70

You can create a formula if you have enough information.
This is called **deriving a formula**.

example

This pentagon has sides which are x cm
or y cm long.
Find a formula for its perimeter P.

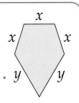

• •

The perimeter is the total length of the sides.
So, $P = y + y + x + x + x$
The formula is $P = 3x + 2y$

Collect like terms.

Sometimes you can use a formula like an equation to
solve a problem.

example

In the above example, $P = 3x + 2y$
Imagine a pentagon with perimeter 13 cm and length $x = 3$ cm.
Find the length y.

• •

$P = 13$, $x = 3$
Substituting into the formula $P = 3x + 2y$
$$13 = 3 \times 3 + 2y$$
Subtract 9 from both sides $13 = 9 + 2y$
Divide both sides by 2 $4 = 2y$
$$2 = y$$

So y is 2 cm long.

Exercise 13b

1 A book has p pages of print and g pages of glossy photographs.
The total mass m of the book is given by the formula
$m = 5p + 10g$
Find m when
  a $p = 20, g = 5$ **b** $p = 100, g = 15$ **c** $p = 42, g = 8$

2 The time, T minutes, to make a cup of tea depends on
the volume, V litres, of water in the kettle and the time,
B minutes, which the tea is allowed to brew, where
$T = 4V + B$.
Find T when
  a $V = 1, B = 2$ **b** $V = 2, B = 5$ **c** $V = 1\frac{1}{2}, B = 4$.

3 This isosceles triangle has sides x cm and
$(x + 5)$ cm long.
Find a formula for its perimeter P.
Find the value of P when $x = 6$.

4 This rectangle has sides n cm and $(n + 2)$ cm long.
Find a formula for
  a its perimeter, P
  b its area, A.
  c Use the formulae to find P and A when $n = 5$.
  d Find n when $P = 20$.

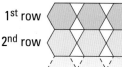

5 A patio is laid row-by-row. It uses hexagonal slabs
(h m^2 each) and triangular slabs (t m^2 each).
Write formulae for the area of
  a one row   **b** 5 rows
  c n rows.   **d** If $h = 1$ and $t = \frac{1}{4}$, find the area of 10 rows.

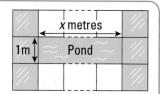

1st row

2nd row

challenge

A rectangular pond is 1 metre wide and x metres long.
Square slabs (edge 1 m) are laid around the pond.
The end slabs are coloured.
Find a formula for the total number x of slabs needed.
Build the formula on a computer spreadsheet for many
different values of x.
Repeat for a pond which is 2 metres wide.

• Construct and solve linear equations

Keywords
Equation
Inverse operation

You can picture an **equation** as a balance.
This balance can be written as the
equation $2x + 1 = 7$

You use **inverse operations** to solve equations.

example

Solve   **a** $2x + 1 = 7$ **b** $\frac{x}{3} - 1 = 4$

a $2x + 1 = 7$

Subtract 1 from both sides. $2x = 6$

Divide both sides by 2. $x = 3$

The solution is $x = 3$.

b $\frac{x}{3} - 1 = 4$

Add 1 to both sides. $\frac{x}{3} = 5$

Multiply both sides by 3. $x = 15$

The solution is $x = 15$.

> You do the same thing to both sides to keep the **balance.**

• The unknown letter may be on both sides of the equation.

example

Solve $5x - 1 = 4x + 13$.

                       $5x - 1 = 4x + 13$

Subtract 4x from both sides. $x - 1 = 13$

Add 1 to both sides. $x = 14$

The solution is $x = 14$.

> $5x - 4x = x$ and $4x - 4x = 0$
> $-1 + 1 = 0$ and $13 + 1 = 14$

Some equations are less straightforward.

example

Solve   **a** $4x = 5x - 13$ **b** $6x = 24 - 2x$

a There are more x's on the right. So, write the equation the other way round.

              $5x - 13 = 4x$

Add 13 to both sides. $5x = 4x + 13$

Subtract 4x from both sides. $x = 13$

The solution is $x = 13$.

b There is a negative number of x's on the right.

                 $6x = 24 - 2x$

Add 2x to both sides. $8x = 24$

Divide both sides by 8. $x = 3$

The solution is $x = 3$.

Exercise 13c

1 Solve these equations using two inverse operations.

a $2x + 1 = 9$	**b** $2x + 7 = 19$	**c** $3x + 7 = 13$
d $5x + 8 = 23$	**e** $4x - 3 = 5$	**f** $10x - 3 = 27$
g $2x - 5 = 9$	**h** $2x + 1 = 8$	**i** $3x + 2 = 11$
j $3x - 5 = 13$	**k** $2x + 3 = 8$	**l** $6x - 7 = 5$
m $\frac{x}{2} + 8 = 13$	**n** $\frac{x}{2} - 4 = 2$	**o** $\frac{x}{4} - 1 = 2$
p $\frac{x}{5} + 9 = 12$	**q** $32 = 6x + 11$	**r** $78 = 5x - 22$
s $71 = 6x + 8$	**t** $7 = \frac{x}{3} + 2$	

> Careful – some contain fractions.

2 Solve these equations which have unknowns on both sides.

a $6x + 3 = 4x + 11$	**b** $7x - 3 = 5x + 11$	**c** $8x + 3 = x + 24$
d $8x - 7 = 6x + 3$	**e** $7x + 2 = 2x + 27$	**f** $5x - 11 = 3x + 1$
g $4x - 6 = 2x$	**h** $4x - 3 = 2x - 3$	**i** $7x = 5x + 17$
j $6x - 1 = 4x + 6$	**k** $5x + 8 = 3x + 3$	**l** $8x + 7 = 5x + 3$
m $2x = 9x - 21$	**n** $2x + 1 = 7 - x$	**o** $x = 20 - 4x$

3 Solve these equations. The solutions involve fractions or negative numbers.

a $x + 7 = 6$	**b** $x + 4 = 1$	**c** $2x + 6 = 2$
d $2x + 1 = 6$	**e** $2x + 3 = 10$	**f** $4x - 1 = 8$
g $3x + 8 = 2$	**h** $5x + 12 = 2$	**i** $2x + 8 = 0$
j $2x - 4 = 1$	**k** $4x - 5 = 8$	**l** $4x + 6 = 1$

4 I think of a number x.

If I subtract the number from 16, I get the number itself.

Find the value of x.

> In questions 4 and 5, try to construct an equation to solve.

5 I think of a number n.

If I double it and add 12, I get the same answer as if I treble it and add 2.

Find the value of n.

---

challenge

In this triangle, the number in each square is found by adding the two numbers in the corner circles on either side of it.

a Find expressions to write in the two empty circles.

b Write an equation in x and find the value of x.

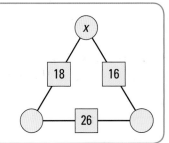

* Solve equations involving brackets and directed numbers

Brackets often occur in equations.

 It is usually best to expand them first.

---

example

Solve $3(5x - 2) = 2(7x + 2)$

$$3(5x - 2) = 2(7x + 2)$$

Expand the brackets. $15x - 6 = 14x + 4$

Subtract $14x$ from both sides. $x - 6 = 4$

Add 6 to both sides. $x = 10$

The solution is $x = 10$.

You need to be careful with negative signs.

Use the rules for multiplying positive and negative numbers.

---

example

Solve $4(3x - 2) - 2(4x - 5) = 26$.

$$4(3x - 2) - 2(4x - 5) = 26$$

Expand the brackets. $12x - 8 - 8x + 10 = 26$

Collect like terms. $4x + 2 = 26$

Subtract 2 from both sides $4x = 24$

Divide both sides by 4. $x = 6$

The solution is $x = 6$.

Check your solution by substituting into the original equation:

$$\text{LHS} = 4(3 \times 6 - 2) - 2(4 \times 6 - 5)$$
$$= 4(18 - 2) - 2(24 - 5)$$
$$= 4 \times 16 - 2 \times 19$$
$$= 64 - 38$$
$$= 26$$

$\text{RHS} = 26$. It checks. ✓

Use curved lines over the brackets.
Note that $4 \times -2 = -8$ and $-2 \times -5 = +10$
When you collect like terms $12x - 8x = 4x$ and $-8 + 10 = +2$

Exercise 13d

1 Solve these equations.

   a $2(x + 5) = 26$ **b** $3(x + 4) = 18$ **c** $2(4x + 3) = 22$

   d $3(2x + 1) = 33$ **e** $3(2x - 1) = 33$ **f** $6(2x - 3) = 42$

   g $5(x - 4) = 10$ **h** $6(4x + 1) = 18$ **i** $5(2x - 1) = 10$

2 Solve these equations.

   a $3(3x + 1) = 2(4x + 6)$ **b** $2(5x + 2) = 4(2x + 3)$

   c $7(x + 1) = 4(x + 4)$ **d** $5(2x - 1) = 3(3x + 4)$

   e $3(6x + 5) = 4(4x + 5)$ **f** $5(2x + 3) = 3(3x + 5)$

   g $4(3x - 2) = 2(5x + 7)$ **h** $6(3x + 6) = 4(5x - 2)$

   i $2(1 + 4x) = 10x - 5$

3 Solve these equations. Collect like terms after expanding the brackets.

   a $3(2x + 1) + 2(4x + 2) = 35$ **b** $2(x + 3) + 3(x + 1) = 24$

   c $5(2x + 3) + 2(5x + 1) = 37$ **d** $2(4x + 3) + 3(2x - 1) = 31$

   e $4(3x - 2) + 8(x + 1) = 100$ **f** $5(2x - 1) + 2(x + 5) = 5$

   g $6(x + 2) + 4(3 - x) = 30$ **h** $5(1 + 4x) - 2(6 - 2x) = 5$

4 Solve these equations. Remember how to multiply positive and negative numbers.

   a $2(3x + 1) - 3(x + 2) = 2$ **b** $5(2x + 3) - 3(3x - 2) = 22$

   c $4(2x - 3) + 2(x - 4) = 10$ **d** $3(4x - 2) + 5(x - 1) = 23$

   e $8(2x - 1) - 3(5x - 3) = 1$ **f** $6(2x - 2) - 3(2x - 3) = 3$

   g $4(3x + 2) + 3(2 - 3x) = 20$ **h** $7(x + 3) + 2(3 - 4x) = 27$

5 Solve these equations.

   a $4x = 18 - 2x$ **b** $6x = 14 - x$ **c** $2x + 3 = 19 - 2x$

   d $6x = 2(15 - 2x)$ **e** $4x - 11 = 3(1 - x)$ **f** $3(2x - 4) = 2(2 - x)$

   g $4 + 2(4x - 7) = 3x$ **h** $3 - 2(5 - 2x) = 5$ **i** $2x - 3(5 - x) = 10$

6 I think of a number. I add 3 to it and then treble the total. My final answer is 36. Find the number.

> In questions 6 and 7, try to construct an equation to solve.

7 I think of a number. I subtract it from 20 and then double what is left. My final answer is 18. Find the number.

---

challenge

In this diagram, a number in a square equals the sum of the numbers in the two circles on either side of the square. Find the expressions (using x) that should be written inside circles A and B.

Write an equation for circle C and so find the value of x.

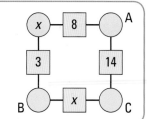

• Draw the graphs of linear functions

Keywords
Equation
Function

This **function** machine shows
the rule *'double and add 3'*

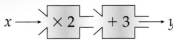

$x \longrightarrow \boxed{\times 2} \longrightarrow \boxed{+3} \longrightarrow y$

The function can be written as an **equation**
$y = 2x + 3$.
You can substitute values for x and find
values for y.

p. 102 Now you can draw the
graph of the equation.

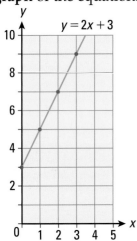

$y = 2x + 3$

These values can be put into a **table**:

x	0	1	2	3
y	3	5	7	9

The values give the **coordinates**
$(0, 3), (1, 5), (2, 7), (3, 9)$

---

example

Draw the graph of $y = 6 - x$, using values of x from 0 to 6.

When $x = 0$, $y = 6 - 0 = 6$ When $x = 2$, $y = 6 - 2 = 4$
When $x = 4$, $y = 6 - 4 = 2$ When $x = 6$, $y = 6 - 6 = 0$

You only really need three
points to draw a straight-
line graph – two to draw
the line, and a third to
check.

The coordinates are $(0, 6)$, $(2, 4)$,
$(4, 2)$ and $(6, 0)$

x	0	2	4	6
y	6	4	2	0

You can use these points to draw
the graph.

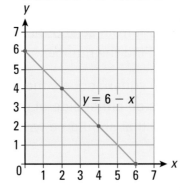

$y = 6 - x$

Exercise 13e

1 For each of these equations, copy and complete this table.

x	0	1	2	3	4
y					

Plot points for each equation on axes labelled as here.

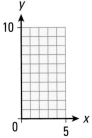

Draw the graph of each equation.

a $y = x + 1$ **b** $y = x - 1$
c $y = 2x + 1$ **d** $y = 2x - 2$
e $y = 8 - x$ **f** $y = 4 - x$

> Use a number line to help you with negative numbers.

> Remember that $2x + 1$ means 'double x and then add 1'.

2 Without drawing any diagrams, find whether each point lies on the given line.

a $(1, 6)$ and $y = x + 5$ **b** $(8, 6)$ and $y = x - 2$
c $(3, 9)$ and $y = 2x + 3$ **d** $(5, 15)$ and $y = 2x - 5$
e $(0, 10)$ and $y = 8x + 2$ **f** $(3, 4)$ and $x + y = 7$

3 In a science experiment, the temperature $y°C$ of a beaker of water is gradually reduced from room temperature over a time of t minutes, as given by

$$y = 20 - \tfrac{1}{2}t.$$

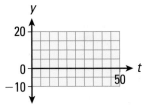

Copy and complete the table and draw the graph of y against t.

The first value is done for you.

a How many minutes does it take for the temperature to fall to $5°C$?
b After how long does ice begin to form?
c What is room temperature?

Time, t mins	0	10	20	30	40	50
Temperature, $y°C$	20					

---

challenge

Use a computer spreadsheet to create a table of values for $y = 2x + 9$.

Use computer software to draw the graph of $y = 2x + 9$ from your spreadsheet.

	A	B
1	x	y
2	0	= 2 * A2 + 9
3	= A2 + 1	= 2 * A3 + 9
4	= A3 + 1	= 2 * A4 + 9
5	= A4 + 1	= 2 * A5 + 9

13e² Equation of a straight line

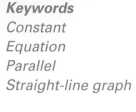

• Recognise the equation of a straight line

Keywords
Constant
Equation
Parallel
Straight-line graph

You can tell what a **straight-line graph** looks like from its **equation**.

p. 104

If x is **constant** (e.g. $x = 4$), the line is parallel to the y-axis.

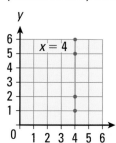

If y is constant (e.g. $y = 3$), the line is parallel to the x-axis.

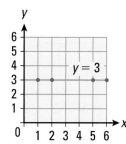

If the equation has both x and y, the line slopes up or down.

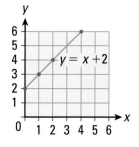

---

example

Draw the graphs of the lines

a $x = 3$ **b** $y = 4$ **c** $y = x - 2$

. . . .

a The line $x = 3$ has points $(3, 0)$, $(3, 1)$, $(3, 2)$ and is parallel to the y-axis.

b The line $y = 4$ has points $(1, 4)$, $(2, 4)$, $(3, 4)$ and is parallel to the x-axis.

c The line $y = x - 2$ has this table of values

x	0	1	2	3
y	-2	-1	0	1

giving the points $(0, -2)$, $(1, -1)$, $(2, 0)$, $(3, 1)$.

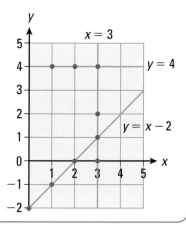

• Straight-line graphs have an equation that can be written in the form $y = mx + c$ where m and c are numbers.

Examples are:
$$y = 2x + 3 \qquad (m = 2, c = 3)$$
$$y = 3x - 4 \qquad (m = 3, c = -4)$$
$$y = x + 1 \qquad (m = 1, c = 1)$$
$$y = -2x + 2 \qquad (m = -2, c = 2)$$
$$y = 4x \qquad (m = 4, c = 0)$$

Exercise 13e²

1 a Copy and complete the table for the equation $y = 2x + 3$.

x	0	1	2	3
y				

b Then draw its graph. Label the x axis from 0 to 4, and the y axis from 0 to 10.

2 a Copy and complete the table for the equations $y = 3x - 2$.

x	0	1	2	3
y				

b Then draw its graph. Label the x axis from 0 to 4, and the y axis from -3 to 8.

3 Without first completing a table, draw the graphs of these equations.

   a $x = 2$ **b** $y = 5$ **c** $x = -2$ **d** $y = 0$

4 For each equation, state whether its graph is:

   i a horizontal straight line   **iii** a sloping straight line
   ii a vertical straight line   **iv** not a straight line

> You do not need to draw the graphs.

   a $x = 4$ **b** $y = -3$ **c** $y = 2x$ **d** $y = 2x^2 + 1$

5 Match the equations to the graphs.
Which is the odd equation out?

$y = x + 1$
$y = 1$
$x = -1$
$y = 2x - 3$
$y = 2x - 2$

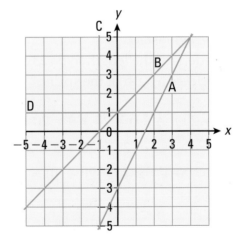

• Interpret and draw linear real-life graphs

Keywords
Conversion graph
Real-life graph

Graphs can be drawn to describe **real-life** situations.
Some real-life graphs are straight lines.

example

Janina goes to the shop for her mother.
This graph describes her journey.
a How far away is the shop?
b How long did it take Janina to get there?
c How long did she spend at the shop?
d Was she faster going or coming back?

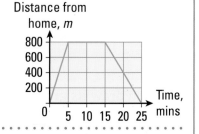

Distance from home, *m*

a The shop is 800 metres away.
b She took 5 minutes to get there.
c She spent $15 - 5 = 10$ minutes at the shop.
d She took $25 - 15 = 10$ minutes to come back. So, she was faster going to the shop.

Graphs can be useful across the whole curriculum.

example

In a Science lesson, the length L cm of a spring is increased
by adding masses of M kg to one end so that $L = 20 + \frac{1}{4}M$.
a Draw a graph of L against M.
b What mass is needed for the length to be 23 cm?
c What is the *unstretched* length of the spring?

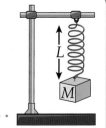

a When $M = 0$, $L = 20 + \frac{1}{4} \times 0 = 20 + 0 = 20$

When $M = 20$, $L = 20 + \frac{1}{4} \times 20 = 20 + 5 = 25$

When $M = 40$, $L = 20 + \frac{1}{4} \times 40 = 20 + 10 = 30$ and so on.
The table of values is

Mass, *M* kg	0	20	40	60	80

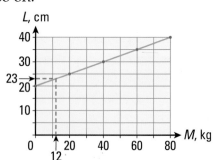

The table gives five points which are plotted
to draw a graph.
b From the graph, $L = 23$ gives $M = 12$.
A mass of 12 kg is needed.
c When the spring is unstretched, $M = 0$ and $L = 20$. The unstretched length is 20 cm.

Exercise 13f

1 This graph converts US dollars ($) to pounds sterling (£).
How many pounds do you get for
a $10 **b** $8 **c** $5?
How many dollars do you get for
d £3 **e** £3.50 **f** £2.50?
g Find the missing number where *dollars = ☐ × pounds.*

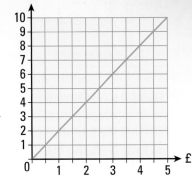

2 This flow diagram approximately converts kilometres
to miles.

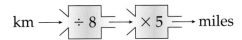

$$km \longrightarrow \boxed{\div 8} \longrightarrow \boxed{\times 5} \longrightarrow miles$$

Copy and complete this table.

Kilometres	8	16	24	40	44	48
Miles						

Use your table to draw a **conversion graph** on axes as
shown here.
Use your graph to change
a 30 km into miles **b** 20 miles into km.

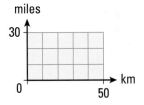

3 This graph describes Peter's walk from his home to the fish
shop and back.
  a How far is it from home to the fish shop?
  b How long does it take Peter to get there?
  c How long does Peter have to wait at the fish shop?
  d How long does it take Peter to come home?
  e Can you give a good reason why he gets
  home more quickly?

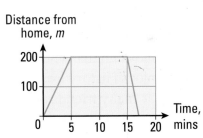

Find the Highway Code on the Internet.
Research stopping distances for cars travelling at different speeds.
a Plot a graph of stopping distance against speed.
b How could you illustrate thinking distance and braking distance
  on your graph?

research

• Draw and interpret non-linear real-life graphs.

Keywords
Interpret
Real-life
Sketch

Real-life graphs may be **sketched** rather than accurately drawn, often without scales on the axes. You need to be able to **interpret** a graph which is given to you.

example

An office uses heating oil which is stored in a tank. This graph shows the level of oil in the tank during one week.
Describe the heating arrangements for the week.

Oil level

M T W Th F S Su → Days

On Monday, Wednesday and Friday, the level stays steady and no oil is used. So there is no heating in the office.
There is also no heating on Saturday and Sunday.
On Tuesday, the level drops sharply. The heating is on.
On Thursday, the level drops less sharply. The heating is on but not fully on.
Late on Friday, the level rises quickly. There is a delivery of oil.

You need to be able to sketch a graph using given information.

example

Sarah enjoys school for most of the time.
Today she has these five lessons, with a short morning break and 45 minutes for lunch.

Lesson	9 a.m.– 10 a.m.	10 a.m.– 11 a.m.	11.15 a.m.– 12.15 p.m.	1 p.m.–2 p.m.	2 p.m.–3 p.m.
Subject	French	History	Mathematics	English	Science

She enjoys English and Science most. She quite enjoys French and Mathematics.
She enjoys History least.
She has many friends and thoroughly enjoys the two breaks in the day.
At the end of the day, she takes an hour to travel home in heavy traffic.
Sketch a graph which shows her level of enjoyment from 9 a.m. to 4 p.m.

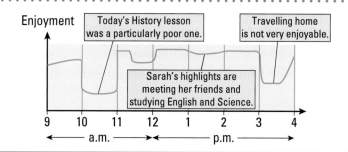

Enjoyment

Today's History lesson was a particularly poor one.

Travelling home is not very enjoyable.

Sarah's highlights are meeting her friends and studying English and Science.

9 10 11 12 1 2 3 4
← a.m. → ← p.m. →

Exercise 13g

1 **a** A baby is born and her weight is measured.
This graph shows changes in her weight over 8 weeks.
Describe these changes by writing a few sentences.

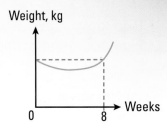

Weight, kg

Weeks

0   8

b As the baby grows into an adult, her weight changes over the years. Describe the changes which take place over 20 years.

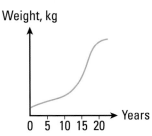

Weight, kg

Years

0 5 10 15 20

2 Jim went on a bike ride lasting 5 hours.
This graph shows his speed during the ride.
Describe his journey.

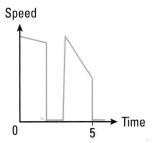

Speed

Time

0   5

3 These two graphs, P and Q, show the brightness of
  a a car's indicator when it is turning a corner
  b a security light which turns on when someone walks by.

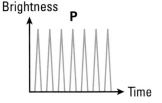

Brightness **P**

Time

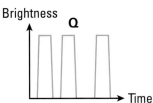

Brightness **Q**

Time

Match P and Q to **a** and **b**.
Write your reasons for deciding which is which.

4 Maria goes on foot to her grandma's house.
She sets off running fast but she gradually tires.
Suddenly she stops at a road and waits a short time until it is safe to cross.
She then walks steadily to reach her grandma's.
Sketch a graph of her speed against the time that she takes.

challenge

David records his heart rate (in beats per minute) during a race.
Sketch a graph of his heart rate over time and describe your graph in words.

Take account of
  • waiting and warming-up
  • changes of speed
  • stopping to tie a shoe lace
  • the last lap.

- Find the gradient of a straight line
- Find the midpoint of a straight line

Keywords
Gradient
Midpoint
Steepness

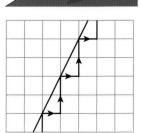

When you travel uphill by car or bus, you say the road is steep. You can measure the **steepness** by finding the **gradient** of the road.

A **sloping** line on a grid also has a gradient.

Draw a staircase on the line with each step going 1 square horizontally. The gradient is the number of squares that each step goes up or down.

- A **rising** line has a **positive** gradient.
  A **falling** line has a **negative** gradient.

---

example

Find the gradient of these two lines, AB and CD.

Line AB has a gradient of 2.
Line CD has a gradient of -3.

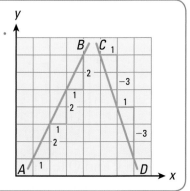

On these axes, the line PQ joins point P to point Q.
P is the point $(3, 1)$ and Q is the point $(7, 5)$.
The **midpoint** M is halfway between P and Q.

The coordinates of M are $\left(\dfrac{3 + 7}{2}, \dfrac{1 + 5}{2}\right) = \left(\dfrac{10}{2}, \dfrac{6}{2}\right) = (5, 3)$

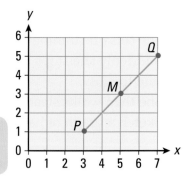

- In general, for points $P(a, b)$ and $Q(c, d)$, the midpoint M is $\left(\dfrac{a + c}{2}, \dfrac{b + d}{2}\right)$.

---

example

Find the midpoint M of the points $E(6, 5)$ and $F(0, -1)$ without drawing in a diagram.

The midpoint M is $\left(\dfrac{6 + 0}{2}, \dfrac{5 + (-1)}{2}\right) = \left(\dfrac{6}{2}, \dfrac{4}{2}\right) = (3, 2)$

Exercise 13h

1 Write down the gradient of these five sloping lines.

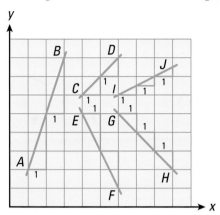

2 Imagine a staircase of steps on each of the lines *KL*, *MN*, *PQ* and *RS*.
Find the gradient of each line.

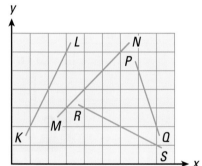

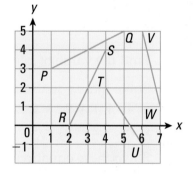

3 Write the coordinates of the midpoint *M* of
   a line *PQ*   **b** line *RS*   **c** line *TU*   **d** line *VW*.

4 Calculate the midpoints of the lines *AB* and *PQ*.

5 Without drawing a diagram, find the midpoints of the
lines joining these pairs of points.
   a (2, 1), (8, 7)   **b** (3, 2), (7, 4)   **c** (8, 1), (0, 5)
   d (6, 0), (2, 5)   **e** (12, 41), (18, 19) **f** (12, 6), (-2, 0)
   g (-1, 8), (5, -2)   **h** (9, 7), (-1, -2)

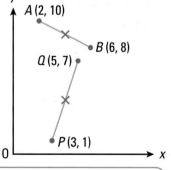

- *M* is the midpoint of *AB*. If *M* is the point (7, -1) and *B* is the point (8, 4), find the point *A*.
- On axes labelled from 0 to 8, draw two lines from the point (4, 6) to the x-axis with gradients of 2 and -2. Join their midpoints. What shape have you drawn?

13a

1 Simplify
a $y + y + y + y$　　　　**b** $y \times y \times y \times y$
c $3 \times 5 \times y$　　　　**d** $3 \times 5 \times y \times y$

2 Simplify by collecting like terms
a $2x + 3y + 4x + 5y$　　**b** $5p + 2q + 3p - 3q$　　**c** $3z + 4 + z - 6$

3 Expand and simplify
a $3(2x + 4) + 4(x + 2)$　　**b** $5(y + 3) + 2(3y - 7)$
c $2(4 - 2y) + 3(3y - 1)$　　**d** $3(x + 4) + 2(3 - 2x)$

13b

4 Find the values of R, S, T and U when $x = 4$, $y = 2$ and $z = 5$.
$$R = 2(x + 3y) \qquad S = y(2z - x) \qquad T = \frac{4z + 2x}{y} \qquad U = z(x^2 + y^2)$$

5 A rectangle is x cm long and $x - 3$ cm wide.
Find a formula for　**a** its area, A
　　　　　　　　　b its perimeter, P.
Use the formulae to find A and P when $x = 5$.

x cm

$x - 3$ cm

13c

6 Find the value of x in this balance.

7 Solve these equations with unknowns on both sides.
a $4x + 1 = 2x + 9$　　**b** $6x + 2 = 2x + 14$
c $8x - 2 = 6x + 4$　　**d** $7x - 2 = 4x + 7$

8 Solve these equations. Take care with the fractions.
a $2x + 5 = 8$　　　　**b** $4x - 1 = 8$　　　　**c** $\frac{x}{2} + 2 = 7$

13d

9 Solve these equations.
a $2(3x + 2) = 22$　　**b** $3(4x + 1) = 15$　　**c** $4(2x - 1) = 20$
d $2(5x + 1) = 3(3x + 2)$　　**e** $3(4x + 3) = 2(5x + 8)$　　**f** $4(3x - 2) = 2(4x + 2)$

10 Expand the brackets and solve the equations.
a $5(x + 2) + 3(x + 4) = 30$　　**b** $4(2x + 1) + 3(2x + 3) = 41$
c $3(2x - 1) + 2(4x + 3) = 31$　　**d** $2(3x - 2) + 4(x + 1) = 50$

11 I think of a number. I subtract it from 2 and then treble what is left.
My final answer is 18. Find the number.

12 For each of these equations, copy and complete this table.

x	0	1	2	3	4
y					

Plot points for each equation on axes, both labelled from -2 to 8.
Draw the graph of each equation and label it.

a $y = x + 1$ **b** $y = x - 1$ **c** $y = 2x - 1$ **d** $y = 8 - x$

13 Label both axes from 0 to 10. Draw the graphs of these lines

a $x = 6$ **b** $y = 5$ **c** $y = x + 1$ **d** $y = 2x$

14 a You can convert euros € into pounds £ with this formula: $£ = \dfrac{3 \times €}{4}$.

€	0	8	12	20
£				

Copy and complete this table using the formula.

b Draw a graph to convert euros to pounds, with both axes labelled from 0 to 20.

    i How many pounds will you get for €16?

    ii How many euros will you get for £3?

15 Khaleda walks the 500 m to the shop in 5 minutes. She spends 3 minutes in the shop and then returns home the same way in 2 minutes.

a Draw a graph to show her visit to the shop on axes as shown here.

b What was her speed (in metres per minute) going from home to shop?

Distance, m

500

0   10   Time, min

16 Sam heats some soup in the microwave for 2 minutes. He takes it out and finds it is not warm enough. He straightaway reheats it for another minute and then leaves it for a further minute before starting to eat it.

Sketch a graph of the temperature of the soup during this time.

17 Draw axes and label both from 0 to 8.
Find the gradient of the line through each of these pairs of points.

a (2, 1), (3, 3)   **b** (1, 3), (2, 6)   **c** (1, 2), (4, 5)   **d** (4, 5), (6, 1)

e (4, 6), (6, 4)   **f** (4, 0), (6, 1)   **g** (6, 1), (8, 7)   **h** (1, 7), (5, 7)

13 Summary

Assessment criteria

- Interpret graphs arising from real situations **Level 6**
- Recognise that $y = mx + c$ represents a straight-line graph **Level 6**

Level 5

1 A restaurant decides to charge for food depending on the weight of the food.

The price is calculated using the formula $p = \frac{1}{2}w + 50$ where p is the price in pence and w is the weight of the food in grams.

a Calculate the price of food weighing 200 g.

b If the price of the food is £3, what was the weight of the food?

Jalen's answer ✔

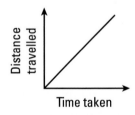

$$a \quad p \quad = \frac{1}{2}w + 50$$
$$= \frac{1}{2} \times 200 + 50$$
$$= 150 \text{ pence or } £1.50$$
$$b \quad p \quad = \frac{1}{2}w + 50$$
$$300 = \frac{1}{2}w + 50$$
$$250 = \frac{1}{2}w$$
$$w \quad = 500 \text{ g}$$

Jalen substitutes $w = 200$ into the equation.

He changes £3 into 300p.

He subtracts 50 from both sides of the equation.

Jalen multiplies both sides of the equation by 2.

Level 6

2 I went for a walk.

The distance-time graph shows information about my walk.

Identify the statement below that describes my walk.

(graph: Distance travelled vs Time taken, showing a straight diagonal line)

A I was walking faster and faster.

B I was walking slower and slower.

C I was walking north-east.

D I was walking at a steady speed.

E I was walking uphill.

Key Stage 3 2002 4–6 Paper 2

14 Geometry

Construction and 3-D shapes

Triangles are used in many structures.
They are used because they form strong
rigid shapes.

What's the point? If structures are not
strong enough they will collapse and
injure people.

✓ Check in

Level 5

1 Measure these angles with a protractor.

a

b

c

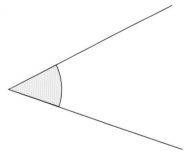

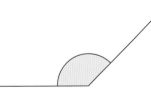

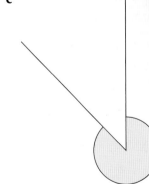

2 Calculate the unknown lengths of these rectangles.

a

6 cm

?

Area = 108 cm²

b

?

8 m

Area = 36 m²

c

?

28 cm

Area = 420 cm²

- Use a ruler and a protractor to construct triangles accurately

Keywords
Congruent   Ruler
Construct   Triangle
Protractor

You can **construct** a **triangle** using a **ruler** and a **protractor**.
You always construct **congruent** triangles, when you are given

> Congruent means the same shape and the same size.

p. 80

either

- two angles and the included side (ASA)

or

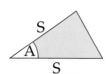

- two sides and the included angle (SAS)

> Included means 'in between'.

example

Construct the triangle *ABC*.

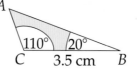

> This is ASA.

a

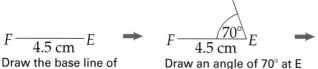

Draw the base line of 3.5 cm using a ruler.

Draw an angle of 110° at C using a protractor.

Draw an angle of 20° at B using a protractor to complete the triangle.

example

a Construct the triangle *DEF*.
b Measure the angle *D*.

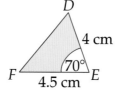

> This is SAS.

a

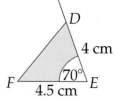

Draw the base line of 4.5 cm using a ruler.

Draw an angle of 70° at E using a protractor.

Mark D at 4 cm from E and draw FD to complete the triangle.

b Measuring angle *D* gives 60°.

Exercise 14a

1 Construct these triangles.
State the mathematical name of each triangle.

a
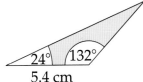
24° 132°
5.4 cm

b
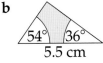
54° 36°
5.5 cm

c
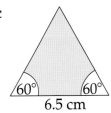
60° 60°
6.5 cm

2 Construct these triangles.
Measure the unknown length in each triangle.

a
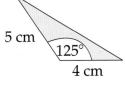
5 cm
125°
4 cm

b
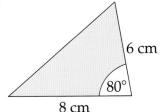
6 cm
80°
8 cm

c
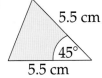
5.5 cm
45°
5.5 cm

3 Calculate the third angle and then construct each triangle.

a
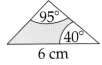
95°
40°
6 cm

b
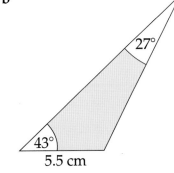
27°
43°
5.5 cm

c
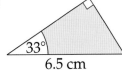
33°
6.5 cm

> Remember: Angles in a triangle add to 180°.

4 A field is in the shape of a triangle.
  a Using a scale of 1 millimetre represents 1 metre, construct an accurate scale drawing of the field.
  b Calculate the smallest length of fencing that is needed to enclose the field.

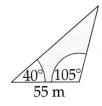
40° 105°
55 m

activity

  a Construct this parallelogram.
  b Measure the lengths of the diagonals.

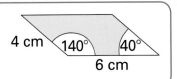
4 cm 140° 40°
6 cm

- Use a ruler and compasses to construct triangles and quadrilaterals accurately

Keywords
Compasses
Congruent
Construct

You can **construct** a triangle using a ruler and **compasses**.

If you know all three lengths, there is only one triangle that you can draw.

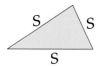 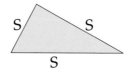

- You always construct **congruent** triangles, when you are given the length of all three sides (SSS).

Congruent means the same shape and the same size.

p. 86

example

a Construct the triangle *ABC*.
b Measure the angles *A*, *B* and *C*.

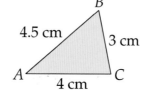

This is SSS. Do not rub out the construction lines.

a

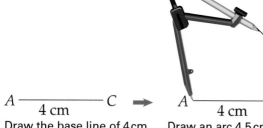

Draw the base line of 4 cm using a ruler.

Draw an arc 4.5 cm from *A* using compasses.

Draw an arc 3 cm from *C*. Draw *AB* and *CB* to complete the triangle.

b Measuring angle *A* = 41°, angle *B* = 60.5° and angle *C* = 78.5°.

You can construct some quadrilaterals by constructing two triangles.

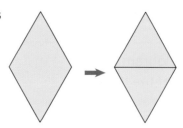

Exercise 14b

1 Construct these triangles, using ruler and compasses. Measure the angles in each triangle and check that the total is 180°.

a

55 mm   55 mm

55 mm

b

4.5 cm   7.5 cm

4.5 cm

c

7 cm   5 cm

6 cm

2 Construct these quadrilaterals using ruler and compasses. What is the mathematical name of each quadrilateral?

a

3 cm   3 cm

6 cm

5 cm   5 cm

b

45 mm   45 mm

60 mm

45 mm   45 mm

c

3 cm   5 cm

6 cm

5 cm   3 cm

3 A teacher asks the students to construct a triangle *ABC* so that angle *A* = 55°, angle *B* = 80° and angle *C* = 45°.
Each child constructs their triangle correctly and all the angles are drawn accurately.
However all the triangles are not identical.

Explain why this is possible.

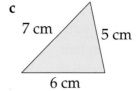

4 A triangle with lengths 3 cm, 4 cm and 5 cm is regarded as special.
a Using compasses, construct this triangle.
b State the type of the triangle.

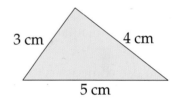

activity

Using compasses, construct these nets of solids.
All the dimensions are in centimetres.
Cut out each net and make the solid.
What is the mathematical name of each solid?

a
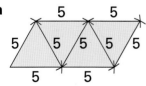

b
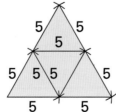

c
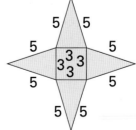

- Use ruler and compasses to construct
  - angle bisectors
  - perpendicular bisectors of lines

Keywords
Angle bisector
Bisect
Compasses
Perpendicular
Perpendicular bisector

To **bisect** an angle, you cut the angle exactly in half.

To bisect a line, you cut the line exactly in half.

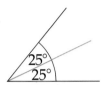

The green line bisects the angle of 50°.

The green line bisects the horizontal line.

You use **compasses** to construct an **angle bisector**.

Do not rub out construction lines.

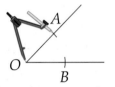

Use compasses to draw equal **arcs** on each line.

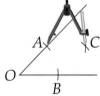

Draw equal arcs from *A* and *B* that intersect at *C*.

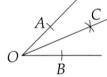

Draw a line from *O* to *C* and beyond.

angle *AOC* = angle *COB*

- **Perpendicular** means 'at right angles'.

You use compasses to construct the **perpendicular bisector** of a line.

Draw equal arcs from *A* and *B* above and below the line.

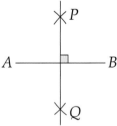

Draw a line from *P* to *Q*.

AX = *XB*

PQ is perpendicular to *AB* and bisects *AB*.
So *PQ* is the perpendicular bisector.

Exercise 14c

1 Draw these angles using a protractor.
Using compasses, construct the angle bisectors.
Use a protractor to check your answers.
   a 80°   **b** 110°   **c** 96°   **d** 56°

2 a Draw a line *AB*, so that *AB* = 8 cm.
   b Using compasses, construct the perpendicular bisector of *AB*.
   c Check that this line **i** is perpendicular to *AB*
                               ii bisects *AB*.

3 a Use a protractor and ruler to draw a 5 cm by 8 cm rectangle.
   b Construct the perpendicular bisector of each side.
   c Draw the lines of symmetry for the rectangle.

4 a Draw a large triangle.
   b Using compasses, construct the angle bisector for each of the three angles.
   c Draw a circle inside the triangle using the point of intersection as the centre.
      The circle should just touch the sides of the triangle.

5 The diagram shows the construction of the angle bisector of the angle *AOB*.
   a State the mathematical names of the shapes *OACB*, *OAC* and *OBC*.
   b Explain why the construction gives the angle bisector.

Did you know?

You can create optical illusions using perpendicular lines.

Which line is longer, *AB* or *CD*?

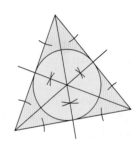

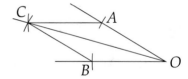

Draw a horizontal line *AB* = 10 cm.
Using compasses, construct the perpendicular bisector of *AB*.
O is the point of intersection.
Draw *CD* = 10 cm, so that *CO* = *OD* = 5 cm.
Find the centres and draw the five circles.

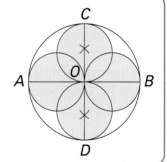

- Use ruler and compasses to construct the perpendiculars
  - from a point to a line
  - from a point on a line.

Keywords
Compasses
Construct
Perpendicular

The shortest distance from a point to a line is the **perpendicular** distance.

You use **compasses** to **construct** a perpendicular from a point to a line.

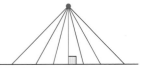

The shortest distance is the red line.

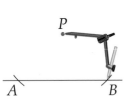

Use compasses to draw equal arcs from P on the line.

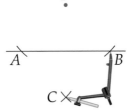

Draw equal arcs from A and B that intersect at C.

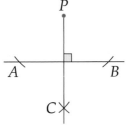

Draw a line from P through C.

Do not rub out construction lines.

You use compasses to construct a perpendicular from a point on a line.

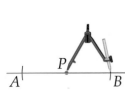

Use compasses to draw equal arcs from P on the line.

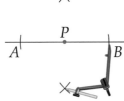

Draw equal arcs from A and B above and below the line.

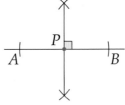

Draw a line through the points of intersection of the arcs.

Do not rub out construction lines.

example

Measure the shortest distance from the point P to the line AB.

P

A ——————— B

First construct the perpendicular from P to the line AB.

Then measure the length PX.

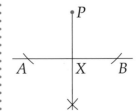

Exercise 14c²

1 Draw a line AB, with a point P above the line.
Using compasses, construct the perpendicular to AB that
passes through the point P and meets AB at X.
Measure the angle PXB.

2 Draw a line AB so that $AB = 10$ cm.
Mark the point P so that $AP = 6$ cm.
Construct the perpendicular to AB that passes through the
point P.

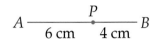

3 A straight line passes through the points
$(0, 0)$, $(2, 1)$ and $(4, 2)$.
a Draw the diagram on square grid paper.
b Construct the perpendicular from the point $(2, 4)$ to
the line.
c Measure the shortest distance from $(2, 4)$ to the line.

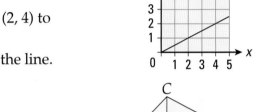

4 Draw a line AB so that $AB = 9$ cm.
Mark the point P on AB so that $AP = 3$ cm.
Construct the perpendicular to AB passing through P.
Mark the points C and D on the perpendicular so that
$PC = PD = 3$ cm.
Join the points A, C, B and D to form a quadrilateral.
a State the mathematical name of the shape $ACBD$.
b Use a protractor to measure the angles A, B, C and D.

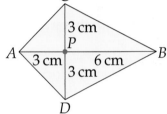

a Using compasses, construct an equilateral
triangle ABC of length 6 cm.
b Construct the perpendiculars from
  i A to BC
  ii B to AC
  iii C to AB
c Draw the lines of symmetry for the equilateral
triangle.

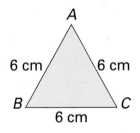

• Describe a locus of a moving point and draw it accurately

Keywords
Equidistant   Rule
Locus
Path
Perpendicular bisector

• The **locus** of an object is its **path**.

Imagine the tip of a sail as it moves around.

The locus is a circle.

Imagine the tip of the beak as it moves up and down.

The locus is a curve.

Imagine the stone as it falls.

The locus is a straight line.

The plural of "locus" is "loci".

• A point that moves according to a **rule** can form a locus.

---

example

Construct the locus of the point that is **equidistant** from the points A and B.

··

The locus is the **perpendicular bisector** of the line AB.

Use compasses to construct the perpendicular bisector.

$A\bullet$ $\bullet B$

Equidistant means 'equal length'.

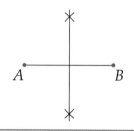

---

example

Draw the locus of the point that is 2 cm from a fixed point O.

··

The locus is a circle of radius 2 cm centre O.
Use compasses to construct the circle.

Exercise 14d

1 Draw and describe in words the locus of
  a a ball thrown straight up in the air
  b the tip of the minute hand on a clock
  c a conker dropping from a tree
  d a competitor on a ski jump
  e the foot of a person doing a somersault on a snow board.

2 **a** Draw an angle *AOB* of 130°.
  b Draw the locus of the point
    that is equidistant from *OA*
    and *OB*.

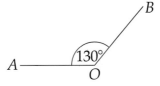

> The locus is the angle bisector.

3 Draw the locus of a point that is 3 cm from a fixed point.

4 **a** Draw a line *AB* = 8 cm.
  b Using ruler and compasses, construct
    the locus of the point that is
    equidistant from *A* and *B*.

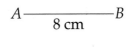

> The locus is the perpendicular bisector of *AB*.

5 The moat in front of a castle wall is 3 metres wide.
  a Using a scale of 1 centimetre to represent
    1 metre, draw a scale drawing.
  b Draw the locus of the point that is as near to the wall as
    possible, but is not in water.

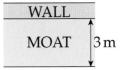

6 Draw the locus of the point that is equidistant from parallel
  lines that are 4 cm apart.

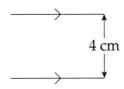

Kyle climbs halfway up a 5 metre ladder.
The ladder starts to slide down the wall and along
the ground.
Kyle remains fixed to the midpoint of the ladder.

Using a scale of 1 cm to represent 1 metre,
draw different positions of the ladder as it slides.

Draw the locus of Kyle.

- Use bearings to specify direction

Keywords
Bearings
Direction
Three-figure bearing

This mountain is called Snowdon.
It is the highest peak in Wales at 1085 metres.

The view is from a mountain ridge called Crib Goch.

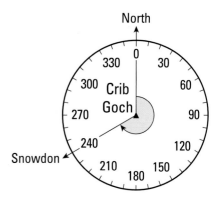

000° is always North.

The **direction** of Snowdon from Crib Goch is 240°.

This angle is called a **three-figure bearing**.
When you use **bearings**

- measure from north
- measure in a clockwise direction
- use three figures.

example

Find the places that are on these bearings from Crib Goch.

a 080°　　　　　　　　**b** 240°　　　　　　**c** 295°

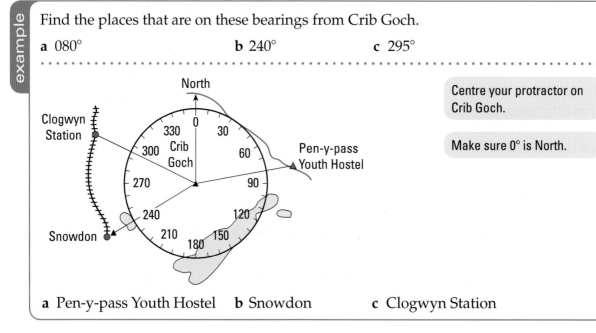

Centre your protractor on Crib Goch.

Make sure 0° is North.

a Pen-y-pass Youth Hostel　　**b** Snowdon　　**c** Clogwyn Station

Exercise 14e

1 The map shows the position of places relative to Middle School.

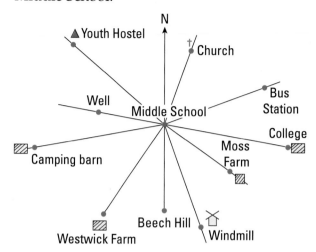

Centre your protractor on Middle School. North is 000°.

Name the places that are on these bearings from Middle School.

a 100°   **b** 160°

c 215°   **d** 125°

e 280°   **f** 020°

g 260°   **h** 070°

i 180°   **j** 310°

2 Copy and complete the table.

Direction	N	NE	E	SE	S	SW	W	NW
Bearing								

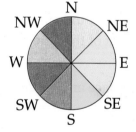

3 Use a protractor to draw accurate diagrams to show bearings at

a 050°   **d** 240°

b 120°   **e** 300°

c 200°

N Remember to start with a North line.

---

challenge

The bearing of Baslow from Bakewell is 045°.

The distance from Bakewell to Baslow is 5 km.

a Draw a scale drawing using a scale of 1 cm represents 1 km.

b Measure the bearing of Bakewell from Baslow.

c Explain why adding 180° to 045° gives your answer to part **b**.

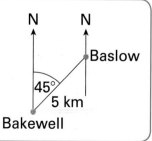

14f Surface area of a cuboid

- Calculate the surface area of cuboids
- Recognise the net of a cuboid

Keywords

3-D   Net
Cuboid   Surface area
Face

- A **cuboid** is a **3-D** shape with six rectangular **faces**.

3-D means '3-dimensional'.

p. 88

When you unfold the cuboid, the six rectangles form a **net**.

The area of the net is the surface area of the cuboid.

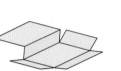

- The **surface area** of the cuboid is the total area of its faces.

There are two green rectangles, two pink rectangles and two blue rectangles.

---

example

A cuboid measures 4 cm by 3 cm by 2 cm.

Calculate the surface area of the cuboid.

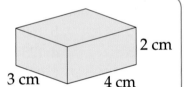

Area of the green rectangle = $4 \times 3 = 12 \text{ cm}^2$
Area of the pink rectangle   = $2 \times 4 =$ 8 cm^2
Area of the blue rectangle   = $3 \times 2 =$ $\underline{6 \text{ cm}^2}$
                                 26 cm^2

Surface area = 26×2
                = 52 cm^2

The units of area are cm^2.

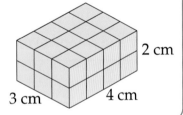

- A cube has six square faces.

---

example

The surface area of a cube is 96 cm^2.

Calculate   **a** the area of one face
                  b the length of one side of the cube.

a A cube has six square faces.
    The area of one face = $96 \div 6$
                        = 16 cm^2

b Length of one side   = $\sqrt{16}$
                        = 4 cm

Area = $4 \text{ cm} \times 4 \text{ cm}$
       = 16 cm^2

Exercise 14f

1 These nets make cuboids.

Each square represents a 1 centimetre square.

Calculate the surface area of each cuboid.

a   **b**   **c**

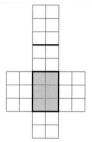

Did you know?

Your skin has a surface area of approximately 1.5 to 2 square metres.

2 A 5 cm by 6 cm by 8 cm cuboid is shown.

Calculate

  a the area of the green rectangle

  b the area of the pink rectangle

  c the area of the blue rectangle

  d the surface area of the cuboid.

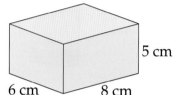

5 cm

6 cm   8 cm

3 Calculate the surface area of these cuboids.

State the units of your answers.

a 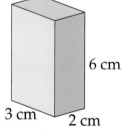   **b** 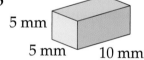   **c**

5 mm

5 mm   10 mm

5 m   4 m   1 m

6 cm

3 cm   2 cm

4 Calculate the surface area of each cube.

State the units of your answers.

  a length = 5 mm   **b** length = 9 m   **c** length = 15 cm

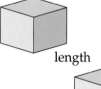

length

5 Calculate the length of one side of a cube, if the surface area of the cube is

  a 600 cm^2 **b** 384 cm^2 **c** 13.5 cm^2

length

The areas of three of the faces of this cuboid are 15 cm^2, 24 cm^2 and 40 cm^2.

Find the length, width and height of the cuboid.

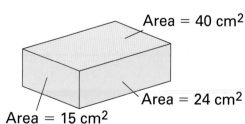

Area = 40 cm^2

Area = 24 cm^2

Area = 15 cm^2

- Calculate the volume of a cuboid

Keywords
Cubic centimetre (cm³)
Cuboid
Dimensions
Volume

- The **volume** is the amount of space inside a 3-D shape.

You measure volume in cubes.

You should use a suitable unit of volume to measure objects.
One common metric unit of volume is a **cubic centimetre (cm³)**.

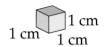

1 cm

1 cm   1 cm

To measure the volume of …

a room

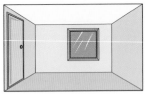

a cereal box

a pin head

you should use …

cubic metres (m³)   cubic centimetres (cm³)   cubic millimetres (mm³)

You can find the volume of a **cuboid** by counting layers of cubes.

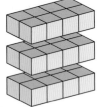

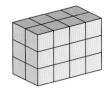

In one layer there are   In three layers there are   The volume is 24 cubes
2 × 4 = 8 cubes   3 × 8 = 24 cubes

This is the same as multiplying the **dimensions** length, width
and height.

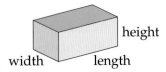

height

width   length

- **Volume of a cuboid = length × width × height**

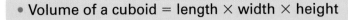

example

Calculate the volume of this cuboid.

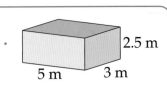

2.5 m

5 m   3 m

Volume of cuboid = length × width × height
           = 5 × 3 × 2.5
           = 37.5 m³

Exercise 14g

1 Choose the most appropriate unit to measure the volume of

    a a chocolate box   **b** a seed   **c** a fish tank

    d a container on a lorry   **e** a snooker ball.

2 Calculate the volume of each cuboid.
State the units of your answers.

a

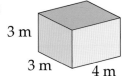

3 m, 3 m, 4 m

b

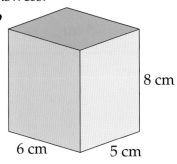

8 cm, 6 cm, 5 cm

c

1.5 m, 5 m, 4 m

Did you know?

The volume of the Heathrow Terminal 5A building is over 2.5 million cubic metres.

3 Calculate the volume of a cube of side 2.5 cm.

4 Calculate the missing lengths.

a

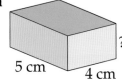

?, 5 cm, 4 cm
Volume = 40 cm³

b

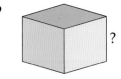

?
A cube
Volume = 216 cm³

c

?, 5 m, 8 m
Volume = 20 m³

5 A box measures 25 cm by 15 cm by 16 cm.

    a Calculate the volume of the cuboid.

    The box is filled $\frac{3}{4}$ full with sand.

    b Calculate the volume of sand.

    c Calculate the height of the sand.

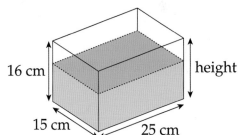

16 cm, height, 15 cm, 25 cm

challenge

Twenty cubes are arranged to form a cuboid.
List the four possible cuboids that can be made using all twenty cubes.
Calculate the surface area of each cuboid.
Which cuboid has the smallest surface area?

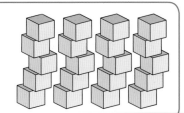

14a

1 Construct these triangles.
Measure the lengths of the sides and calculate the perimeter of each triangle.

a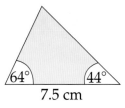

b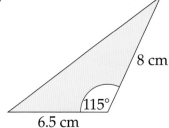

c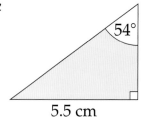

14b

2 Construct these triangles, using ruler and compasses.
State the mathematical name of each triangle.

a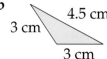

b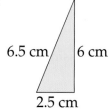

c 6.5 cm 6 cm 2.5 cm

14c

3 a Draw a large triangle.
b Construct the perpendicular bisector for each of the three sides.
c Draw a circle passing through the vertices of the triangle, using the point of intersection as the centre.

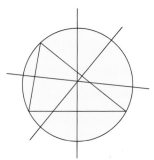

14c²

4 Copy this diagram.
Using compasses, construct a vertical wall through the dot to separate the giraffe from the person.

5 Copy the diagrams on square grid paper.
Draw the locus of the point that is equidistant from P and Q.

a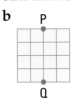

b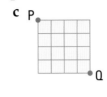

c

> Equidistant means 'equal length'.

6 Measure the three-figure bearings of these places from Manchester.

a Leeds   b Liverpool
c Sheffield   d Preston
e Bradford   f Chester

> You may need to trace the map and extend the lines.

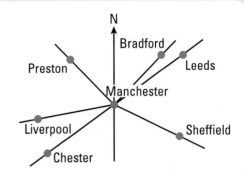

7 Calculate the surface area of these cuboids.

a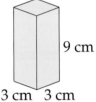
9 cm
3 cm   3 cm

b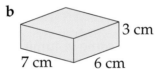
3 cm
7 cm   6 cm

c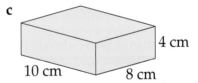
4 cm
10 cm   8 cm

8 Calculate the length of one side of the cube, if the surface area of the cube is

a 294 cm^2 b 1536 cm^2 c 235.5 cm^2

length

9 Copy and complete the table for the cuboids.

	Length	Width	Height	Volume
a	9 m	8 m	8 m	
b	15 mm	10 mm	20 mm	
c	2.5 cm	2 cm	8 cm	
d	5 m	3.5 m	3.2 m	
e	6 cm	2 cm		42 cm^3
f	4 m	4 m		48 m^3
g	7 cm		20 cm	280 cm^3
h	9 cm		32 cm	288 cm^3

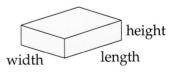
height
width   length

Assessment criteria
- Use straight edge and compasses to do standard constructions **Level 6**
- Calculate the surface area and volume of a cuboid **Level 6**

1 Using compasses and a straight edge, construct the perpendicular bisector of the line AB.
You must leave your construction lines.

A————————B

Steph's answer ✔

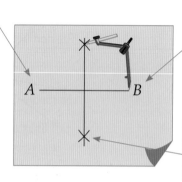

Steph draws 2 arcs with the compasses centred at *A*.

Without altering the compasses, she draws 2 more arcs with the compasses centred at *B*.

Steph draws the perpendicular bisector through the points of intersection of the arcs.

2 The drawing shows two cuboids that have the same volume.

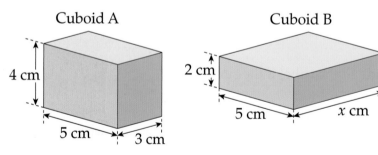

Cuboid A

Cuboid B

4 cm

5 cm   3 cm

2 cm

5 cm x cm

a What is the volume of cuboid A?
Remember to state your units.

b Work out the value of the length marked x.

Key Stage 3 2002 4–6 Paper 2

Analysing data

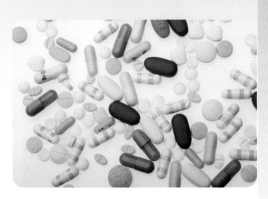

Modern medical treatments can be very expensive. Scientists and doctors conduct clinical trials to produce statistics on the effectiveness of a medicine, and how safe it is to use.

What's the point? Doctors use these statistics to help them decide if the benefit of a treatment outweighs its cost.

 **Check in**

Level 4

1 Pete and Maria both recorded the number of points they scored in ten games of basketball.

Pete	5	0	6	8	5	7	4	9	3	9
Maria	7	5	7	6	7	4	7	6	5	7

a Find the mode and the range of each set of scores.
b Which player had the best set of scores? Use the mode and the range to explain your answer.

Level 5

2 Two Year 8 classes took part in a four-week recycling competition.
The bar chart shows the number of points they scored.
Which class did best in the competition?
Explain your answer.

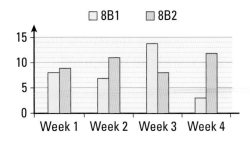

• Calculate statistics for sets of discrete data

Keywords
Average   *Mode*
Mean   *Range*
Median   *Statistic*

Three different **averages** are often used to make sense of data. Each one tries to describe a typical value.

> The **mode** is the most common value in a set of data.

> The **median** is the middle value when the data is put in order.

> To find the **mean**, add up all the values, and then divide by the number of items.

Averages are useful for describing typical values in real life.

example

Find the mode, the median and the mean of these sets of data.

a The number of pets owned by seven students:
   2, 4, 4, 4, 5, 7, 9
b The ages of six members of a family: 3, 7, 12, 13, 16, 21
c The number of flowers on nine different plants:
   6, 3, 5, 5, 9, 2, 6, 4, 1

. . . .

a The mode is 4 pets.
   The data is already in order, and the median is 4 pets.
   To find the mean, first add the values: $2 + 4 + 4 + 4 + 5 + 7 + 9 = 35$.
   The mean is $35 \div 7 = 5$ pets.
b There are no repeated values, so there is no mode.
   There is an even number of values, so there are two 'middle' values.
   The median is half-way between them: 12.5 years old.
   The mean is $72 \div 6 = 12$ years old.
c This set of data has two modes: 5 and 6 flowers.
   To find the median, first put the data in order:
   1, 2, 3, 4, 5, 5, 6, 6, 9.
   The median is 5 flowers.
   The mean is $41 \div 9 = 4.56$ flowers.

> In part **c**, the mean does not give you a possible value - you can't have 4.56 flowers.

Another important **statistic** is the **range**.
This tells you about the **spread** of the data.

> • Range = maximum value − minimum value

In example **a** above, the range is $9 - 2 = 7$ pets.

Exercise 15a

1 Four student in class 8A who used the 'MyFace' website recorded the number of messages they received each day.

Amy   3, 5, 5, 5, 6, 6, 2

Jen   4, 4, 8, 9, 9, 11

Selma 5, 6, 1, 2, 5, 7, 8, 4, 6, 2, 6, 6

Jo   2, 1, 7, 8, 5, 3

   a How many days did each person keep records for?

   b Find the **mode** of each of these sets of data.

2 Mrs Morgan asked student in class 8B to find out about mobile phone use. Some student asked people how many text messages they had sent the previous day.

Kalid   3, 5, 9   Emily   4, 5, 4, 7, 1

Dan   2, 6, 7, 9   Steph   5, 0, 8, 7, 3, 9

James 2, 3, 6, 8, 8, 9, 11

   a Who asked most people?

   b Calculate the **median** of each person's data.

3 Five basketball players recorded the number of points they scored in each game that they played in a tournament.

Sandra 5, 5, 5, 5   Abbie   3, 6, 7, 9, 15

Lizzie   3, 4, 5, 6   Jill   3, 6, 9, 19, 13, 7

Maya   2, 9, 7, 2

   a How many games did each person play?

   b Calculate the **mean** score for each player.

4 Work out the **range** of each of these sets of data.

   a Number of people living in five houses: 1, 1, 4, 6, 9

   b Number of absences for five student: 5, 4, 3, 9, 6

   c Number of books borrowed from the school library by six student: 9, 5, 0, 6, 4, 8

   d Mass (in kilograms) of 5 cats: 4.8, 6.3, 2.1, 5.8, 2.2

discussion

Can you make up examples of sets of numbers where:

a The mean, median and mode are all equal?

b The mean and median are the same, but the mode is smaller?

c The mode is bigger than the median, and the median is bigger than the mean?

d The mode is 1, the median is 2 and the mean is 3?

- Calculate statistics for sets of discrete data and grouped continuous data
- Recognise when it is appropriate to use the range, mean, median and mode

Keywords

Average	Mean
Frequency	Median
table	Mode
Grouped	Modal class
continuous	Range

You can calculate statistics for data in a **frequency table**.

example

p. 166

The frequency table shows the number of goals scored during a season by members of a football club.

Number of goals	Frequency
0	12
1	7
2	3
3	4
4	1

a How many players are included in the table?
b Find the **mean**, **median**, **mode** and **range** of the number of goals scored.

a The total number of players is $12 + 7 + 3 + 4 + 1 = 27$.
b The mode is the number of goals with the highest frequency, which is 0 goals.

The median is the middle value when the data are arranged in order.
The 14th value is the median, and this is 1 goal.

> The table puts the data into numerical order.

The mean is the total number of goals divided by the total number of players. To calculate the total number of goals, add an extra column to the table.
The total number of goals scored is
$0 + 7 + 6 + 12 + 4 = 29$.
The total number of players is 27.
The mean is $29 \div 27 = 1.07$ goals per player.

The range is the difference between the maximum and minimum numbers of goals scored. The range is $4 - 0 = 4$ goals.

Number of goals	Frequency	Totals
0	12	$0 \times 12 = 0$
1	7	$1 \times 7 = 7$
2	3	$2 \times 3 = 6$
3	4	$3 \times 4 = 12$
4	1	$4 \times 1 = 4$

For **grouped continuous** data, the **modal class** is the only **average** that can be found easily. This is the interval that contains the highest frequency.

Exercise 15b

1 This frequency table shows the number of pets owned by the students in class 8C5.

Number of pets	Frequency
0	10
1	12
2	7
3	2

   a How many students' data are shown in the table?

   b What is the modal number of pets owned by the students in 8C5?

   c What is the range of the number of pets owned by people in 8C5?

2 Students in class 8P were asked to record the number of portions of fruit and vegetables that they ate one day.

Portions of fruit and vegetables	Frequency
0	1
1	2
2	5
3	4
4	9
5	6
6	4
7	1

   a How many students' data are shown in the table?

   b What is the modal number of portions eaten?

   c What was the median of the number of portions eaten?

3 The table shows the number of absences for the students in class 8K during one term.

Number of absences	Frequency
0	10
1	5
2	4
3	2
4	3
5	3
6	2
7	0
8	1

   a Find the total number of students whose data are shown in the table.

   b Redraw the table with an extra column to show the total number of absences.

   c Find the overall total number of absences for the whole class.

   d Use your answers to parts **a** and **c** to calculate the mean number of absences per student.

The table shows the heights of students in class 8KT.

   a What is the modal class for this set of data?

   b Why is the modal class the only average that can be worked out easily?

Height, h cm	Frequency
$170 \leqslant h < 180$	3
$160 \leqslant h < 170$	9
$150 \leqslant h < 160$	14
$140 \leqslant h < 130$	5

• Interpret graphs and diagrams for discrete and continuous data

Keywords
Bar chart
Frequency diagram
Interpret
Modal class
Pie chart

Statistical diagrams can help you to **interpret** data.

A **pie chart** lets you compare a part to the whole.

p. 168

example

This pie chart shows the eye colours of people in a class.

Estimate the proportion of the total number of people who had each eye colour.

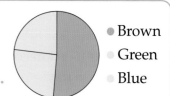

• Brown
• Green
• Blue

· ·

Just over half the people had brown eyes.

Just over a quarter of the people had green eyes.

Just over a fifth of the people had blue eyes.

p. 170

A **bar chart** makes it easy to compare one category of discrete data with another.

example

This bar chart shows the colours of the cars in a car park. Make a list of the colours in order of popularity.

· ·

The bar chart makes it easy to see that silver is the most popular colour. The other colours, in order, are: red, green, blue, black.

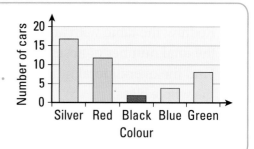

A **frequency diagram** can be used to compare categories of continuous data.

example

The frequency diagram shows the heights of a group of people.

Find the **modal class** for this data, and the class with the lowest frequency.

· ·

The modal class is 160−170 cm. The class with the lowest frequency is 190−200 cm.

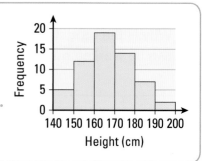

Exercise 15c

1 The pie chart shows the attendance at four different films shown at a cinema one evening.

Use the pie chart to estimate the percentage of the total cinema audience who attended each film.

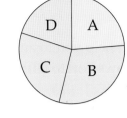

Did you know?

Cinema attendances fell from around 1.4 billion in 1951 to around 53 million in 1984 and climbed back to 176 million admissions in 2002.

2 The bar chart shows the results of a survey about pet ownership.

Frequency — Number of pets owned

a What was the modal number of pets owned by people who took part in the survey?

b How many people took part in the survey?

c What was the total number of pets owned by people who took part in the survey?

d What was the mean number of pets owned by people who took part in the survey?

3 The frequency diagram shows the finishing times of the competitors in a marathon.

a How many runners finished the race?

b Find the modal class of the finishing times.

c Find the number of runners who had had a finishing time less than 2 hours 30 minutes.

d Find the number of runners who had a finishing time between 2 hours 25 minutes and 2 hours 45 minutes.

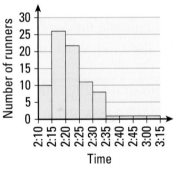

Number of runners — Time

discussion

Redraw the chart from question **2** as a pie chart.

Would question **2** be easier or harder to answer with this chart instead of the bar chart? Explain your answer.

• Interpret simple line graphs for time series

Keywords
Extrapolate
Time series

Any statistical diagram can help you to analyse a set of data, but a **time series** graph allows you to tell a story.

example

This graph shows the average number of children born to women in the UK from 1960 to 2006. Describe the main features shown on the graph.

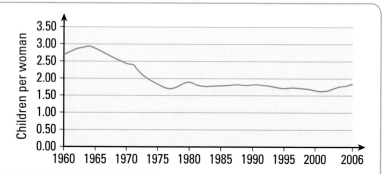

The average number of children born to each woman increased from about 2.7 in 1960 to nearly 3 in 1965. After that, there was a fairly steady decrease to around 1.7 children per woman by about 1977. Since then the number has remained relatively stable, varying between about 1.6 and 1.9 children per woman.

Sometimes a time-series graph is **extrapolated** - this means that it is used to predict future data.

example

This graph shows the number of children born per woman in Italy. Comment on the main features of the graph and the data shown.

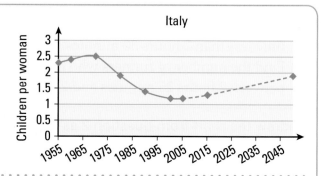

Italy

The graph shows data from 1955, and includes projected data as far as 2050. The individual data points are marked, so we can see the actual measurements and predictions as well as the trend.
The number of children born per woman declined from a peak of 2.5 in about 1970 down to about 1.2 in 2000. The number is predicted to rise again, to about 1.9 children per woman in 2050.

Exercise 15d

1 The chart shows the depth of water in a harbour.

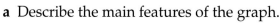

a Describe the main features of the graph.

b Captain Jack's boat can only enter or leave the harbour when the depth of water is above 2.5 m. What is the earliest time that he can enter the harbour? What is the latest time that he can leave?

Did you know?

The depth of water in a harbour is governed by the pull of the moon, nearly 400 000 km away!

2 This chart shows the changes in the prices of goods (the consumer price index) during the 20th Century.

Describe the main features of the graph.

Consumer Price Index

discussion

The graph shows the progress of the women's world record for the high jump.

Use the Internet to check the current women's world record for the high jump.

Describe the main features of the graph.

Do you think that the record will increase much in the future?

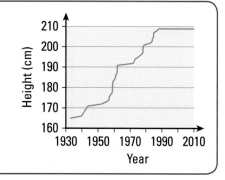

• Construct scatter diagrams and understand correlation

Keywords
Correlation
Scatter diagram

This **scatter diagram** shows the scores obtained by a group of people in two fitness tests taken a week apart.

It shows that people had similar scores on both tests. This is what you might expect − a person's fitness would not change much over one week.

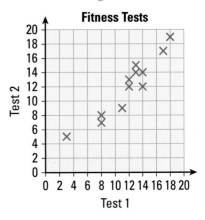

Fitness Tests

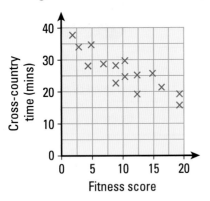

This scatter diagram shows that people with higher fitness scores tend to have shorter finishing times in a cross–country race.

This scatter diagram shows the heights and Spanish test scores for a group of pupils.

There is no clear pattern. There is no reason to expect a connection between people's heights and their Spanish scores.

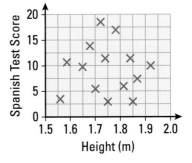

• **Correlation** describes the connection between two sets of data.

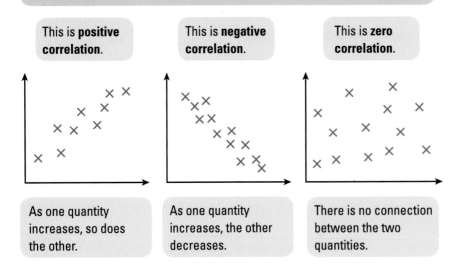

This is **positive** correlation.	This is **negative** correlation.	This is **zero** correlation.
As one quantity increases, so does the other.	As one quantity increases, the other decreases.	There is no connection between the two quantities.

Exercise 15e

1 Matt collected the scores for ten people in a Maths test and a Science test, and started to draw a scatter diagram.

Maths	10	16	15	8	18	11	9	4	19	20
Science	12	14	12	5	16	9	6	7	16	18

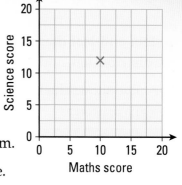

a Copy the diagram, and complete it using the data from the table.

b Describe and explain any correlation in your scatter diagram.

2 Pat gathered data about the height and arm-span of ten people.

Height (cm)	165	162	148	149	151	153	139	149	134	140
Arm-span (cm)	163	163	145	147	149	155	142	153	137	138

a Use the data in the table to plot a scatter diagram.

b Comment on the pattern shown in your diagram.

3 Josh wanted to see if there was any correlation between the number of emails that people received in one day, and the number of text messages they received. The table shows the results for twelve people.

Emails	12	14	9	2	0	8	15	14	11	6	4	5
Texts	4	3	8	2	6	1	8	5	3	1	2	14

a Draw a scatter diagram for Josh's data.

b Explain whether or not there is a correlation between the numbers of emails and the numbers of text messages received by the people surveyed.

---

discussion

Sandy decided to find out whether there was a connection between people's height and their weight.

She first went out and measured the weight of ten people, and recorded this data in a table.

She then went out and measured the heights of another ten people, and recorded this data in the same table.

Weights of 10 people (kg)	75	49	68	83	92	71	64	39	49	67
Heights of 10 people (cm)	158	149	168	176	185	190	167	188	175	164

Explain why Sandy would not be able to produce a sensible scatter diagram from the data in this table.

• Construct and interpret stem-and-leaf diagrams

Keywords
Distribution
Statistics
Stem-and-leaf diagram

A **stem-and-leaf diagram** makes it easy to see the 'shape' of the **distribution**, and to calculate **statistics**.

The table shows the heights of twenty people in a class.

Heights in centimetres

159	173	170	154	181	163	165	180	178	150
160	163	164	171	157	181	177	159	168	151

18	0	1	1			
17	0	3	7	7	8	
16	0	3	3	4	5	8
15	0	1	4	7	9	9

Key | 15 | 4 = 154 cm

Always include a key.

The multiples of 10 are the 'stem'.
The units are the 'leaves'.

You can easily find the median and the range of the data.
The median of the heights is 164.5 cm (half-way between the 10th and 11th values.)
The range of the heights is 181 cm − 150 cm = 31 cm.

p. 236

A back-to-back stem-and-leaf diagram can be used to compare two sets of data.

example

This back-to-back stem-and-leaf diagram shows the heights of the boys and the girls in a class. Compare the two sets of data.

Girls		Boys			
	17	1	1	2	
3	16	3	4	7	8
8 6 5 1	15	1	5	8	
9 5 2	14	2	8		
7 5 5	13				

Key | 14 | 8 = 148 cm

On average, the boys are taller than the girls:
  The modal class of the boys' heights is 160–170 cm.
  The modal class of the girls' heights is 150–160 cm.

The boys' heights are more spread out than the girls':
  The range of the boys' heights is 172 cm − 142 cm = 30 cm
  The range of the girls' heights is 163 cm − 135 cm = 28 cm.

• When you compare two sets of data, you should compare one type of average and the range.

Exercise 15f

1 This stem-and-leaf diagram shows the numbers
of tickets sold for twenty one different performances of a play.

25	0	0	0	0	0
24	2	8			
23	0	3			
22	3	5	6		
21	2	4	7	7	
20	1	2	4	9	
19	4				

Key | 21 | 7 = 217 tickets

a Find the median number of tickets sold.

b Find the modal class of the number of tickets sold.

c Find the range of the number of tickets sold.

2 A teacher compared the scores of one of her classes on two tests.

Test 1 Scores (in numerical order)

18	21	24	24	27	30	31	32	32	34
35	35	36	37	39	42	44	46	48	48

Test 2 Scores (in numerical order)

24	25	25	26	29	30	32	35	36	38
38	41	41	43	44	48	49	50	50	50

a Construct a back-to-back stem-and-leaf diagram for this set
of data.

p. 170

b Describe the distribution of the scores on the two tests, using your
diagram to help calculate suitable statistics.

---

discussion

You could have used bar charts or frequency diagrams to represent the data in the
questions above.

What are the advantages and disadvantages of using stem-and-leaf diagrams
instead of bar charts or frequency diagrams?

1 Find the mean, median and range of each of these sets of numbers.
 a 4, 8, 16, 19, 25
 b 34, 67, 92, 108
 c 3.5, 9.2, 7.3, 8.3, 4.1
 d 106.3, 88.9, 71.4, 58.7, 91.9

2 The students in a class were asked how many people live in their house.
 The table shows the result.

Number of occupants	2	3	4	5	6	7	8
Frequency	3	5	11	6	4	0	1

 For this set of data, find
 a the mode   **b** the median   **c** the mean   **d** the range.

3 This bar chart shows the number of house sales in two areas in a town.

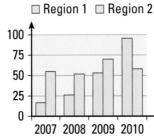

 Describe the main trends shown by this chart.

4 A department store has five floors: ground, 1, 2, 3 and 4.
 There are up and down escalators between each floor.
 Each escalator takes one minute to go up or down one floor, and
 it takes 30 seconds to walk between escalators on each floor.
 Monica starts on the ground floor, and travels up to the top floor
 as quickly as possible.
 Draw a time-series graph for her journey.

5 Sketch a scatter diagram to show the pattern you would expect to see
 when the correlation between variables is
 a positive   **b** negative   **c** no correlation.
 In each scatter diagram, suggest what the two sets of data could be.

6 The ages (in years) of 20 customers in a shop were

| 15 | 61 | 42 | 33 | 38 | 29 | 53 | 17 | 44 | 32 |
| 39 | 45 | 41 | 26 | 22 | 44 | 43 | 49 | 55 | 60 |

Draw a stem-and-leaf diagram for this set of data.

7 The table shows the number of cars issued by two car hire offices in a town, for 20 business days.

Office 1

6	11	21	24	25	9	13	23	13	25
19	7	22	15	17	25	10	8	25	25

Office 2

8	36	36	16	36	34	36	24	36	36
36	27	36	29	36	36	11	36	36	32

Draw a stem-and-leaf diagram for this set of data, and use it to describe the distribution of the data.

Maths life

Electricity in the home

Have you ever thought about how many things you have around the house that use electricity? Have you considered how much electricity the various things use? As energy costs rise, more and more people are keeping an eye on how they use their electricity.

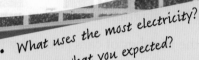

- What uses the most electricity?
- Is that what you expected?
- What fraction of the total electricity does it use?

- What uses the least electricity?
- Why do you think that is?

- Why do you think that the fridge and freezer use so much electricity?

- Where do you think that savings in the use of electricity could most easily be made?

Electricity usage in a typical household

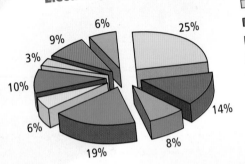

- lighting
- tv and audio
- computer and games console
- fridge and freezer
- kettle
- cooker
- microwave
- washing machine and tumble dryer
- other

25%, 14%, 8%, 19%, 6%, 10%, 3%, 9%, 6%

Switch off to save money

Consumers are wasting up to £200 a year on electricity bills by leaving appliances on standby rather than switching them off, according to recent research.

A typical microwave oven uses more electricity to run its clock than it does to cook food! Although cooking the food uses much more power than the running the clock, most microwave ovens are in standby mode for at least 99% of the time.

`8.45`

Item	power used when on (W) A	power used on standby (W) B	hours in use per day C	hours on standby per day D	power used per day (WH) (A x C) + (B x D)
Television	200	7	6.5	17.5	
Satellite TV	30	13	5	19	
DVD player	12	7	1.5	22.5	600
Main light	100	—	6	0	
Microwave oven	700	5	0.1	23.9	
Desktop computer	125	15	4	20	
Laptop computer	29	2	4	20	

- Complete the final column of the table.
- Which item uses the most electricity each day? Which uses the least?
- What would happen if the items that are left on standby were turned off instead? Would the same items use the most and least electricity per day?

Fridge A £99.99

Size (h) 85cm (w) 48cm (d) 49.5cm
Fresh food storage
- ❄ volume 86 litres
- ❄ manual defrost

Freezer compartment
- ❄ volume 10 litres
- ❄ 1 star rating ★

Energy efficiency class 'A'
Energy consumption 139kWh/year

Fridge B £179.99

Size (h) 144cm (w) 54.4cm (d) 57cm
Fresh food storage:
- ❄ volume 245 litres
- ❄ auto defrost

Freezer compartment
- ❄ none

Energy efficiency class 'A'
Energy consumption 164kWh/year

Fridge B £299.99

Size (h) 85cm (w) 55cm (d) 61.2cm
Fresh food storage
- ❄ volume 122 litres
- ❄ auto defrost

Freezer compartment
- ❄ volume 18 litres
- ❄ 4 star rating ★ ★ ★ ★

Energy efficiency class 'A'
Energy consumption 234kWh/year

Electricity costs 11p per kWh

- What is the yearly cost of running each fridge?
- If you were buying a new fridge, what things would influence your choice? Would it just be running cost?
- What does the star rating for the frozen food storage mean?
- Which fridge would you choose if frozen food storage was important for you?

ENERGY   Fridge/Freezer
Manufacturer model
More efficient
A
B
C
D
E
F
G
Less efficient
A

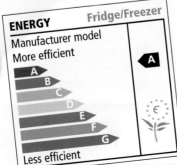

The fridges are all described as Energy efficiency class 'A' but they use different amounts of energy per year.

Why do you think that is?

Try to find out what the Energy efficiency classes mean.

Assessment criteria
- Interpret graphs and diagrams **Level 5**
- Compare two distributions using range and one of mode, median or mean **Level 5**
- Communicate interpretations and results of a statistical survey **Level 6**

Level 6

1 The stem-and-leaf diagram shows the number of people in a lift in a store for 15 journeys.

0	2	4	4	5	8	9
1	0	1	1	6	7	7
2	3	3	4			

Key 1 | 6 represents 16 people

a The lift can hold 25 people. Was it ever full? Explain your answer.

b What was the range of the number of people in the lift?

c What was the median of the number of people in the lift?

Leo's answer ✔

Leo knows 2 | 4 represents 24 people.

Range = highest value − lowest value

a No, never full as 24 people was the most in the lift.

b 24 − 2 = 22 people

c Median is the middle value of the 15 ordered numbers.

0	2	4	4	5	8	9
1	0	1	1	6	7	7
2	3	3	4			

The 8th value is 11.
The median is 11 people.

Level 5

2 The graph shows the date each year that frogs' eggs were first seen.

a On what date in 1997 were the frogs' eggs first seen?

b At the beginning of the year, the warmer the weather, the earlier frogs' eggs are first seen.
What can you say about the weather at the beginning of 1991?

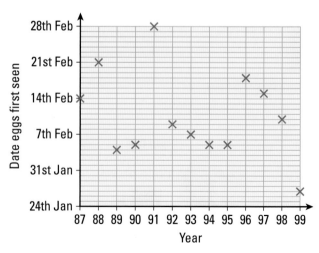

Key Stage 3 2007 4–6 Paper 2

Calculation+

The shape of the Earth is rounded with a bulge around the equator. However, scientists often approximate this to a perfect sphere as many calculations are easier with a regular shape.

What's the point? You can make complex problems much simpler by knowing how to make approximations.

Check in

Level 5

1 Calculate these using a mental method.
   a $13.6 + 7.5$ **b** $2.57 + 3.9$ **c** $13.4 - 8.59$ **d** $7.65 - 4.29$

2 Calculate these using a written method.
   a $43.72 + 514.2 + 3.47$ **b** $23.8 + 147.3 + 61.97$

3 Calculate these using mental methods.
   a 21×0.3 **b** $252 \div 12$ **c** 12×1.4 **d** $340 \div 15$ **e** 7.1×21

4 Calculate these using written methods.
   a 9×3.73 **b** 6×3.34 **c** 23×1.7 **d** 18×2.4

5 Calculate these using written methods giving your answer as a decimal to 1 dp where appropriate.
   a $55 \div 7$ **b** $40 \div 9$ **c** $336 \div 12$ **d** $720 \div 16$

- Consolidate and extend a range of mental strategies for addition and subtraction
- Make and justify estimates and approximations
- Identify the information necessary to solve a problem

Keywords
Approximation
Calculation
Information

- You should write down the **information** you know and the information you are trying to find out when you are solving a problem. This makes it easier to solve the problem by changing it into a **calculation**.

example

Here are the distances in kilometres between four towns.
Hanif walks from Deeport to Aton and then to Ceeley.
Jack walks from Deeport to St Bees and then to Ceeley.
Who walks the furthest distance and by how much?

Aton			
4.2 km	St Bees		
6.85 km	3.15 km	Ceeley	
2.65 km	5.4 km	7.6 km	Deeport

Hanif's journey = Deeport to Aton + Aton to Ceeley
  Approximate first:
  $2.65 + 6.85 \approx 3 + 7$
  $= 10$
  So a good **approximation** is 10 km.
  $2.65 + 6.85$
  $= 9.5$ km

Jack's journey = Deeport to St Bees + St Bees to Ceeley
  Approximate first:
  $5.4 + 3.15 \approx 5 + 3$
  $= 8$
  So a good approximation is 8 km.
  $5.4 + 3.15$
  $= 8.55$ km

Hanif walks further by $9.5 - 8.55$
  $= 0.95$ km

> Write down each person's journey and read the distances from the table.

> You could use compensation to work out the answer, for example $2.65 + 7 - 0.15$
> $= 9.65 - 0.15 = 9.5$ km

> The final part of the problem is a mental subtraction

Exercise 16a

1 A road runs from Preston to Colne. The distance between places on the road are shown in kilometres.

a How far is it from Preston to Burnley?

b Is it further from Preston to Accrington, or from Accrington to Colne? Explain your answer.

c Mr Mulachy is a teacher. He travels from his home in Blackburn to his school in Brierfield every day. How many kilometres does he travel in a week?

Colne
Brierfield 7.2km
Burnley 5.49km
Accrington
Preston   Blackburn   10.02km
16.4km   9.74km

2 Read this information carefully and then answer the questions.

Bernice is 1.4 m tall.   Stephanie is 0.3 m taller than Bernice.
Shabeena is 0.18 m shorter than Bernice.   Carla is 0.25 m shorter than Stephanie.
Ingrid is 0.08 m shorter than Stephanie.

a Who is the tallest student and what is their height?

b How much taller than Shabeena is Ingrid?

c What is the difference in height between Carla and Bernice?

3 Here are some items for sale in a shop. Work out the cost of these orders and the change they should be given.

a Malcolm buys a memory pen and a book. He pays with a £20 note.

b Jameela buys a mobile phone and a memory pen. She pays £50.

c Yuri buys a DVD, a computer game and a book. He pays £25.

d Valerie buys a DVD and a book. Natasha buys two identical memory pens. Who spends the most and by how much?

DVD   Computer Game   Mobile Phone

£8.95   £6.99   £36.35

Memory Pen   Book

£7.20   £4.89

4 Five students at Verifast School run in the 100 m race. Here are their times.

Algenon	14.3 seconds
Barry	14.08 seconds
Cris	13.9 seconds
Dominic	14.37 seconds
Eli	14.6 seconds

a How much longer did the slowest person take compared to the fastest person?

b Which two runners were 0.18 seconds apart?

- Consolidate written methods for + and −
- Check by doing the inverse operation
- Break a problem down into smaller steps

Keywords
Inverse operation

Some problems can be broken down into smaller steps.

> **example**
>
> Tom records the weights of all the parts of a space shuttle before it launches.
>
> ```
> 2 booster rockets  = 1.18 million kg
> separate fuel tank = 0.75 million kg
> payload            = 0.0249 million kg
> crew + other       = 0.0015 million kg
> shuttle body       = ?
> Total weight       = 1.998 million kg
> ```
>
>
>
> Use this information to calculate the weight of the shuttle body.
>
> Step 1 Find the weight of all the parts using addition.
>
>
>
> Break the problem into two smaller steps.
>
> Step 2 Subtract the weight of all the parts from the total weight of the shuttle.
>
>
>
> This is 41 600 kg, so it is still quite heavy!!
>
> Weight of shuttle body = 0.0416 million kg

p. 96 You can often check your answer by performing an **inverse operation**.

> **example**
>
> Lorna and Gina run the 200 m race at the school sports day.
> Lorna's time is 27.8 secs   Gina's time is 30.07 secs
>
> Sam works out the difference between Lorna's time and Gina's time as 27.29 secs.
> **a** How do you know Sam's answer is wrong?
> **b** What is the correct answer?
>
> **a** Sam can check his answer using addition, because
>   Difference + Lorna's time = Gina's time
>   27.29 secs + 27.8 secs = 55.09 secs
> This is not Gina's time, so Sam knows he has made a mistake.
> **b** Set out the calculation in the correct columns.
>   Lorna is 2.27 seconds faster than Gina.
>
>

Exercise 16b

1 Tron is a robot chef. He measures all his ingredients very precisely.
Work out the total weight of each of his recipes.

Risotto	
24.7 g	Butter
605 g	Onions
245.4 g	Rice
520 g	Water
2.036 g	Salt
224.8 g	Mushrooms

Spiced Rice	
14.34 g	Ghee
212.7 g	Rice
520 g	Water
3.207 g	Salt
1.08 g	Pepper
6.2 g	Turmeric

2 Veronica has measured the perimeter of the main school building.
Here is a plan showing the measurements she has made.

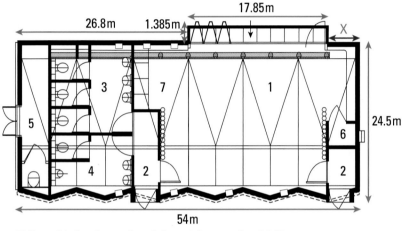

a What is the length of the side marked **X**?

b What is the perimeter of the school building?

Did you know?

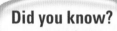

Decision Maths helps people design satellite navigation systems which can quickly find the shortest route between two places.

puzzle

A satellite navigation system is trying to calculate the shortest route from Ayton to Gewizzle.

a Find the shortest route from Ayton to Eckerslike. Clearly show the towns visited and the total distance travelled.

b Will the shortest route by distance be the quickest? Explain your answer.

c Investigate finding the shortest route between other places.

d Can you find the shortest route which visits all the towns and starts and finishes

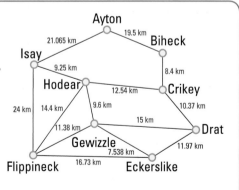

- Consolidate a range of mental strategies for multiplication and division
- Check by doing the inverse operation
- Break a problem down into smaller steps

Keywords
Inverse operation

Some problems involving multiplication and division can be solved by breaking the working out into smaller steps.

example

Karen pays £7460 for printing 2000 holiday guidebooks.
These are the prices the printing firm charges for printing each holiday guidebook:

12p per page
85p for the cover

How many pages are there in Karen's guidebook?

. . . .

Step 1 – Find the cost of one guidebook.

Cost of 1 guidebook = total cost ÷ number of guidebooks
$$= £7460 ÷ 2000$$
$$= £3.73$$

> Divide by 1000 and then divide by 2.

Step 2 – Find the cost of one guidebook without the cover.
Cost of all pages = 373p − 85p
$$= 288p$$

> Change all amounts into pence.

Step 3 – Find the number of pages.
Number of pages = cost of all pages ÷ cost of one page
$$= 288 ÷ 12$$
$$288 ÷ 12 = (240 ÷ 12) + (48 ÷ 12)$$
$$= 20 + 4$$
$$= 24 \text{ pages}$$

> Use mental method of partitioning

- You should always check your working by performing an **inverse operation**.

Karen's guide has 24 pages + 1 cover
$$= 24 × 12p + 85p$$
$$= £3.73$$
Total cost of 2000 guides $$= £3.73 × 2000$$
$$= £7460$$

Exercise 16c

1 Jody is trying to improve her fitness levels.
When she is cycling, Jody's heartbeat is 84 beats per minute.
When she is running, Jody's heartbeat is 92 beats per minute.
Jody cycles for 21 minutes per day and runs for 19 minutes per day.
Does Jody's heart beat more in total when she cycles or when she runs?
Explain and justify your answer.

2 Debbie pays £56 300 for printing 10 000 holiday guidebooks.
These are the prices the printing firm charges for printing each holiday guidebook.
How many pages are there in Debbie's guidebook?

13p per page
95p for the cover

3 Here are some items for sale on the 'Nut-e-nuts' website.

Type of nut	Cost per kg
Almonds	£8.85
Peanuts	£3.75
Walnuts	£6.95
Pecans	£11.69

Use an approximation to decide if each person has enough money for the cost of their orders. Explain and justify your answers.
a Maurice orders 5 kg of almonds and 4 kg of peanuts. He has £65.
b Jenna orders 11 kg of walnuts and 12 kg of pecans. She has £215.
c Boris orders 2 kg of almonds, 3 kg of peanuts and 5 kg of pecans. He has £95.

4 Every person is recommended to consume five portions of fruit and vegetables every day. A 150 ml glass of orange juice counts as one daily portion.
A carton of orange juice contains 1000 ml (= 1 litre).
a How many recommended daily portions of orange juice are there in one carton?
b A family of four decide to each drink 150 ml of orange juice every day.
How much orange juice will they drink in one week?
How many cartons of orange juice will they need to buy?

- Consolidate a range of written methods for
  multiplication and division
- Identify the information necessary to solve a problem
- Check by doing the inverse operation

Keywords
Calculation
Equivalent
Standard method

You should write down the information you know and the
information you are trying to find out when you are solving a
problem.

example

Here are the prices of buying calculators.

Number ordered	DAZIO CX 283	DAZIO CX 283P	SHIP TQ 83S	SHIP TQ 83SE
1 – 5	£3.45	£3.85	£4.85	£5.15
6 – 14	£3.30	£3.70	£4.49	£4.99
15 – 30	£3.19	£3.55	£4.30	£4.89
Over 30	£3.09	£3.40	£4.19	£4.79

Gina buys 35 DAZIO CX 283P calculators.
Noreen buys 23 SHIP TQ 83SE calculators.
Who spends the most money on calculators and how much more
does she spend?

Write down the relevant information:

Change into **equivalent** whole
number **calculations**:

	Make	Price each	Number
Gina	DAZIO CX 283P	£3.40	35
Noreen	SHIP TQ 83SE	£4.89	23

$$35 \times 3.40 \rightarrow 35 \times 340$$
$$23 \times 4.89 \rightarrow 23 \times 489$$

Multiply the decimals by 100.

Use an appropriate method, such as the **standard method**:

$$35 \times 340 = 11\ 900$$
$$23 \times 489 = 11\ 247$$

Write down the total cost for each person (remember to divide by 100):

Gina's total   = £3.40 × 35 = £119.00
Noreen's total = £4.89 × 23 = £112.47

The final part of the problem is a mental subtraction:
Gina spends £119.00 − £112.47 = £6.53 more than Noreen.

Exercise 16d

1 Here are the offers from three phone companies for text messages.

a Klaus buys 35 text messages from Four. How much money would he save if he switched to Yello to buy his text messages?

Number of texts	CO2	Yello	Four	Skyte
1 – 9	4.5p	3.8p	4.3p	4.1p
10–49	4.2p	3.7p	4.1p	4.0p
50–99	3.9p	3.6p	3.9p	3.9p
Over 100	3.6p	3.5p	3.7p	3.8p

b Xuan buys 180 text messages a week from Skyte. How much money would he save each week if he switched to Yello to buy his text messages?

c How much money would Xuan save in a year if he switched?

2 a Hector saves £8.40 a week for his holiday for 12 weeks. If he is on holiday for 14 days, how much money does he have to spend each day?

b Anna takes 8 days to complete a long distance walk. Each day she walks the same distance of 9.25 miles. Louise completes the same walk in 5 days. How far does Louise walk each day? What assumption do you need to make about Louise's journey?

3 Calculate the rate of pay for 1 hour for each of these workers.

a Anton works in an office for 8 hours a day, for 5 days a week, and gets paid £251.20 a week.

b Habib works for an emergency service. He works 4 shifts each lasting 12 hours in 1 week. His weekly pay is £393.60.

c Hannah works in advertising. She works 7 hours a day. In the month of May she works 23 days. Her monthly pay for May is £2125.20.

- Calculate accurately selecting mental methods, written methods or using a calculator
- Record working and method, showing all the steps
- Estimate, approximate and check working

Keywords
Accuracy
Approximation
Calculation
Estimate
Inverse operation
Unitary method

You should write down all the steps of your working out, and choose the most appropriate method.

example

Flour comes in three different-sized packets.
Work out which packet is the best value for money.

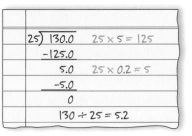

Calculate the amount you get for 1p in each packet:

Packet A   1p will buy you $400 \div 80$ grams of flour

This is a **mental calculation**, using factors ($\div 10$ and then $\div 8$).

$400 \div 80 = 5\,g$

Packet B   1p will buy you $454 \div 87$ grams of flour

This is best done with a **calculator (estimate $\approx 450 \div 90 = 5$).**

$454 \div 87 = 5.218\,39...\,g$
$\qquad\qquad = 5.22\,g\ (2\,dp)$

This is an example of the **unitary method**.

Packet C   1p will buy you $130 \div 25$ grams of flour

This could be done using a **written method**.

$130 \div 25 = 5.2\,g$

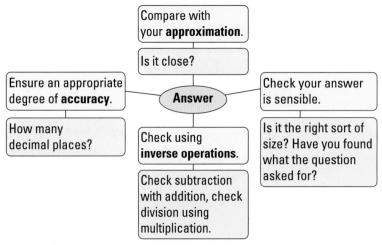

Packet B is the best value for money.

Once you've worked out your answer, you should check it is correct:

Compare with your **approximation**.

Is it close?

Ensure an appropriate degree of **accuracy**.

How many decimal places?

Answer

Check your answer is sensible.

Is it the right sort of size? Have you found what the question asked for?

Check using **inverse operations**.

Check subtraction with addition, check division using multiplication.

Exercise 16e

1 ChocChoc biscuits come in three different-sized packets. Work out which packet is the best value for money by calculating the cost of one biscuit for each packet.

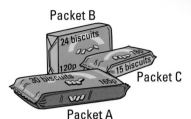

Packet B
Packet C
Packet A

2 Choose the most appropriate method (mental, written or calculator) for solving each of these calculations. In each case, explain your choice and then use that method to solve the problem.

Oliver goes on a sponsored charity walk from Maryport to Liverpool, dressed as a giant leek.
He takes 17 days to walk from Maryport to Liverpool.
Each day he walks the same distance.
He returns by car along the same route in 3 hours at an average speed of 47.6 mph.
He raises £28.63 for charity for each mile he walks.

i How far did Oliver travel each day on his charity walk?

ii How much money did Oliver raise for charity by completing his walk?

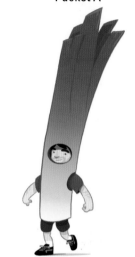

3 Jayne lives in Halifax and works in Manchester. Her journey to work each day is 55 km. She is trying to decide whether it is better to travel to work by car or by train. Here are some ideas she has written down.

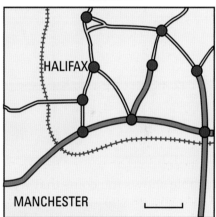

HALIFAX

MANCHESTER

Travelling by car...	
Car insurance	= £280.45 (each year)
Road tax	= £180 (yearly)
Servicing	= £195 (twice a year)
MOT	= £50.63 (each year)
Fuel costs	
Petrol	= 113.9 p per litre
Consumption	= 12.3 km per litre
Travelling time	
Each journey lasts about 55 mins	

Travelling by train...	
Monthly season ticket	= £285.29
Daily return ticket	= £13.75
Travelling time	
Home to station	= 19 mins walk
Journey on train	= 38 mins
Station to work	= 13 mins walk

Jayne works for 46 weeks a year. She has a 4-week holiday in August.
Write a short report recommending which form of transport Jayne should take. Explain and justify your answer.

16 Summary

Assessment criteria
- Break a complex calculation into simpler steps **Level 5**
- Identify the necessary information to solve a problem **Level 5**
- Check a result by working the problem backwards **Level 5**

1 A box contains 150 drawing pins and weighs 50 grams.
The empty box weighs 12.5 grams.

Calculate the weight of one drawing pin.

Kayla's answer ✔

$$50 - 12.5 = 37.5g$$

$$37.5 \div 150 = 0.25g$$

She finds the weight of the drawing pins without the box.

Kayla finds the weight of one drawing pin.

Kayla checks her answer.
$0.25 \times 150 + 12.5 = 50g$ ✓

2 A drink from a machine costs 55 p.

The table shows the coins that were put into the machine one day.

Coins	Number of coins
50 p	31
20 p	22
10 p	41
5 p	59

How many cans of drink were sold that day?

Show your working.

Key Stage 3 2001 4–6 Paper 2

Number Calculation+

17 Functional maths

Real life, functional maths relies on using mathematical processes and applications.

Representing

Using mathematical reasoning

Using mathematical procedures

Interpreting and evaluating

Communicating

Miss Perry is planning a trip for year 8.
They will travel from Birmingham to Sarlat in France by coach and ferry.

She has to work out the cost of the trip for 50 students.

Here are the costs for the whole journey.

Coach	£3460
Ferry berths	£875
Accommodation	£1475
Food	£1450
Insurance	£516
Activities	£1700

1 Miss Perry has to pay deposits to some of the companies.
   Work out how much she will need to pay for these items.

   a accommodation   10%   **b** coach   15%

   c activities   25%   **d** ferry births   20%

   e insurance $12\frac{1}{2}\%$

2 In order to pay the deposits Miss Perry will need to obtain   There are 50 students
   money in advance.

   a What is the total cost of the company deposits?

   b What is the deposit that she will need to collect from each student?

      Miss Perry does not want exact amounts if they involve
      pence, so work out a sensible deposit that covers the costs
      but is not too large. Explain your thinking.

3 It is decided to round up, to the nearest £10, the full amount
   each student must pay. The extra money will be used for
   emergencies and returned if not used.

   a What is the total cost to each student?

   b After paying their deposits, how much does each student still owe?

   c The school allows parents 10 weeks to pay the rest of the money.
      How much will they pay each week?

4 The parents would like to know how the money is going to be spent so the Cooper's School illustrates the costs in a letter.

Miss Perry works out the percentages using a calculator.

          9.23385

She rounds the percentage to the nearest whole number and shows that the ferry bill is 9% of the total.

> Divide the ferry costs by the total cost and multiply by 100 to convert the decimal to a percentage.

a Finish the calculations for Miss Perry.

b What should the total percentage be?

5 Some of the bills have to be paid in euros (€). The school pays its bills with cheques.

> To convert £ p to € e use
> $$e = \frac{6 \times p}{5}$$

Coach bill

Ferry bill

Accommodation bill

Activities bill

a Which cheques have been converted properly into euros?

b Which two companies' payments have been mixed up?

> To convert € e to £ p use
> $$p = \frac{5 \times e}{6}$$

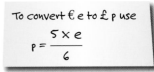

6 Use the formula to convert these Euro prices into GB pounds.

€3.00   €2.40   €45   €119.99

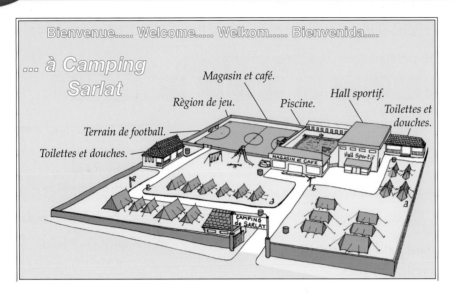

Bienvenue...... Welcome...... Welkom...... Bienvenida.....

... à Camping Sarlat

Magasin et café.
Règion de jeu.
Piscine.
Hall sportif.
Toilettes et douches.
Terrain de football.
Toilettes et douches.

The students are staying in tents. There are three sizes of tent: 2 person, 3 person and 4 person.

1 Working with a partner use the information given to calculate the missing quantity for each tent.

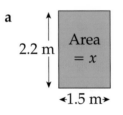
a 2.2 m, Area = x, 1.5 m

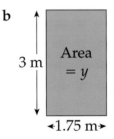
b 3 m, Area = y, 1.75 m

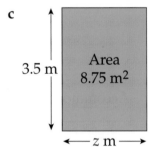
c 3.5 m, Area 8.75 m², z m

2 The students are shown to their tents. Here are the first five tents – A to E.

A sleeps 4
B sleeps 2
C sleeps 2
D sleeps 4
E sleeps 3

Again with a partner, use these clues to work out which tents Carl, Cherry, John, Kadeja and Magnus are in.

Boys and girls are in separate tents.

- 15 pupils are put in these tents: seven girls and eight boys.
- John's tent is at the end of the row.
- Cherry shares a tent with three other girls.
- The four boys in the tent beside Carl's tent make a lot of noise.
- Kadeja likes her tent because it is far away from the noisy boys' tent!

The students are given a map of the camp.

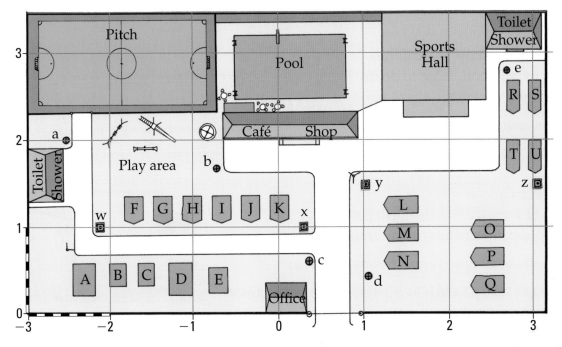

3 a What would you find at these coordinates?
   i (0.5, 2.7)   **ii** (2.2, 3.3)   **iii** (-2.5, 2.8)   **iv** (-0.4, 2.1)   **v** (-1.5, 2.0)

b Which tent is at each of these coordinates?
   i (1.4, 0.6)   **ii** (3.0, 1.8)   **iii** (-2.3, 0.4)   **iv** (-1.0, 1.2)   **v** (-1.6, 0.5)

c Which building would you be standing beside at the coordinates (0.0, 0.0)?

4 Kelly is standing in the middle of the centre circle of the football pitch.
Give the coordinates for her position.

5 There are 5 bins around the site, marked 🔲. and 4 water taps marked ⊕.
Give the coordinates for the bins labeled a – e the taps labeled w – z.

6 a Which grid squares are shown here?

   a   **b**   **c**

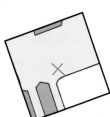   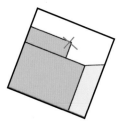   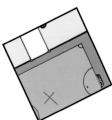

b In each case give the grid reference of the spot marked ✕.

On the first day at Camp Sarlat there is a sports day.

Morning

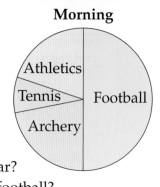

Afternoon

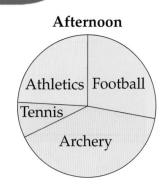

1 The pie charts show the activities which the students chose to do in the morning and in the afternoon.

  a In the morning,
    i which choice was the least popular?
    ii what fraction of students played football?

  b In the afternoon,

There are 50 students

    i which choice was the most popular?
    ii approximately how many students did athletics?

  c Overall, what was the most popular choice?

2 Five teams take part in a five-a-side soccer competition. These are the results.

Round 1				
High 5	2	v	Superstars	4
Champions	3	v	Cheetahs	1
High 5	2	v	All Stars	2
Cheetahs	0	v	Superstars	2
Champions	2	v	All Stars	1

Round 1				
High 5	3	v	Cheetahs	2
All Stars	1	v	Superstars	1
High 5	0	v	Champions	0
All Stars	2	v	Cheetahs	5
Champions	2	v	Superstars	2

  a How many goals were scored in total in the competition?

  b What is the modal average number of goals scored in all the matches?

  c Copy this table of results and complete it. You can work with a partner.

	Games				Goals		Points
	played	won	drawn	lost	for	against	
All Stars	4						
Champions	4						
Cheetahs	4						
High 5	4						
Superstars	4						

Points scoring system

win = 3 pt
draw = 1 pt
lose = 0 pt

  d Calculate the mean average for the number of goals scored in all matches.

  e There is a tie for first place. Without playing another match, explain how you would decide who was the winning team.

3 Four students take part in an archery competition.
Each competitor fires four arrows. Their scores are shown below the targets.

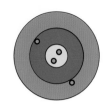   

23 points   17 points   20 points   20 points

a Using this information, how points do you get for a hit in the
   i red circle   **ii** blue circle   **iii** gold bull's eye?

b What is the mean average of the students' scores?

4 Five people raced in a 100 m sprint.

a Round their times to the nearest $\frac{1}{10}$th of a second.
   i 16.35 s   **ii** 14.37 s   **iii** 17.33 s   **iv** 15.08 s   **v** 14.62 s

b Write the rounded times in order, from fastest to slowest.

5 In the shot put, each competitor has three puts. These are the results in metres.

a The sum of the best two throws are used to decide the winner. List the competitors in order from first to fifth.

Name	Put 1	Put 2	Put 3
Darren	6.8	7.1	6.3
Hamed	5.9	6.9	6.6
Reece	5.8	6.8	6.8
Hussain	6.2	7.2	6.5
Carl	7.0	6.8	7.4

b If, instead, the mean average of all three puts is used to decide the winner, work out the new positions.

6 Ronald has three practice puts
   the first put is 6.3 m
   the second put is 8.7 m
   the mean average of the three puts is 7.5 m
How long was the third put?

The group is going on an expedition and must pack their own rucksacks. To be safe and comfortable a rucksack should weigh no more than one fifth ($\frac{1}{5}$) of your body weight.

Delica 45 kg   Lau It 35 kg   Dan 70 kg

1 a Calculate the maximum weight of each students' rucksacks using the above proportion.

Think how to deal with answers that are not whole numbers.

b Ian has 4.2 kg in his rucksack. What is the least that he should weigh?

c Who is closest to the mean weight of the six students?

Eddy 40 kg   Ahmed 61 kg   Maggie 50 kg

This is the route the students will take from Camp Sarlat.

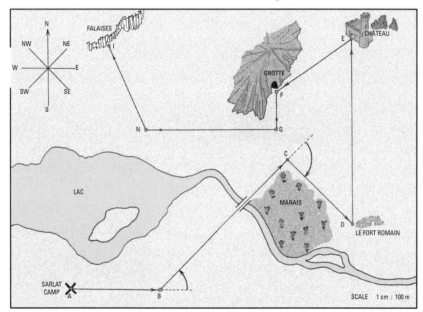

2 a What is the distance and direction of travel between these points?

    i B to C   **ii** C to D   **iii** D to E   **iv** E to F   **v** F to G

> The distance and direction of travel from points A to B is approx. 250 m, East.

b At point B the students turn towards the bridge. Is this turn clockwise or anticlockwise?

c How many degrees is the turn at point C; is it clockwise or anticlockwise?

3 a The Roman fort was occupied from 35 BC to 65 AD. How many years is this?

b In the cave are drawings that were made in 2010 BC. How long ago is this?

At the end of the journey the students learn to mountaineer.

On The Rocks!

4 Measure these angles to the nearest degree.

  a **i** $\widehat{ABC}$ **ii** $\widehat{BCD}$ **iii** $\widehat{CDE}$ **iv** $\widehat{DEF}$

  b **i** $\widehat{KLM}$ **ii** $\widehat{LMN}$ **iii** $\widehat{MNO}$

  c Use your knowledge of angles around a point to find these reflex angles.

    i $\widehat{GHI}$ **ii** $\widehat{HIJ}$ **iii** $\widehat{MNO}$

5 The scene is drawn to a scale of 1 cm : 1 m (1 : 100)

  a To the nearest half metre give theses distances in real life.

    i HI   **ii** MN   **iii** ED   **iv** LM

  b One climber has finished. Approximately, how high above the ground is she?

The day started badly for Miss Perry — her tent leaked in the night and she is not pleased.

Mr Powell thinks that with the help of some students he can make a new tent for her.

1 Here are the measurements for the tent.

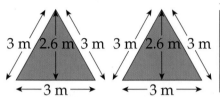
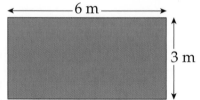

a What is the total area of the material Mr Powell used for the tent?
Give your answer to the nearest 1 m².

b The tent was cut from a 6 m by 7 m piece of material. How much material was wasted?

Things become worse still. Ms. Perry refuses to use the showers — they are just too dirty for her! She has a private shower.

The students have to carry the water to her shower in containers.

2 Tariq and Emma argue about who has carried the most water.
Tariq carries 5 full jerrycans and 1 litre bottle of water.
Emma carries 3 full jerrycans and 11 litre bottles of water.

=

a They both carried an equal amount of water.
How much water does one full jerrycan hold?

b How much water is in a full can if, instead
   i 4 cans + 11 bottles = 6 cans + 5 bottles
   ii 3 cans + 3 bottles = 1 cans + 12 bottles

While waiting to board the coach to go home, the students gather in the play area.

Sam has placed his sandwich on the roundabout which is rotating slowly in a clockwise direction.

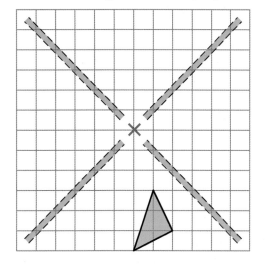

3 On graph paper draw the centre of rotation and the position of the sandwich. Beginning from the start position, rotate the shape through

   a 90° in a clockwise direction and draw the image.

   b 270° in a clockwise direction and draw the image.

4 Claire sits on the see-saw. She weighs 37 kg. Which of the weights shown can be used to balance her?

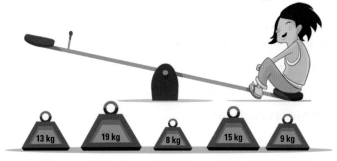

13 kg   19 kg   8 kg   15 kg   9 kg

Miss Perry calls to the students from a plane. She explains that her best friend Rupert happened to be flying by and offered her a lift home. She decided to hurry back and compete all her unfinished marking.

5 The distance from Camp Sarlat to Birmingham is 550 miles. Rupert can fly at an average speed of 100 m.p.h. How long will it take them to fly home?

17

Assessment criteria

- Solve problems by breaking them down into smaller tasks and using a range of methods, including ICT; give solutions to an appropriate degree of accuracy — Level 6

- Interpret, discuss and combine information presented in a variety of mathematical forms — Level 6

- Give short, reasoned arguments using mathematics and explanatory text — Level 6

- Use logic to establish the truth of a statement — Level 6

- Find the information needed to solve problems — Level 5

- Check to see if results are reasonable — Level 5

- Solve word problems and investigations from a range of contexts — Level 5

- Describing situations mathematically using symbols, words and diagrams — Level 5

- Draw simple conclusions and explain the reasoning — Level 5

Check in and Summary answers

Check in

1 **a** 0.47, 0.5, 0.512, 0.52, 0.55
  b -10, -6, -4, 3, 5, 9
2 **a** -5   **b** -3   **c** -9
3 **a** 35   **b** 3   **c** 54   **d** 9
4 **a** 7, 14, 21   **b** 1, 2, 3, 4, 6, 12
5 2, 3, 5, 7, 11

Summary

2 **a** My number must be even.
  b My number could be odd or even.

Check in

1 **a** 3000 **b** 56 **c** 46   **d** 8.5
2 **a** 132   **b** 36 **c** 8   **d** 9
3 **a** 20   **b** 8   **c** 100   **d** 4
4 **a** P = 12, A = 6 cm²
  b P = 12, A = 5 cm²
  c P = 12, A = 8 cm²

Summary

2 **a** 12 cm   **b** 1.2 m   **c** 0.12 km

Check in

1 The answer to this question
  depends on where you live and
  what time of year it is!
2 **a** 0.5   **b** 0.4   **c** 0.375
3 **a** 0.35   **b** 0.635   **c** 0.007

Summary

2 **a** $\frac{1}{3}$ or 0.333…   **b** 3

Check in

1 **a** 0.3   **b** 7.4   **c** 0.05
2 0.23, 0.3, 0.35, 0.39, 0.4
3 **a** £30   **b** 3.5 kg   **c** 18 m

Summary

2 **a** 7 out of 10 is the same as 70%
     10 out of 20 is the same as 50%
  b You could put many different
     numbers in this sentence. One
     example is '1 out of 20 is the
     same as 5%'

Check in

1 66
2 **a** 16   **b** 100   **c** 180
3 **a** 5   **b** 4   **c** £4.50
4 **a** 800 km   **b** 3

Summary

2

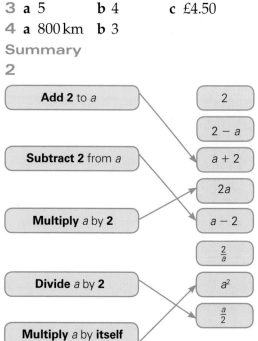

Check in

1 a acute   **b** obtuse   **c** straight
   d reflex   **e** right

2 a 105°   **b** 125°

3 a a = 90   **b** b = 50   **c** c = 72

Summary

2 a 8 faces

   b You should have a drawing of
    a cube, cuboid or pentagonal
    pyramid on isometric paper.

Check in

1 a i 3000   **ii** 3500   **iii** 3460
   b i 5000   **ii** 5300   **iii** 5280

2 a 95   **b** 56   **c** 12.1   **d** 6.3

3 a 86.1   **b** 67.8

4 a 390   **b** 480   **c** 0.58   **d** 48.5

5 a 153   **b** 195   **c** 228   **d** 198

6 a 480   **b** 16   **c** 4770   **d** 13

Summary

2 a 4410   **b** 2.5

Check in

1 a 9   **b** 6   **c** 7   **d** 20

2 a 7   **b** 8

3 8

4 a 56   **b** 56 ÷ 8 = 7   56 ÷ 7 = 8

Summary

2

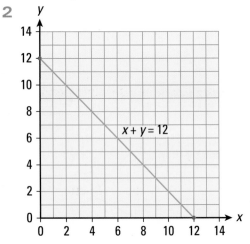

Check in

1 a (3, 1)   **b** (-3, -1)   **c** (-1, -2)

2 a D   **b** C   **c** B   **d** A

Summary

2

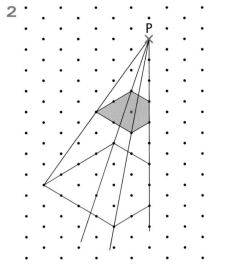

Check in

1 $2^2 = 4$ $3^2 = 9$ $10^2 = 100$

2 a 7, 11, 15, 19

   b This is still the same sequence, but
    with 19 at the end.

   c 23

3 a 2   **b** 10

Summary

2 a $4n + 2$ **b** $3n + 3$

   c $2(5n - 3)$ or $10n - 6$

Check in

1 a Number of
books

0

1   [Book][Book][Book][Book]

2   [Book][Book][Book][Book][Book][Book]

3 or more   [Book][Book][Book][Book][Book]

[Book] = 2 books

b

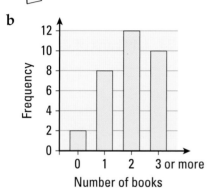

2

Number on dice	Frequency
1	10
2	8
3	12
4	14
5	9
6	7

3 a 5, 5   b 6, 7   c 5, 4

Summary

2 a $60 \div 5 = 12°$ per student,
$96° \div 12° = 8$ students

b $360° \div 24 = 15°$ per student,
$15° \times 9 = 135°$

12

Check in

1 a 12   b £12   c 72 g

2

Fraction	Decimal	Percentage
$\frac{17}{20}$	0.85	85%
$\frac{39}{50}$	0.78	78%
$\frac{25}{25}$	0.96	96%

Summary

2 Dark grey area $= 9 \times 9 + 3 \times 3$
$= 90\,cm^2$

Grey area $= 9 \times 3 + 9 \times 3 = 54\,cm^2$

Dark grey area : Grey area $= 90 : 54$
$= 10 : 6$
$= 5 : 3$

Check in

1 a 3   b 4

2 a €20   b €50

3 10

Summary

2 I was walking at a steady speed.

Check in

1 a 45°   b 135°   c 315°

2 a 18 cm   b 4.5 m   c 15 cm

Summary

2 a 60 cm³   b $x = 6$ cm

Check in

1 a **Pete** the range is 9.
There are two modes – 5 and 9.
Maria the range is 3.
The mode is 7.

 b Maria has the better scores
because her mode is high and
there is a small range in her
data set.

2 8b2 did best because they gained
the highest score in three out of four
weeks. Although they did much
worse in week 3, in week 4 they
compensated by doing well.

Summary

2 a 15th February

 b It was colder for longer or it
became warmer later in the year.

16

Check in

1 a 21.1 b 6.47 c 4.81 d 3.36

2 a 561.39 b 233.07

3 a 6.3 b 21 c 16.8 d 22 r10
 e 149.1

4 a 33.57 b 20.04 c 39.1 d 43.2

5 a 7.9 b 4.4 c 28 d 45

Summary

2 $50 \times 31 = 1550$, $20 \times 22 = 440$,
$10 \times 41 = 410$, $5 \times 59 = 295$,
$155 + 440 + 410 + 295 = 2695$,
$2695 \div 55 = 49$ cans of drink